ESSENTIAL A

and some Clinical Applications

J. S. P. LUMLEY
M.B., B.S., F.R.C.S.

*Assistant Director Surgical Professorial Unit and
Honorary Consultant Surgeon at
St. Bartholomew's Hospital, London
Examiner in Anatomy for
the Royal College of Surgeons of England.*

J. L. CRAVEN
B.Sc., M.D., F.R.C.S.

*Senior Lecturer in Surgery and
Honorary Consultant Surgeon at
the Welsh National School of Medicine, Cardiff
Examiner in Pathology for
the Royal College of Surgeons of England.*

*Both Formerly Assistant Lecturers at
University College, London*

J. T. AITKEN
M.D.

*Professor of Anatomy at
University College, London*

SECOND EDITION

CHURCHILL LIVINGSTONE
EDINBURGH LONDON AND NEW YORK

1975

CHURCHILL LIVINGSTONE
Medical Division of Longman Group Limited

Distributed in the United States of America by Longman Inc., 19 West 44th Street, New York, N.Y. 10036, and by associated companies, branches and representatives throughout the world.

©LONGMAN GROUP LIMITED 1975

First Edition	1965
Reprinted	1969
Reprinted	1972
Reprinted	1973
Second Edition	1975
Reprinted	1977
Reprinted	1978

ISBN 0 443 01181 8

Library of Congress Catalog Card Number 74–77031

Printed in Great Britain by
T. & A. Constable Ltd., Edinburgh

ESSENTIAL ANATOMY

and some Clinical Applications

PREFACE TO THE FIRST EDITION

Preclinical medical and dental students labour to-day under a weight of ever expanding subjects and books, so that some justification needs to be given for producing yet another textbook.

As teachers we know that the profusion of data in anatomy often obscures many important and essential facts, and we have seen students, lacking a critical and methodical approach, perform badly in examinations. This concise book omits much detail and avoids unnecessary repetition. Short notes on relevant histology and embryology have been included and as far as possible the New York (1963) nomenclature has been used.

We have tried to emphasise a methodical approach to the subject by the description of structures in a consistent manner, and to this end the book-mark may prove a useful *aide mémoire*. The diagrams have been chosen with care and their simplicity should make them easy to understand.

This combination of brevity, method and regional description will, we hope, help the student to be selective both in his dissection and in his revision for the second professional examination.

We are greatly indebted to Professor J. Z. Young for his encouragement, guidance and the facilities of his department. Many colleagues have also helped in the process of sifting and emphasising. We are grateful to Mrs. J. Astafiev, departmental artist, who has made our drawings and diagrams comprehensible. Mr. Charles Macmillan and the staff of E. & S. Livingstone Ltd. have been, as always, very helpful in all stages of the preparation of this work.

1965.   THE AUTHORS.

PREFACE TO THE SECOND EDITION

The confidence of students in this book has been well demonstrated by its continuing demand. Although principally written for students in their preclinical years, increasing numbers of postgraduate students have found the book satisfactory reading in preparation for higher degrees and diplomas. At many medical schools, the time available for the study of gross anatomy has been much reduced and compressed into one year.

In an effort to meet these extra demands a new chapter describes some of the basic processes in prenatal development, the order of presentation of the parts of the body has been altered, and some of the descriptions have been compressed. The references to clinical applications however have been increased.

A selection of typical X-ray pictures has been included. The authors are indebted to Mr Andrew Rowlands and the Photographic Department at St Bartholomew's Hospital, London, for their help with these illustrations. All the diagrams have been retitled by Mr Robin Hipps who has also modified some original drawings and prepared some new ones.

Churchill Livingstone has given encouragement and much technical help, and has been most cooperative in the preparation of the new edition.

J.S.P.L.
J.L.C.
1975   J.T.A.

METHOD OF DESCRIPTION

JOINTS

1. Classification:
   - (a) bony
   - (b) fibrous
   - (c) cartilaginous
   - (d) synovial
2. Bones:
   - (a) names
   - (b) shapes
   - (c) articular covering
3. Ligaments:
   - (a) capsule
   - (b) capsular thickenings
   - (c) accessory
4. Intracapsular structures:
   - (a) synovial membrane
   - (b) discs
   - (c) ligaments, tendons, fat pads
5. Functional aspects:
   - (a) movements (muscles involved)
   - (b) stability (bones, ligaments and muscles)
   - (c) Relation to line of weight
6. Blood and nerve supply
7. Relations
8. Bursae

ORGANS

1. Definition
2. General outline:
   - (a) shape
   - (b) size
   - (c) surfaces
   - (d) situation
   - (e) colour
   - (f) consistency
3. Relations
4. Blood supply
5. Nerve supply
6. Lymph drainage
7. Histology
8. Embryology
9. Functional aspects

VESSELS AND NERVES

1. Origin
2. Course
3. Termination
4. Relations
5. Branches

MUSCLES

1. Attachments
2. Actions
3. Nerve supply

CONTENTS

Chapter   *Page*

GENERAL INTRODUCTION   1

1   The Structure of the Body   2

2   Embryology   18

3   The Vertebral Column   33

THORAX   41

4   The Thoracic Wall and Diaphragm   42

5   The Thoracic Cavity and Heart   52

6   Other Mediastinal Structures   63

7   The Pleura and Lungs   72

8   The Autonomic Nervous System and Lymph Drainage   81

ABDOMEN AND PELVIS   85

9   The Abdomen and Peritoneum   86

10   The Abdominal Alimentary Tract   95

11   The Liver, Spleen and Pancreas   113

12   The Kidneys, Suprarenal Glands and Posterior Abdominal Wall   121

13   The Pelvis   131

14   The Perineum   152

15   The Blood Vessels, Lymph Drainage and Nerves   158

UPPER LIMB   165

16   The Shoulder Region   166

17   The Axilla and Upper Arm   178

ix

Chapter		Page
18	The Elbow and Forearm	184
19	The Wrist and Hand	198
20	The Fascia, Veins, Lymph Drainage and Nerves	207
	LOWER LIMB	211
21	The Hip and Thigh	212
22	The Knee, Leg and Dorsum of the Foot	227
23	The Foot	244
24	The Fascia, Veins, Lymph Drainage, Nerves, and Posture	254
	HEAD AND NECK	261
25	The Skull, Scalp and Face	262
26	The Orbit, Nose and Mouth	276
27	The Temporomandibular Joint, Pharynx and Larynx	295
28	The Ear, Intracranial Region and Cranial Nerves	308
29	The Neck	324
30	The Vessels, Nerves and Lymph Drainage	331
	CENTRAL NERVOUS SYSTEM	343
31	Introduction	344
32	The Forebrain	349
33	The Brain Stem and Cerebellum	363
34	The Spinal Cord and Reticular Formation	375
35	The Afferent and Efferent Pathways	379
36	The Meninges and Blood Supply	384
	Index	397

GENERAL INTRODUCTION

CHAPTER 1

THE STRUCTURE OF THE BODY

The body is formed of innumerable cells and varying amounts of intercellular substances. They may be grouped into (a) the tissues, (b) the cells of the body fluids, and (c) the mobile cells of the macrophage (reticulo-endothelial) system. Aggregations of one or more tissues form the functional units (the organs) of the body. All the cells, tissues and organs subserving a particular function are classified as a system.

The Cell

Cells are composed of a protoplasmic gel, the protoplasm of the nucleus being called karyoplasm and that of the cell body, cytoplasm. The resting nucleus is surrounded by an elastic nuclear membrane and contains a large amount of basophil staining chromatin which, in the dividing cell, is grouped to form the chromosomes.

The cytoplasm is limited by a thin cell membrane and within it are found a number of intracellular inclusions, the organelles. These comprise the mitochondria, Golgi apparatus, endoplasmic reticulum and the centrosome. The mitochondria are often small rod-shaped granules with inward projecting folds, the cristae. They are rich in enzymes and are essential for the metabolism of the cell. The Golgi apparatus is situated near the nucleus and consists of a number of vesicles and a smooth-walled membranous component. It is probably concerned with cell secretion. The endoplasmic reticulum is a membranous lattice network scattered throughout the cytoplasm; it is concerned with protein synthesis. The centrosome is a spherical area of clear cytoplasm placed near the nucleus and is concerned with cell division.

Occasionally the growth of a group of cells in the body may become uncontrolled with the resultant development of a local swelling known as a tumour, a newgrowth or a neoplasm. This abnormal process is known as neoplasia. If infiltration or spread of the neoplastic tissue around the body occurs the condition is said to be malignant. Cancer is one form of malignant neoplasm. A change in the form or function of a tissue or organ is often referred to as a lesion. Death of a tissue is called necrosis.

THE SYSTEMS AND ORGANS

The systems and organs of the body are composed of epithelial, connective, muscular and nervous tissues.

EPITHELIAL TISSUE

This forms a protective covering over the internal and external surfaces of the body and is characterised by having a minimal amount of inter-

2

cellular substance and a tendency to form sheets. It may be simple, transitional or stratified.

1. Simple epithelium consists of a single layer of cells on a basement membrane. It is described as squamous (pavement), cubical or columnar, depending on the shape of its cells. Squamous cells are found lining the alveoli of the lungs, the blood vessels (endothelium) and the serous cavities (mesothelium). Cubical cells line the ducts of many glands. Columnar cells are often ciliated and may be modified as mucus-forming goblet cells; they line much of the alimentary, respiratory and reproductive tracts.

2. Transitional epithelium contains two or three layers of cells, most of which are attached to the basement membrane and are nucleated. It lines the urinary tract, is stretchable and does not desquamate. It contains few glands.

3. Stratified squamous epithelium also has a number of layers of cells. Those in contact with the basement membrane are columnar stratified cells. The more superficial cells are flattened and the surface cells are enucleate and continually being rubbed away (desquamated). This form of epithelium covers the exterior of the body and lines both ends of the alimentary tract.

Skin

This consists of two layers, an outer epidermis and an inner dermis (corium). The epidermis is composed of keratinised stratified squamous epithelium. Hair follicles, sweat and sebaceous glands and nails are modifications of the epidermis.

The dermis is a layer of vascular connective tissue moulded closely to the epidermis and merging in its deeper part with the subcutaneous tissues. Lying in the dermis are the coiled tubular sweat ducts opening on to the skin surface, and the compound alveolar sebaceous glands opening into the hair follicles. In the subcutaneous tissue are the roots of the hairs and the sweat glands.

Mucous and Serous Membranes

These line the wet internal surfaces of the body and consist of an epithelium and a corium. The epithelium is usually of a simple variety with many mucous or serous cells but the urinary tract is lined by transitional epithelium, and the respiratory tract by pseudostratified columnar ciliated epithelium with mucous cells. The serous membranes line the closed body cavities (the coelome), bursae, etc. The corium is composed of connective tissue. In the alimentary tract it contains a thin sheet of smooth muscle—the muscularis mucosae.

Glands

These are epithelial outgrows modified to produce secretions. These secretions may pass on to the epithelial surface (exocrine glands) or into the blood stream (endocrine glands). Exocrine glands may be unicellular

3

(goblet) or multicellular. The latter may be simple (containing one duct) or compound where numerous small ducts open into a single main duct. The secretory part of the gland may be the same diameter as the duct (tubular), globular (acinar), oval (alveolar) or intermediate, e.g. tubulo-alveolar. The secretions of the exocrine glands may be formed by disintegration of the whole cell (holocrine, e.g. sebaceous glands), dis-integration of the free end of the cell (apocrine, e.g. mammary glands) or without cellular damage (merocrine or epicrine, e.g. most endocrine and other glands).

CONNECTIVE TISSUE

This is characterised by having a large amount of intercellular sub-stance. It forms areolar tissue, the packing material of the body, and supporting tissues, ligaments, cartilages and bone.

Areolar Tissue

The intercellular substance is semisolid and composed of proteins and mucopolysaccharides. Three types of fibres are found: coarse collagen fibres which are white (in bulk), flexible, inelastic and arranged in bundles; elastic fibres which are yellowish (in bulk), less frequent and branching; reticular fibres which form a very fine silver-staining network throughout the tissues.

The cells are of five main varieties: large slender poorly-staining fibro-blasts, closely concerned with the production of the three types of tissue fibres; tissue macrophages which are phagocytic; oval plasma cells with their cartwheel-like staining nucleus, concerned with antibody produc-tion; granular basophilic mast cells, concerned with histamine and heparin production; the cyst-like fat-containing cells.

The relative amounts of cells and intercellular substances vary throughout the body. Subcutaneous tissue forms superficial and deep fascia. These contain a variable amount of fat and fibrous tissue. Superficially, fat is usually predominant but deeper, the fascia forms a well-defined fibrous sheet over the muscles. In other places condensations of non-elastic fibrous tissue form ligaments, tendons and aponeuroses. Ligaments are usually related to joints, maintaining their stability; tendons join the muscles to the bones by blending with the periosteum; aponeuroses are thin flattened tendinous sheets through which muscles gain wider attachments.

Supporting Tissues

1. Cartilage: This is an avascular firm tissue composed of cells (chondrocytes) in an abundant matrix. It is formed from an overlying fibrous layer, the perichondrium, and classified, according to its pre-dominant fibres, into hyaline cartilage, fibrocartilage and yellow, elastic cartilage.

(a) Hyaline cartilage contains many cells, a few fine collagen-like fibres and is found in the rib cartilages and over most articular surfaces. It also forms the precursor in cartilaginous ossification.

(b) Fibrocartilage contains many dense fibrous bundles, fewer cells and is present in the intervertebral discs, over the articular surface of bones which ossify in membranes, e.g. the mandible, and in intra-articular cartilages, e.g. the menisci of the knee.

(c) Yellow, elastic cartilage contains elastic fibres and is found in the auricular, epiglottic and arytenoid cartilages of the head.

2. Bone: This is a hard supporting tissue composed mainly of inorganic calcium salts impregnating a network of collagen fibres. The basic unit is composed of concentric layers around a central vessel, the arrangement being known as a Haversian system. The bone cells (osteocytes) lie within lacunae between the layers and their processes pass into canaliculi in the bone. Compact bone is dense and strong and forms the outer part of most bones. Inside, the cancellous (spongy) bone consists of a network of trabeculae around intercommunicating spaces; the osteocytes lie within lacunae in the trabeculae. The outer surface of a bone is covered by a thick fibrous layer, the periosteum, many of the cells of which are the granular, bone-forming osteoblasts.

The shape of the bones of the body, the proportion of compact to cancellous tissue and the architecture of the trabeculae, are arranged to give maximum strength along with economy of material. Both genetic and local factors influence the shape and size of a bone. Adjacent muscles or organs (e.g. the brain) mould the bone to some extent. Many of these properties of bone can be investigated in the living person by means of X-rays (Fig. 1.1).

Bones are classified as long, short, flat or irregular.

Long bones are present in the limbs. The body (shaft) is a cylinder of compact bone surrounding a medullary cavity which is filled with some spongy bone and a large amount of yellow fatty marrow. The two ends are formed of spongy bone with a thin outer shell of compact bone. The trabeculae in the cancellous bone are laid down along the lines of force. In the developing long bone, blood-forming tissue is found in the ends, but not normally in the adult.

The short bones are found in the carpus and tarsus. They consist of spongy bone covered with a thin layer of compact bone.

The flat bones, e.g. the scapula, give attachment to muscles and form a protective covering (the bones of the skull vault). They consist of two layers of compact bone with a thin intervening spongy layer (the diploë in the skull).

The remaining irregular bones may contain red, blood-forming, marrow (the vertebrae), or air sinuses being then called pneumatic bones (some bones of the face).

Excessive force applied to a bone may cause it to fracture and in such injuries the adjacent soft tissues may be damaged both by the force and by the broken ends of the bone. Knowledge of the anatomical relations of the bone enables the doctor to predict the likely association of nerve, artery and muscle injury with a bone fracture. A break in the overlying skin is a serious complication of fractures, as it allows entry to infecting organisms. In these circumstances the fracture is said to be compound.

5

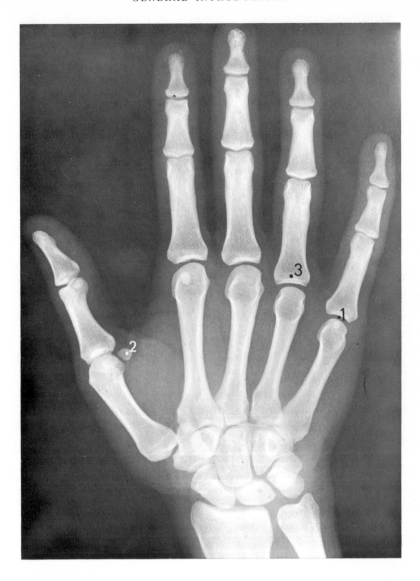

FIG. 1.1
Radiograph of adult hand. Note the joint lines (1), the sesamoid bones (2), and the bony trabeculae (3).

OSSIFICATION

Bone may develop in a fibrous tissue model (membranous ossification) or in cartilage which has replaced the membranous model (cartilaginous ossification).

Membranous ossification usually starts in the fifth to sixth week of

A   B

FIG. 1.2

Radiograph of young person showing unfused epiphyses (1, 2, 3 and 4). Note the clear zone (epiphyseal cartilage, 5) which separates the body of the bone from the epiphysis. Compare A and B and note that the method of printing has been reversed. In A the dense tissues appear white but in B they are dark. Both methods of reproduction are used in the text in an effort to obtain a clear contrasty picture.

intra-uterine life, and is found in the bones of the skull vault, the bones of the face and the clavicle (partly).

Cartilaginous ossification occurs in all long bones except the clavicle. A primary centre appears for the body about the eighth week of intra-uterine life and secondary centres for each end between birth and puberty. Fusion of the body and these centres occurs about the 18th year in males. Secondary centres appear and fuse up to a year earlier in the female. Further ossification centres may develop at puberty in areas of major muscle attachment. Examples are the processes of the vertebrae and the crests of the scapula and the hip. They fuse with the rest of the bone about the 25th year.

DEVELOPMENT OF A LONG BONE (Fig. 1.2)

A long bone develops from a cartilaginous model possessing an outer perichondrium and an irregular cartilaginous matrix; the deep layers of the perichondrium have pronounced osteogenic properties.

The first changes occur in the cartilage cells of the middle of the body (the **diaphysis**). They become greatly enlarged and the matrix is correspondingly reduced and calcified. The cells die and undergo shrinkage, leaving spaces known as primary alveoli. The deeper layer of perichondrium around the middle of the body starts to produce bone and is then known as the periosteum. Blood vessels and bone cells (the bone-forming osteoblasts and the bone-removing osteoclasts) pass inwards from the periosteum to the calcified zone. The multinucleated osteoclasts initiate absorbtion of the calcified material producing larger spaces, the secondary alveoli. Osteoblasts come to line the secondary alveoli and layers of bone are deposited. Some osteoblasts are incorporated into the bone, becoming the bone cells (osteocytes). Ossification extends up and down the body from this primary centre. The cells of the adjacent cartilage come to lie in parallel longitudinal rows and are subsequently replaced in the manner already described. This form of ossification is known as endochondral (cartilaginous).

Secondary centres of ossification (the **epiphyses**) appear later in life. Osteogenic cells invade the calcified cartilage after the cells have undergone hypertrophy, death and shrinkage. The layer of cartilage left between the epiphysis and the diaphysis is known as the **epiphyseal plate.** The part of the diaphysis bordering the plate is known as the **metaphysis;** the cartilage adjacent to the metaphysis is continually being ossified. New cartilage cells are formed in the epiphyseal plate. Growth in length of the bone continues until the cartilage cells stop multiplying and fusion of the diaphysis and epiphysis then occurs. The internal architecture of the bone is remodelled by osteoclastic and osteoblastic activity. Simultaneous laying down of layers of bone around the body by the periosteum increases the girth of the bone and is known as subperiosteal ossification; it is a form of membranous ossification.

Epiphyses may be classified into three types: pressure epiphyses seen at the ends of weight-bearing bones, traction epiphyses occurring at the site of muscle attachments, and atavistic epiphyses being functionless skeletal remnants.

Injury in a young person can dislodge the epiphysis from the metaphysis, e.g. a fall on the outstretched arm may produce a slipped epiphysis of the lower end of the radius.

THE SKELETON

The skeleton is divisible into an axial part (the bones of the head and trunk) and an appendicular part (the bones of the limbs). The upper limb is joined to the trunk by the mobile pectoral girdle, and the lower limb by the stable pelvic girdle.

Joints (Figs. 1.1, 1.2)

These are unions between two or more bones and may be of four types: bony, fibrous, cartilaginous or synovial.

1. Bony—The three elements of the hip bone are joined by bony union, as are the occipital and the sphenoid in the skull after completion of the second dentition.

2. Fibrous—The bony surfaces are united by fibrous tissue. They comprise the skull sutures, the articulations of the roots of the teeth, and the inferior tibiofibular joint.

3. Cartilaginous—These may be primary or secondary. In the primary cartilaginous joints the bony surfaces are united by hyaline cartilage as seen in the union of the body and the ends in a developing long bone.

In the secondary cartilaginous joints (the symphyses) the bony surfaces are covered with hyaline cartilage and united by a fibrocartilaginous disc. These joints all lie in the midline and comprise the intervertebral discs, the symphysis pubis and the manubriosternal junction.

4. Synovial—The bony articular surfaces are covered with hyaline cartilage (with the exception of the temporomandibular and sternoclavicular joints where they are covered with fibrocartilage). A fibrous capsule is attached near to the articular margins of the bones. The surfaces of the interior of the joint, except those covered by cartilage, are lined by a delicate vascular synovial membrane which secretes a watery synovial fluid into the joint cavity.

The capsule may possess ligamentous thickenings, and accessory extracapsular and intracapsular ligaments may pass across the joint. Fibrous intra-articular discs are present in some joints, occasionally completely dividing their cavity (e.g. temporomandibular joint). Tendons occasionally enter the joint cavity by piercing the capsule (biceps brachii) and fat pads may be present between the capsule and the synovial lining (knee joint).

Muscles or tendons crossing superficial to the joint may be protected by a synovial sheath or sac whose fluid prevents excessive friction. The sacs are known as **bursae** and the cavity may communicate with that of the joint.

FUNCTIONAL ASPECTS OF JOINTS

Movement—Bony, fibrous and primary cartilaginous joints are immobile, secondary cartilaginous joints are slightly mobile, and synovial joints are freely mobile.

Synovial joints are subdivided into a number of varieties according to the movements possible at the joint. These varieties are listed below and the movements are best understood by examining the examples given.

(a) Hinge—elbow and ankle joints.
(b) Pivot—proximal radio-ulnar joint and the dens articulation of the atlanto-axial joint.

(c) Condyloid—wrist and metacarpo- and metatarso-phalangeal joints.

(d) Saddle—carpometacarpal joint of the thumb.

(e) Ball and socket—hip and shoulder joints.

(f) Plane—intercarpal joints and joints between the articular processes of adjacent vertebrae.

Stability—This may be due to bony, ligamentous or muscular factors and is usually inversely related to the mobility of the joint. Many of these functional aspects of joints may be assessed in an X-ray examination of the part. Displacement of the articulating surfaces of a joint is known as dislocation. Dislocation of a joint may follow severe injury and is always associated with damage to the capsular and accessory ligaments. There may also be fractures of the bony structures of the joint and occasionally damage to closely related nerves and vessels. Chronic inflammatory processes are prone to affect the bone ends (osteoarthritis) and synovial membranes (rheumatoid arthritis), and joints thus affected may be deformed and painful.

MUSCULAR TISSUE

This is a contractile tissue. There are striated, smooth, and cardiac varieties.

1. Striated (voluntary) muscle acts mainly on the bony skeleton or as a diaphragm, but it is also found around the pharynx and larynx and forms some sphincters. It is composed of unbranched fibres of sacroplasm limited by a membrane, the sarcolemma, and contains many nuclei. Each fibre has a motor end plate and contains many contractile units, the myofibrils, which have alternating dark (A) and light (I) bands. A dark line (the Z disc) crosses the middle of the I band. The bands of adjacent myofibrils coincide, giving the muscle fibre its striated appearance. Each fibre is enveloped and attached to its neighbour by a fibrous endomysium and bundles of fibres are enclosed by a fibrous perimysium. A muscle composed of many bundles is surrounded by an epimysium.

The motor nerve supply of the muscle comes from the anterior horn cells of the spinal cord. The sensory supply arises in the spindles and tendon organs as well as less specialized touch and pain endings. Impulses from the sensory endings pass into the posterior horns of the spinal cord. Muscles have a very rich blood supply.

Muscles of the Skeleton

These are formed of voluntary fibres. The muscles are attached at each end, usually to bone, either directly or through tendons and aponeuroses and cross one or more joints. Occasionally two muscles meet at a common stretchable union known as a raphé, e.g. mylohyoid muscles.

Muscle fibres are arranged either parallel to the direction of the action (sartorius) or obliquely to it (rectus femoris). In muscles of equal volume, a parallel arrangement of fibres gives greater movement but less power than an oblique arrangement.

When a movement occurs at a joint, the muscles concerned in producing it are known as the prime movers and those opposing it, as antagonists.

10

Muscles contracting to steady the joint across which movement is occurring, and other joints involved are known as synergists. A further type of action is known as the action of paradox, in which a muscle gradually relaxes against the pull of gravity, e.g. lowering a weight by relaxing the back muscles.

2. Smooth (unstriated, involuntary) muscle is present in the walls of most vessels and hollow organs of the body. It is composed of un-branched spindle-shaped fibres with a single central nucleus and containing many unstriated myofibrils. The fibres are arranged in interlacing bundles.

3. Cardiac muscle is found in the heart. It consists of short branched cylindrical fibres joined end to end. The adherent ends of adjacent fibres form the dark intercalated discs. Each fibre contains a single central nucleus and striated myofibrils resembling those of voluntary muscle.

NERVOUS TISSUE
This is capable of excitability and conductivity. It consists of functional units (neurons) and supporting cells which in the central nervous system are the neuroglial cells, and in the peripheral nervous system, the Schwann cells.

The neuron consists of a cell body, the perikaryon, and processes, usually an axon and one or more dendrites. The cell bodies are situated in the central nervous system or in peripheral ganglia. They possess a large nucleus and well-marked cellular inclusions. The axon (fibre) begins at a small axon hillock on the cell body and carries impulses away from the cell body. This often long slender process ends by dividing into many branches which have small terminal knobs, the boutons, related to the cell bodies or branches of other neurons. The relationship is known as a synapse. (A rather specialised synapse is formed when a nerve ends on a muscle fibre at a motor end plate.)

Axons may give off one or more short collateral branches. Many axons are surrounded by a myelin sheath. This sheath is interrupted about every millimetre or so and the constriction is called a node of Ranvier. In the peripheral nervous system each internodal segment of sheath is produced by a Schwann cell, the nucleus of which is seen on its surface. These cells play an important role in peripheral nerve regeneration. In the central nervous system oligodendroglia probably takes the place of the Schwann cells. Fibres of the peripheral nervous system are also covered by a thin fibrous membrane, the neurilemma. Dendrites are usually short unmyelinated processes carrying action potentials to the cell body. The volume over which the dendrites of a single cell extend is known as the dendritic field.

Afferent neurons carry information towards the central nervous system and efferent neurons carry instructions away from it. Within the central nervous system afferent and efferent neurons are often connected by many intercalated (internuncial or intermediate) neurons.

The neurons are organised to form the central and peripheral nervous systems. The former comprises the brain and spinal cord (p. 344) and the latter the cranial nerves (p. 314), spinal nerves and the autonomic nervous system (see below).

Neuroglia consists of astrocytes, oligodendroglia and microglia.

Astrocytes are stellate cells with large nuclei and numerous processes which may be of the thick protoplasmic variety, as found mainly in the grey matter, or the thin fibrous variety found mainly in the white matter. Some of the processes end on blood vessels and the astrocytes are thought to be concerned with the nutrition of the neurons. Oligodrendroglia are oval dark-staining cells processing few processes. They probably function as the Schwann cells of the central nervous system. Microglia are small mobile phagocytic cells and form part of the macrophage system.

Ependymal cells are columnar in shape and line the cavities of the brain and spinal cord. In certain regions the ependyma is modified to form the choroid plexuses of the brain which produce the cerebrospinal fluid.

Spinal Nerves

The 31 paired spinal nerves (8 cervical, 12 thoracic, 5 lumbar, 5 sacral and 1 coccygeal) are formed within the vertebral canal, each by the union of a ventral and a dorsal root. The roots are formed from a number of rootlets which emerge from the anterolateral and posterolateral sulci of the spinal cord. The ventral root carries efferent (motor) fibres from the cord and the dorsal root, afferent (sensory) fibres to the cord. The cell bodies of the sensory fibres are situated in a ganglion on the dorsal root. The spinal nerves are therefore a mixture of motor and sensory fibres. Each nerve leaves the vertebral canal through an intervertebral foramen and soon divides into a large ventral and smaller dorsal ramus.

The adjacent ventral rami of most regions communicate to form plexuses (cervical, brachial and lumbosacral) while those of the thoracic region become the intercostal and subcostal nerves (p. 46). The dorsal rami pass backwards into the postvertebral muscles and divide into medial and lateral branches. These rami supply the muscles and skin over the posterior aspect of the body but give no branches to the limbs. Tumours within the vertebral canal or a protusion from a degenerate intervertebral disc may compress a spinal nerve and produce segmental sensory and motor dysfunction. Knowledge of the anatomical distribution of the individual nerves will enable the site of the disease to be identified.

Autonomic Nervous System

This system supplies glands and smooth and cardiac muscle. All its fibres arise from neurons of the visceral columns of the brain and spinal cord (p. 346) and synapse with peripheral ganglion cells before reaching the organs they supply. The system is divisible into two complementary parts, sympathetic and parasympathetic, which leave the central nervous system at different sites and usually have opposing effects on the structures they supply. Most viscera are innervated by both parts, the sympathetic preparing the body for fight or flight, and the parasympathetic controlling its vegetative functions.

Sympathetic system—Each ventral ramus of the 1st thoracic to the 2nd lumbar nerves gives a bundle of myelinated (pre-ganglionic) fibres to the sympathetic trunk. The bundles arise near the formation of a ramus and are called rami communicantes; they form the sympathetic outflow of the central nervous system. Each ventral ramus later receives a bundle of unmyelinated (post-ganglionic) fibres from the sympathetic trunk—a ramus communicans. The peripheral ganglia of the system lie within the two parallel sympathetic trunks alongside the vertebral column. The trunks extend from the base of the skull to the coccyx and have 3 cervical, 12 thoracic, 4 lumbar and 5 sacral ganglia. The preganglionic fibres from the thoracolumbar outflow may synapse: (i) in the adjacent ganglion, (ii) in other ganglia higher or lower in the chain, (iii) in the collateral ganglia situated in the plexuses around the aorta (e.g. coeliac). Each preganglionic fibre may synapse with 15 or more ganglionic cells, thus giving rise to widespread activity. A number of preganglionic fibres end in the medulla of the suprarenal gland.

Postganglionic (unmyelinated) fibres may: (i) return to a spinal nerve in a ramus communicans to be distributed to peripheral smooth muscle, e.g. arterial walls, (ii) pass along the major arteries and their branches to be distributed to the organs these supply, (iii) form named nerves, e.g. cardiac, running to the viscus concerned.

The cell bodies of the sympathetic fibres supplying the upper and lower limbs are situated in ganglia in the upper thoracic and lumbar regions respectively. Surgical removal of these ganglia may be undertaken to improve the blood supply to the tissues of the limb, and less commonly, to reduce excessive sweating.

Parasympathetic system—This system receives preganglionic fibres from four cranial nerves (oculomotor, facial, glossopharyngeal and vagus) and the 2nd, 3rd and 4th sacral nerves (craniosacral outflow). The peripheral ganglia of this system are near the organs they supply, usually in its walls. There, are, however, four well-defined, isolated, parasympathetic ganglia associated with the cranial nerves (p. 340). The postganglionic fibres are usually short and unmyelinated.

Afferent (e.g. pain) fibres from the viscera are present in both sympathetic and parasympathetic systems and pass to the central nervous system without synapsing. Their subsequent paths are similar to those of somatic pain (p. 380). Afferent (reflex) fibres from the lungs, heart, bladder, etc, and visceral sensations of nausea, hunger, rectal distension, etc. also reach the central nervous system, probably along parasympathetic pathways.

THE CELL-CONTAINING BODY FLUIDS

These comprise mainly the blood and lymph.

Blood consists of cells and plasma, slightly less than half its volume being cellular.

Blood cells—these are the red and white blood corpuscles and the

13

platelets. The red blood corpuscles are enucleate biconcave discs. They contain the pigment haemoglobin and are concerned with the transport of blood gases. The white blood cells are less numerous, nucleated and larger. Their cytoplasm may be granular (neutrophils, eosinophils and basophils) or nongranular (lymphocytes and monocytes). Neutrophils are the most numerous of the granular cells. They have a lobulated nucleus and fine granular cytoplasm staining with neutral dyes. Eosinophils usually have a lobulated nucleus and eosinophilic cytoplasmic granules. Basophils have a kidney-shaped nucleus and basic-staining coarse granules.

Lymphocytes have a large darkly staining nucleus and pale basophilic cytoplasm; monocytes are similar but slightly larger. Platelets are small subcellular elements concerned in blood clotting.

The red blood corpuscles, granular white corpuscles and platelets are all formed in the red bone marrow, the lymphocytes in the lymph nodes and the monocytes in the macrophage system.

Bone marrow is a pulp-like tissue contained within all bones; it may be red or yellow.

Red marrow is present in parts of most bones at birth. It is composed of a reticular network of fine collagen fibres and contains red and granular white cells and their precursors, large multinucleate megakaryocytes which give rise to the platelets, and a few plasma cells and monocytes. Yellow marrow is less vascular and contains many fat cells. It gradually replaces the red marrow and, in the adult, the latter is present only in the vertebrae, ribs, sternum and flat bones. Anaemia is a deficiency of circulating haemoglobin and may be caused by chronic blood cell loss, newgrowths affecting the bone marrow or by insufficient blood precursors such as iron and vitamin B_{12}. In most chronic and severe anaemias there is a compensatory increase in the amount of red marrow found in the bones.

THE CARDIOVASCULAR SYSTEM

This comprises the heart (p. 52) and blood vessels, the latter being the arteries, veins, capillaries and sinusoids.

The walls of the arteries possess three coats: an intima, composed of an endothelial lining and a small amount of connective tissue; a media, composed mainly of elastic tissue in the larger arteries, and almost entirely of smooth muscle in the smaller (arterioles) and medium sized arteries; an outer fibrous adventitia. The coats of the veins correspond to those of the arteries but the media contains less smooth muscle and elastic fibres. In the larger veins the adventitia is thicker than the media. In most veins, valves are present, formed of folds of endothelium, and help to determine the direction of flow. The capillaries, which unite the arteries and veins, have their walls formed of a single endothelial layer of large angular flattened cells.

The direct union between two vessels is called an anastomosis. Sinusoids are thin-walled, dilated channels uniting arteries and veins and are found in the bone marrow, liver, spleen and suprarenal glands. Their endothelial lining contains many mobile cells of the macrophage system.

In some situations blood passes through two capillary beds before returning to the heart; this constitutes a portal circulation. The passage of blood from the stomach, intestine, pancreas and spleen through the liver exemplifies such a system.

Reduction of the blood supply to a region is known as ischaemia and this is of particular importance in the heart and brain. One important degenerative arterial disease which can affect the vessels is arteriosclerosis and this is very prevalent in developed countries. The arterial narrowing produced by the disease may cause local intravascular clotting (thrombosis) to occur. A local thrombus may also be flushed into the blood stream (forming an embolus) and block distal smaller vessels. Local death of an area of tissue or organ due to reduction of its blood supply is known as an infarction.

Lymph consists of cells and plasma. The cellular and protein proportions are less than in blood.

Lymph cells—mainly lymphocytes.

THE LYMPH SYSTEM

This collects tissue fluid and conveys it to the blood stream. It comprises the lymph capillaries and vessels, the lymph nodes and aggregations of lymph tissue in the spleen, thymus and around the alimentary tract.

The lymph capillaries are larger than those of the blood; they are composed of a single layer of endothelial cells. The lymph vessels resemble veins and possess many paired valves. The larger collecting vessels open into the venous system near the formation of the brachiocephalic veins.

A lymph node is an aggregation of lymph tissue along the course of a lymph vessel. It is bean-shaped with a number of afferent vessels (conveying lymph to the node) entering its convex surface, and an efferent vessel (carrying lymph away from the node) leaving its hilus. It is surrounded by a fibrous capsule from which fibrous trabeculae pass inwards. It is filled with a reticular network of fine collagen fibres, and the cells are either primitive (lymphocyte precursors) or fixed macrophages. Numerous lymphocytes and a few monocytes lie freely within the meshwork but they are absent peripherally, leaving a subcapsular lymph space. The cells of the outer part of the node (cortex) are densely packed and form oval masses called follicles. The centre of the follicle and the hilar (medullary) regions of the node contain loosely packed lymphocytes.

Lymph aggregations elsewhere in the body consist of a mixture of follicles and loosely packed lymphocytes.

Bacterial infections produce inflammatory responses in the regional lymph nodes. In many malignant diseases neoplastic cells spread via the lymph vessels to the regional lymph nodes and there develop to such an extent as to completely replace the normal tissue of the lymph node and occlude lymph flow. The stagnation of lymph within the tissues due to obstruction of flow produces a swelling of the tissues known as lymphoedema.

15

THE MOBILE CELLS OF THE BODY

These form the macrophage (reticulo-endothelial) system. They are capable of ingesting foreign material and are an important defence against micro-organisms. They are found in the lymph tissue (macrophages), blood (monocytes), connective tissue (tissue macrophages), nervous tissue (microglia), and the sinusoids of the bone marrow, liver, spleen and suprarenals (reticulo-endothelial cells).

ORIENTATION

The anatomical position, about which anatomical relations are orientated, is one in which the person stands upright with feet together, eyes looking forward and arms straight down the side of the body, with the palms facing forward.

Structures in front are termed anterior (ventral) and those behind, posterior (dorsal). Structures above are superior (cranial, rostral) and those below, inferior (caudal). Structures may be nearer to (medial) or further from (lateral) the midline and those in the midline are called median. A sagittal plane passes vertically anteroposteriorly through the body and a coronal plane passes vertically at right angles to a sagittal plane. Transverse (horizontal) planes pass horizontally through the body.

Movements—Forward movement in a sagittal plane is usually flexion and backward movement, extension. Owing to rotation of the lower limb during development, backward movement of the leg extends the hip and flexes the knee; downward movement of the toes is flexion. Upward movement at the ankle joint is dorsiflexion (extension) and downward movement is plantar flexion (flexion). Movement away from the midline in the coronal plane is abduction and movement towards the midline is adduction. Side to side movement of the neck and trunk is termed lateral flexion. Circumduction is the movement when the distal end of a bone describes the base of a cone whose apex is at the proximal end. Rotation occurs in the long axis of a bone; in the limbs it may be medial, towards the midline or lateral, away from it.

RADIOGRAPHIC AND RADIO-ISOTOPIC EXAMINATION OF THE BODY

The study of normal and disordered anatomy in the living human subject by means of X-rays has developed enormously in the last 60 years. Plain radiographs will demonstrate most bony features, for bone is markedly radiopaque in comparison to the soft tissues of the body. The use of ingested or injected substances, with an absorptive capacity for X-rays different from the body tissues, has allowed many organs to be examined. For example, the ingestion of barium sulphate by mouth, or its introduction per anum by an enema, allows the upper or lower parts of the gastro-intestinal tract to be examined. The gall bladder can be examined radiographically by some iodine-containing substances (taken by mouth or by intravenous injection) which are excreted by the liver into the bile. Certain radiopaque substances are excreted by the kidneys and thus the structure of the kidney and the ureters can be examined. Direct injection of radiopaque substances into arteries, veins, lymph vessels, the subarachnoid space, bladder and joints also allows radiographic examination of these structures (Figs. 1.1, 10.1, 11.3, 12.1).

Some radio-isotopes when ingested or injected are preferentially localised in certain organs. The gamma-camera allows a fairly precise localisation of the radio-isotope by measuring its emissions and in this way the thyroid, liver, kidney, pancreas and brain can be indirectly studied (Fig. 11.2).

CHAPTER 2

EMBRYOLOGY

Embryology is the study of development from the time of fertilisation of the mature female ovum by the male spermatozoon to the time of birth. During this period of about nine calendar months the embryo undergoes a process of growth and differentiation. Interruption, or delay, of the process will almost certainly give rise to congenital abnormalities. Thus a

FIG. 2.1

Early development of fertilised egg. The bold numbers indicate the age in days after fertilisation.

1. Zona pellucida 2. Ectodermal germ layer 3. Endodermal germ layer 4. Embryonic disc 5. Trophoblast 6. Exocoelomic cavity 7. Syncytiotrophoblast 8. Cytotrophoblast 9. Amnioblast 10. Amniotic cavity 11. Extra-embryonic mesoderm (e.e.m) 12. Developing yolk sac 13. Exocoelomic cyst 14. Extra-embryonic coelome 15. Somatopleuric e.e.m. 16. Splanchnopleuric e.e.m. 17. Yolk sac 18. Body stalk 19. Chorion

clear knowledge of normal human development will enable the mechanisms of the production of embryological defects to be understood (Fig. 2.1).

The mature ovum is about 120 μm in diameter and is surrounded by a thick coat known as the **zona pellucida.** As it is expelled from the ovary it is caught by fimbriae of the uterine tube and drawn into the ampulla, probably by suction. Here it may be fertilised by a spermatozoon but its life cycle without fertilisation is only 12–24 hours. Although only one spermatozoon is necessary for fertilisation many others are probably necessary to aid penetration of the zona pellucida by the fertilising sperm. The mature female and male germ cells contain only half the adult number (haploid) of chromosomes. Fusion of the two germ cells to form the **zygote** restores the adult number (diploid) of chromosomes. During the 3–6 days after fertilisation the zygote is passed to the uterine cavity by contraction of the muscular walls of the uterine tube and by the cilia of the epithelial lining. Failure of this transport can give rise to an ectopic pregnancy in which the embryo develops in the uterine tube or even in the abdominal cavity or on the ovary.

During the passage to the uterus the zygote undergoes cellular division, each cell being called a blastomere. Once the 12–16 cell stage has been reached the structure is known as the **morula** (mulberry) and two distinct cell types are present. The smaller outer cells line the zona pellucida and are nutritive in function, and the larger inner cells (**inner cell mass**) are destined to become the future embryo.

Once the morula has reached the uterus, fluid from the uterine cavity enters its intercellular spaces. Confluence of these spaces produces a central cavity and the structure is now known as a **blastocyst**. The zona pellucida disappears at this stage and allows enlargement of the blastocyst and its implantation into the uterine wall. This occurs between 7 and 11 days. The cells which surround the cyst are known as the **trophoblast**, while the cells of the slower dividing inner cell mass come to lie at one end of the cyst and are known as the **embryoblast**. By the 8th day the embryoblast consists of two layers of cells, a flattened layer, adjacent to the cavity, known as the **endodermal germ layer** and a higher columnar layer, adjacent to the trophoblast, known as the **ectodermal germ layer**. At this stage another cavity develops between the ectodermal layer and the trophoblast; this is the **amniotic cavity** (and the cells lining the trophoblast side of the cavity are known as **amnioblasts**). The ectodermal and endodermal layers together form the **germ disc**. By the 9th day a further layer of cells is developing within the blastocyst known as the **extra-embryonic mesoderm** (Heuser's membrane or **primary mesenchyme**). It lines the trophoblast and is probably formed from it, being continuous with the periphery of the embryonic endoderm. At this stage the cavity of the blastocyst is known as the **exocoelomic cavity** (**primitive yolk sac**). Between the 9th and 14th days the exocoelomic cavity is gradually obliterated by an increase of extra-embryonic mesoderm and by the development of the **secondary** (**definitive**) **yolk sac**. The yolk sac is lined by endoderm but it is uncertain whether its formation is due to a cavity developing within the endoderm or whether a layer of endoderm grows out from the periphery of the germ disc and nips off part of the exocoelomic cavity to form the sac. By the 13th day the exocoelome is represented only by one or more **exocoelomic cysts**. The extra-embryonic mesoderm splits to form a further cavity, the **extra-embryonic coelome**. In this way the extra-embryonic mesoderm is divided into two parts; an inner layer surrounding the yolk sac, germ disc and the enlarging amniotic cavity, (**the extra-embryonic splanchnopleuric mesoderm**),

19

and an outer layer lining the trophoblast, the **extra-embryonic somatopleuric mesoderm**. The two layers are continuous as a narrow **body stalk** at one end of the embryonic disc and this stalk will develop into the **umbilical cord**. The trophoblast and somatopleure together make up a structure known as the **chorion** and this forms a vital link between the developing embryo and the uterus.

While the embryo is passing along the uterine tube, the uterine lining, influenced by hormones produced by the corpus luteum, undergoes the so-called **decidual reaction**. Menstruation is inhibited, the endometrial glands proliferate and the endometrial vascularity increases. After losing the zona pellucida the blastocyte becomes at first adherent and then embedded in the uterine wall, usually posteriorly. The endometrial covering of the blastocyst is now called the **decidua capsularis**, that between the embryo and the uterine muscle the **decidua basalis** and that over the remainder of the uterus the **decidua parietalis**. After implantation the trophoblast undergoes rapid proliferation. Cell definition is lost in its outer layer, the nuclei lying in a common cytoplasm called the **syncytiotrophoblast**. An inner layer of cells remains definable and is known as the **cytotrophoblast**. Syncytiotrophoblast with the underlying cytotrophoblast extends in finger-like processes known as **primary villi** into the decidua. As organisation progresses the extra-embryonic mesoderm of the chorion grows into the primary villi and they are then known as **secondary villi**. When branches of the future umbilical artery and vein have developed within the mesoderm the villi are called **tertiary villi**. The maternal tissue between the villi becomes a collection of blood lakes, the **intervillous spaces**.

GENERAL BODY FORM

By the beginning of the 3rd week (15th day) the oval-shaped embryonic disc, made up of ectodermal and endodermal layers, lies between the amniotic and yolk sacs (Fig. 2.2). Both the disc and the sacs are surrounded by splanchnopleure. The body stalk of extra-embryonic mesoderm joins these structures to the chorion. About the 14th day a midline endodermal area of thickening develops at the end of the disc away from the body stalk, this is the **prochordal plate** (future mouth area). In this region the endoderm and ectoderm are closely adherent and remain so throughout development. The area later becomes the **buccopharyngeal membrane**. The prochordal plate is at the cephalic end of the disc, and the body stalk is at the caudal end. The embryo can thus be orientated. During the 15th and 16th days a midline differentiation occurs in the caudal half of the disc to form the **primitive streak**. From this region cells stream forward between the ectoderm and endoderm on either side of the midline to form a third germinal layer known as the **mesodermal germ layer.** The mesoderm extends forwards on each side of the prochordal plate reaching the midline beyond it to form the **cardiogenic mesoderm** which will later contain the **pericardial cavity**.

At the cephalic end of the primitive streak there is a thickening known as the **primitive knot (Hensen's node)** in which there is a central pit, the **primitive pit.** About the 17th day a midline collection of cells, the

head process, grows forward from Hensen's node between the ectodermal and endodermal layers to reach the prochordal plate. For a short time the head process replaces the endoderm being in direct contact with the

FIG. 2.2
Development of the embryonic disc. The bold numbers indicate the age in days after fertilisation.

1. Ectoderm   2. Endoderm   3. Prochordal plate (oral membrane)   4. Primitive streak   5. Primitive knot with central pit   6. Notochordal process   7. Allantois   8. Splanchnopleuric extra-embryonic mesoderm (e.e.m)   9. Somatopleuric e.e.m.   10. Pericardial cavity   11. Cloacal membrane   12. Notochord   13. Neurenteric canal   14. Clefts in lateral plate mesoderm (beginning of intra-embryonic coelome)   15. Pericardioperitoneal canal   16. Intra-embryonic mesoderm   17. Neural crest   18. Neuroectoderm   19. Neural groove   20. Somitic mesoderm   21. Intermediate mesoderm   22. Lateral plate mesoderm   23. Dorsal aorta   24. Communication between intra- and extra-embryonic coelomes   25. Neural tube

yolk sac. About the 18th day the head process becomes canalised to form the **notochordal (neurenteric) canal** which temporarily unites the amniotic and yolk sac cavities. The head process soon folds along its longitudinal axis to form a solid column of cells known as the **notochord**, this being the precursor of the vertebral column. The neurenteric canal becomes obliterated and the endoderm reunites beneath the notochord to separate it from the yolk sac. This process is completed by the end of the 3rd week.

The midline area of ectoderm caudal to the primitive streak is closely related to the endodermal layer. Together they form the **cloacal membrane** which will later become the **urogenital** and **anal membranes**. A diverticulum arises from the yolk sac adjacent to the cloacal membrane, and extends into the body stalk. It is known as the **allantois**. Although the allantois of lower animals plays an important role in the developing urogenital system it remains rudimentary in man. By the end of the 3rd week of development three embryonic germ layers have appeared and some differentiation has already taken place, the embryonic disc becoming elongated and pear-shaped with a recognisably wider cephalic end. The ectoderm and endoderm remain in contact at the prochordal plate and at the cloacal membrane, and the precursors of the vertebral column (notochord) and the pericardial cavity are already discernable. Development now enters the **embryonic period** (4th–8th weeks) during which time longitudinal and side-to-side folding of the disc turns it into a recognisable body form, and the main organ systems are laid down.

The ectodermal surface of the embryonic disc is carried by the longitudinal (**head** and **tail folds**) and side-to-side folding of the disc over all aspects of the embryo. The head fold not only swings the buccopharyngeal membrane (prochordal plate) to the ventral surface of the embryo, it also brings the pericardial region to the ventral surface, caudal to the buccopharyngeal membrane. The tail fold brings the cloacal membrane to the ventral aspect of the embryo, and both the head and tail folds tend to narrow the attachment of the embryo to the body stalk. The simultaneous ventral folding of the sides of the embryonic disc enclose an endoderm-lined tube of yolk sac which extends from the buccopharyngeal membrane to the cloacal membrane. This tube is the future alimentary tract and its connection to the yolk sac is soon only a narrow stalk, the **vitelline duct**. The further development of the embryo can now be considered as being from three concentric cylinders (representing the three germ layers). They are curved longitudinally to form a 'C', the opening of which is attached to the chorion by the body stalk, which in turn contains the remains of the yolk sac. The outer cylinder (representing the ectoderm) is not completed ventrally until:

(a) the pericardial region has come to lie caudal to the buccopharyngeal membrane.

(b) some communications between the extra-embryonic coelome and a new cavity within the mesoderm (the intra-embryonic coelome) have been closed.

(c) the development of the alimentary and urogenital systems allows completion of the anterior abdominal wall (Fig. 2.3).

As the ectoderm comes to surround the embryo, the amniotic cavity, which started as a small cavity adjacent to the ectoderm, also expands and surrounds the embryo. The embryo is now enclosed in the amniotic cavity, the body stalk being narrowed down to the thin elongated umbilical cord. The three primitive germ layers become differentiated during the folding process into the tissues and organs of the body. As an understanding of mesodermal differentiation is the key to this process it will be considered first.

MESODERMAL GERM LAYER (Figs. 2.2 and 2.4)

The primitive mesoderm is formed from the primitive streak and extends forwards on either side of the notochord and buccopharyngeal membrane; it also forms the midline pericardial region, the latter coming to lie caudal to the buccopharyngeal membrane after development of the head fold. The mesoderm on each side of the midline differentiates into a medial block of **paraxial mesoderm** and the laterally placed **lateral plate mesoderm**. From the end of the third week the paraxial mesoderm on each side of the midline becomes transversely divided into the segmented blocks known as **somites**. This process starts adjacent to the cranial end of the notochord and progresses in caudal sequence. It is customary to express the age of the embryo between the 4th and 6th weeks by the number of somites that have appeared, these being discernable on external examination. By the end of the 4th week approximately 30 pairs of somites have appeared and by the end of the 5th week 42–44 pairs are present. Some of the most cranial and caudal pairs eventually disappear to equate to the adult number of 31 pairs of spinal nerves. By the 6th week the embryo has taken up a definite form and the crown to rump measurement (**crown-rump length**) is thereafter used to tabulate growth.

Each somite differentiates into a ventromedially placed **sclerotome** and a dorsalateral **dermomyotome**. The sclerotome in turn differentiates into young connective tissue (mesenchyme) which forms the bone, cartilage and packing tissue of the trunk. During the 4th week each sclerotome migrates medially and surrounds the notochord, forming the vertebral column. Each adult vertebral body is in fact intersegmental in position, i.e. it is formed from the halves of two adjacent somites. The nucleus pulposus of the adult intervertebral disc is produced by mucoid degeneration of the notochord. The skull is also partly developed from the sclerotomes. Initially two distinct parts, the **neurocranium** surrounding the brain, and the **viscerocranium** forming the face, are present.

The dermomyotome has two distinct elements, an outer **dermatome** and an inner **myotome**. The dermatome migrates deep to the ectoderm to form the dermis and subcutaneous tissues of the body. The myotome differentiates into young muscle cells (**myoblasts**) which form the striated somatic musculature of the body. A smaller dorsal block of the myotome (**epimere**) is innervated by the dorsal ramus of a spinal nerve while the larger ventral part of the myotome (**hypomere**) is innervated by its ventral ramus. Not all striated muscle, however, is somitic in origin. The muscles derived from the pharyngeal arches, e.g. those of mastication, of facial expression and of the pharynx and larynx develop from the mesenchymal core of the arch. It is debated whether the limb musculature develops from the mesenchymal core of the limb bud or whether the appropriate somitic myotomes are carried into the limb bud with the ventral rami of the respective spinal nerves. Further uncertainty exists about the development of the extrinsic eye muscles and the tongue muscles. It is thought that the eye muscles may be derived from the so-called pre-otic myotomes situated on either side of the prochordal plate, and the tongue muscles by the ventral migration of occipital myotomes. Each myotome acquires its appropriate cranial nerve innervation.

By the end of the 3rd week clefts appear within the lateral plate mesoderm. These clefts coalesce to form a longitudinal cavity on each side

Fig. 2.3

Longitudinal sagittal section of a 30 day embryo. Transverse sections of the embryo at sites A–D are shown in Fig. 2.4. The two arrows are in the enlarging amniotic cavity.

1. Placental site   2. Body stalk (umbilical cord)   3. Yolk sac (vitello-intestinal duct)
4. Forebrain   5. Eye rudiment   6. Buccopharyngeal membrane   7. Pericardial sac
8. Head fold   9. Notochord   10. Foregut   11. Lung bud   12. Heart tube   13. Dorsal pancreatic bud   14. Spinal cord   15. Ventral pancreatic bud   16. Midgut   17. Amniotic ectoderm   18. Extra-embryonic mesoderm   19. Hindgut   20. Allantois   21. Cloacal membrane

of the midline, the **intra-embryonic coelome**. The lateral plate mesoderm is thus divided into a layer lining the ectoderm, known as **somatopleuric mesoderm,** and a layer covering the endoderm, known as **splanchnopleuric mesoderm**. Coincident with the development of the intra-embryonic coelome within the lateral plate mesoderm a further space is forming within the pericardial mesoderm—the pericardial cavity. The latter unites with the coelome on each side to form a single ∩-shaped cavity. The longitudinal cavities adjacent to the pericardial sac become the **pericardioperitoneal canals** from which develop the future pleural sacs. Whilst these cavities are uniting, the clefts in the lateral plate mesoderm extend into the extra-embryonic mesoderm and the extra-

24

embryonic coelome. A free communication soon exists between intra-embryonic and extra-embryonic coelomic cavities. The intra-embryonic somatopleuric mesoderm becomes continuous with the extra-embryonic mesoderm over the amniotic cavity, and the intra-embryonic splanchno-pleuric mesoderm becomes continuous with the extra-embryonic mesoderm

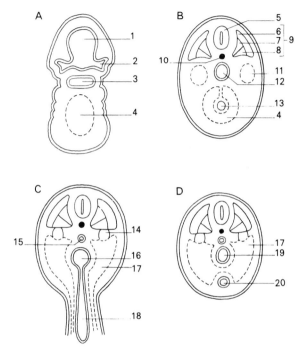

FIG. 2.4
Transverse sections of 30 day embryo cut at sites shown in FIG. 2.3.

1. Forebrain vesicle   2. Eye rudiment   3. Stomodeum   4. Pericardial cavity
5. Neural tube   6. Dermatome   7. Myotome   8. Sclerotome   9. Somitic mesoderm
10. Notochord   11. Pericardioperitoneal canal   12. Foregut   13. Primitive heart
tube   14. Intermediate mesoderm   15. Dorsal aorta   16. Midgut   17. Peritoneal
cavity bounded by lateral-plate mesoderm   18. Yolk sac in body stalk   19. Hindgut
20. Allantois

over the yolk sac (Figs. 2.3, 2.4). The communication between intra-embryonic and extra-embryonic coelomic cavities is limited and does not extend cranially into the pericardial cavity or into the short length of intra-embryonic coelome immediately adjacent to it on each side (the pleural cavities).

The communications are thought to have a nutritional function for the embryo but with the development of the umbilical and placental circulation the intra-embryonic coelome becomes cut off. The extra-embryonic coelome is obliterated by the enlarging amniotic sac. The reformed coelomic cavity on each side comes to surround the gut, while the splanchnopleuric mesoderm from each side unites dorsally and ventrally to form the **dorsal** and **ventral mesenteries** of the gut. The splanchnopleuric mesoderm also forms the smooth muscle, connective tissue and blood vessels of the gut and its derivatives. The future pericardial, pleural and peritoneal cavities are formed from the intra-embryonic coelome by septa developing cranial and caudal to the pleural cavities. The separation of the midline pericardium from the pleural cavities is by two transverse folds known as the **pleuropericardial membranes**. The folds overlie the **common cardinal veins** which remain in position as the pericardium descends and the lungs expand, stretching the pericardioperitoneal canals over them. The folds separating the pleural cavities from the peritoneal cavity later form part of the diaphragm. The diaphragm is formed largely from a single midline ventral mass, the **septum transversum**, lying between the pericardium and the cranial lip of the yolk sac. Additionally paired transverse dorsolateral folds, the **pleuroperitoneal membranes**, grow out to fuse with the septum transversum in front, and the mesentery of the lower oesophagus behind. The diaphragm is completed by peripheral contributions from the body wall. In the abdomen the dorsal mesentery is retained from the lower oesophagus to the upper rectum, being most easily recognisable as the small gut mesentery and being greatly expanded and folded to form the greater omentum. The ventral mesentery is absent below the level of the first part of the duodenum which means that the two lateral compartments of the coelomic cavity can unite to form a single peritoneal cavity (p. 94).

Urogenital Development (Figs. 2.2 and 2.4)

A longitudinal non-segmented condensation of mesoderm develops between the paraxial and lateral plate mesoderm known as the **intermediate cell mass (nephrogenic cord)**. This region develops successively craniocaudially into the **pronephros**, **mesonephros** and **metanephros**. Of the first two components only the **mesonephric duct (Wolffian duct)** persists. The metanephros forms the secreting part of the adult kidney, and a **ureteric bud** from the caudal end of the mesonephric duct forms the collecting system. The mesonephric duct persists in the male as the ductus deferens but disappears in the female. A further tube, the **paramesonephric (Müllerian) duct** appears in the 6th week. It lies parallel and medial to the mesonephric duct and, like the latter, it opens into the terminal part of the alimentary canal, the **cloaca**. In the male the paramesonephric duct regresses but in the female it persists and the cranial portion (opening directly into the peritoneal cavity) persists as the uterine tube. The lower portion of the two paramesonephric tubes unite in the midline in the female to form the uterus and upper vagina.

During the 4th week a septum, the **urorectal fold**, begins to grow caudally from the cranial lip of the allantois. In the 6th week the septum reaches and fuses with the cloacal membrane while laterally it fuses with the wall of the pelvis. The septum thus subdivides the cloaca into a ventrally situated **primitive urogenital sinus** receiving the mesonephric and paramesonephric ducts, and a dorsally situated **anorectal canal**. Similarly it subdivides the cloacal membrane into the **urogenital** and **anal membranes**. The portion of the primitive urogenital sinus cranial to the point of entry of mesonephric duct is the definitive bladder and proximal urethra and that caudal to it the distal urethra. As development proceeds the distal end of each mesonephric duct is gradually incorporated into the wall of the sinus so that the ureter opens independently into the sinus. By further incorporation and differential growth, the ureter comes to enter the bladder portion of the sinus. A communication between the bladder and the allantois, the **urachus**, may persist but usually forms the median umbilical ligament of the adult. In the male the mesonephric duct comes to enter the more distal part of the urogenital sinus which forms the prostatic and membranous urethra. The prostate gland is formed from urethral outgrowths. In the female the fused paramesonephric ducts enter the distal part of the urogenital sinus. The portion of the sinus above this point of entry makes a small contribution to the urethra. The remainder forms the adult vestibule and a small portion of the vagina.

The external genitalia develop from swellings around the urogenital and anal membranes which usually rupture during development. At the end of the 3rd week mesoderm from the primitive streak migrates and surrounds the cloacal membrane forming a midline **cloacal eminence** adjacent to the allantois, and, on each side, a medial **genital fold** and a lateral **cloacal** (**labioscrotal**) **swelling.** After the separation of the urogenital and anal membranes the part of the cloacal swelling adjacent to the anal membrane comes to surround the latter as the **anal fold**. In the female the genital folds border the urogenital membrane and then become the labia minora, the cloacal swellings becoming the labia majora. The cloacal eminence becomes known as the **genital tubercle** and later forms the clitoris. In the male the genital folds become the **urethral folds** and form the body of the penis. A groove along the ventral aspect becomes enclosed and forms the bulbous and spongy urethra. The cloacal eminence (genital tubercle) forms the glans penis. The cloacal swellings become the **scrotal swellings** which fuse in the midline to form the adult scrotum.

The gonads develop in the 4th week as the **gonadal ridge** of mesoderm situated on each side of the midline, between the mesonephros and the dorsal mesentery. The primitive germ cells are first formed from the endoderm of the yolk sac adjacent to the allantois but they migrate dorsally and along the dorsal mesentery to reach the gonadal ridges in the 6th week.

Cardiovascular Development (See also p. 59)

The cardiovascular system is an early mesodermal derivative distributing nutriment through the embryo. The blood vessels are derived from clusters of primitive mesodermal cells known as **angioblasts**. Confluence of intercellular clefts within the clusters form blood channels. The angioblasts lining the channels become the flattened endothelium of the vessels, while the clumps of cells enclosed within the channels become the red blood cells. White cells develop later. This process is first seen in the walls of the yolk sac but is rapidly followed in the chorion and within the embryo itself. The heart starts to develop at the end of the 3rd week as two tubes which initially lie ventral to the pericardium but come to lie dorsal to it as the head fold develops. About this time the tubes fuse and invaginate the pericardium to produce the **dorsal mesentery**. Early in the 4th week the heart becomes disproportionally elongated and buckles in ∽-shaped fashion within the pericardium. The main arteries and veins thus become more closely related over the cranio dorsal aspect of the

FIG. 2.5

Development of the systemic venous system (A, B and C) and of the portal venous system (D and E). The dotted lines represent vessels which disappear.

1. Sinus venosus   2. Right common cardinal vein   3. Left common cardinal vein   4. Anterior cardinal vein   5. Posterior cardinal vein   6. Subcardinal vein   7. Supracardinal vein   8. Azygos vein   9. Right umbilical vein   10. Left umbilical vein   11. Right vitelline vein   12. Left vitelline vein   13. Hepatic vein joining IVC   14. Portal vein   15. Superior mesenteric vein   16. Splenic vein   17. Ductus venosus   18. Superior vena cava   19. Brachiocephalic veins   20. Coronary sinus   21. Adult azygos vein   22. Hemiazygos and accessory hemiazygos veins   23. Definitive inferior vena cava (shaded)   24. IVC link with hepatic veins   25. Renal veins   26. Neural tube   27. Sympathetic chain   28. Primitive midgut   29. Liver   30. Kidney

pericardium (see also p. 60). The dorsal mesentery of the pericardium breaks down and the defect, situated between the arteries cranially and the veins caudally, becomes the **transverse sinus**. The first heart beat occurs about the 4th week. As the circulation is not established at this time, the main effect is to produce some ebb and flow of blood and also possibly produce movement of fluid between the intra- and extra-embryonic coelomic cavities.

The **dorsal aortae** develop on each side of the notochord in the 4th week. They are joined by the umbilical and vitelline arteries and give off segmental branches. At the head end of the body the dorsal aortae pass ventrally around the primitive foregut as the first pharyngeal arch arteries and then turn, and form the **ventral aortae**. The latter soon unite and enter the cranial end of the heart tube. Further paired **aortic arch** vessels appear in association with the development of the other pharyngeal arches (p. 301), and they link the ventral with the paired dorsal aortae. Caudal to this level the dorsal aortae fuse. The paired vitelline arteries also fuse to form three unpaired branches, the coeliac, superior mesenteric and inferior mesenteric arteries which pass to the foregut, midgut and hindgut respectively. The umbilical arteries are initially branches of the paired dorsal aortae, but later become separate branches from the iliac vessels. Each is represented in the adult as the internal iliac and superior vesical arteries and the lateral umbilical ligament. Segmental branches from the fused dorsal aortae pass to the various mesodermal and ectodermal derivatives.

Venous development parallels that of the arteries (Fig. 2.5). Paired vitelline and umbilical veins pass to the sinus venosus of the heart. The primitive embryonic vessels consist of pairs of cardinal veins running the length of the embryo and being divided into anterior and posterior portions with respect to a pair of common cardinal veins which connect them to the sinus venosus of the heart. Further venous development can best be understood by reference to Fig. 2.5.

ENDODERMAL GERM LAYER (Figs. 2.2, 2.3 and 2.4)

It has been shown that with the longitudinal and side-to-side folding of the embryo the primitive endodermal lining of the yolk sac is fashioned into a longitudinal tube extending between the buccopharyngeal and the cloacal membranes. This forms the primitive gut. The gut remains attached to the yolk sac by a stalk of diminishing diameter, the vitelline duct. A series of paired vitelline arteries form around the duct and communicate with the dorsal aortae, but when the latter fuse the vitelline arteries also fuse and become reduced to three midline arteries, the coeliac and the superior and inferior mesenteric arteries.

The **primitive foregut** extends from the buccopharyngeal membrane to approximately the level of origin of the liver bud. The buccopharyngeal membrane breaks down in the 3rd week. Between the 4th and 5th weeks the cranial end of the foregut acquires a series of paired lateral pharyngeal grooves which divide the adjacent mesoderm into six bars of tissue known as the pharyngeal (branchial) arches. The derivatives of the arches are considered on pages 290, 301, 329. In the region immediately caudal to the last pair of pharyngeal arches, and preceding their full development, a ventral midline **respiratory (tracheobronchial) diverticulum** appears which grows caudally. In the 6th week the diverticulum bifurcates to form the paired **lung buds**. The lung buds grow into the pericardio-peritoneal canals and acquire a covering of splanchnopleuric mesoderm which develops into the connective tissue, smooth muscle and blood vessels of the adult organ. The lining of the canal becomes the pulmonary and parietal pleura. Below the respiratory diverticulum the foregut becomes the oesophagus, and the caudal part develops into the stomach and proximal duodenum. Elongation of the primitive tube in the region of the stomach and duodenum produces a kink, the duodenum coming to lie on the right side of the body and its dorsal mesentery in this region fuses with the posterior abdominal wall coelomic mesoderm. The ventral mesentery of the foregut stops at the approximate position of the liver bud but passes from the anterior body wall to the lower oesophagus, stomach and upper duodenum. The mesentery is continuous with the mass of mesoderm forming the septum transversum. The dorsal mesentery of the enlarging stomach, which comes to lie transversely, elongates to form a dependent fold known as the greater omentum, the layers of which adhere to each other. A clear understanding of the fate of the ventral and dorsal mesenteries of the foregut will greatly facilitate an understanding of the adult peritoneal cavity (see p. 94).

As the foregut only has a ventral mesentery a free edge of the mesentery can be expected at the lower end of the foregut. The edge becomes partly obscured by the ventrally placed liver bud growing and enlarging within the substance of the ventral mesentery. The liver divides the ventral mesentery into the falciform ligament which passes from the anterior body wall to the liver, and the lesser omentum from the liver to the gut. In the adult the free edge referred to extends from the umbilicus to the liver as the lower border of the falciform ligament (containing the obliterated umbilical vein), is obscured by the liver in its middle portion and then continues as the right border of the lesser omentum (containing the bile duct, hepatic artery and portal vein). The transverse position taken up by the stomach and the enlargement of the liver combine to enclose the right half of this region of the coelomic cavity as a separate compartment known as the omental bursa (lesser sac). As the liver bud enlarges within the ventral mesentery it comes into contact with the septum transversum which extends dorsally from the ventral wall forming a mass of mesoderm across the ventral mesentery. The septum transversum contributes mesodermal elements to the bile ducts, and cords of liver cells penetrate into its substance. The pancreas develops from a ventral bud adjacent to the liver bud and a more proximal dorsal bud from the foregut directly. Differential growth and rotation of the duodenum bring the buds together to form the adult pancreas.

The midgut extends from the position of the liver bud to approximately the junction of the middle and distal thirds of the adult transverse colon (the part supplied by the superior mesenteric artery). As already stated the midgut has no ventral mesentery and the dorsal mesentery becomes stretched as the midgut undergoes marked elongation. In the 6th week the enlargement of the midgut outstrips the enlargement of the abdominal cavity and loops of gut are extruded into the jelly-like extra-embryonic mesoderm of the body stalk (umbilical cord). The loops begin to return in the 10th week but in doing so they make a 270° counter-clockwise (as viewed from the ventral surface) turn about the axis of the superior mesenteric artery. The gut has returned to the abdomen by the 12th week and is nearly in its adult position (p. 94).

The hindgut, extends from the midgut to the cloacal membrane and forms the distal colon, the rectum and upper anal canal. The terminal hindgut (cloaca) partakes in the development of both the urogenital system (bladder) and the alimentary system (rectum), and has been studied above. The anal membrane usually disappears after the 9th week but may be present at birth.

ECTODERMAL GERM LAYER (Figs. 2.2, 2.3 and 2.4)

The primitive ectoderm initially forms the dorsal aspect of the embryonic disc, being continuous at its periphery with the ectoderm lining of the amniotic cavity. At the beginning of the 3rd week the midline cranial portion of ectoderm becomes differentiated, into the **neural plate**, the future nervous system. The midline grooving, folding and tube formation of this region to form the central nervous system is considered on page 345. The neural crest, a dorsal longitudinal plate of cells on each side of the neural tube, becomes differentiated into the ganglia of the dorsal roots and the cranial nerves, their peripheral and central branches, the ganglia of the autonomic nervous system and also the medulla of the suprarenal glands.

The remainder of the ectoderm extends to surround the developing embryo and forms the epidermis and skin derivatives, under which develops the mesodermal dermis. The ectoderm also contributes to the formation of the cutaneous and mammary glands. In early development the ectoderm over the prochordal plate is depressed to form a pit, the **stomodeum**. Mesodermal condensations around the stomodeum during the 5th week raise ectodermal processes which develop into the face (p. 274). The early breakdown of the buccopharyngeal membrane (3rd to 4th week) has created some uncertainty as to which structures in the mouth are ectodermal and which are endodermal in origin. Probable ectodermal derivatives are the gums, enamel organs of the teeth, nasal sinuses and the parotid salivary glands. A midline ectoderm diverticulum from the stomodeum known as **Rathke's pouch** extends dorsally to the base of the brain and contributes to the development of the pituitary gland. An area of ectoderm on each side of the head adjacent to the developing optic cup (itself an outgrowth from the brain) becomes the lens of the eye. The ectoderm covering the pharyngeal arches has transverse clefts (pharyngeal clefts) which mostly disappear. The first, however, contributes to the formation of the external acoustic meatus (p. 301).

The ectoderm over the cloacal membrane is depressed to form a pit, the **proctodeum**. The migration of mesoderm raises ectodermal folds around the membrane which have already been referred to. The folds form the external genitalia and also the lower part of the anal canal. The anal membrane ruptures usually at the end of the 9th week.

The limb buds appear at the end of the 5th week, the upper limbs preceding the lower. The debate as to whether the muscles are derived from somitic or core mesoderm has already been referred to but the nerves, arising from the ventral rami, have a well-marked segmental organisation. The digits are developed by the formation of four longitudinal grooves at the distal extremity of each limb. Initially the limbs project laterally but with the formation of the joints they come to lie more ventrally. A 90° axial rotation of the limbs (the direction being reversed in the upper and lower limbs) brings the elbows to point dorsally and the knees ventrally.

By the end of the 2nd month of development the embryo has taken on the familiar appearance with a large head, short limbs and wide body stalk. The period extending from the 3rd month to birth is known as the **fetal period** during which time the age of the fetus is expressed by its crown-rump or crown-heel length. During this period the head becomes relatively smaller, the limbs longer and the umbilical cord thin and elongated. The external genitalia also develop during this period.

Up to the 2nd month of development the uterine decidual reaction around the embedded trophoblast (the decidua capsularis and the decidua basalis) is uniform. Subsequently, however, with the increasing size of the fetus the decidua capsularis becomes thinned and the decidua basalis thickens to take up the disc-like form of the placenta. By the 3rd month the uterine cavity is obliterated with the progressive enlargement of the amniotic cavity. The extra-embryonic coelome is also obliterated, the amniotic membrane fusing with the chorion. Both membranes are continuous with the placenta at its margins. In the early stages of development, the chorion is evenly covered by villi. By the 3rd month, however, most villi have atrophied except those near the site of attachment of the body stalk. These villi increase in size and the whole area becomes the future placenta. The maternal surface of the full-term placenta is divided into about 20 smaller lobes (**cotyledons**). Each consists of 3 or 4 **villous stems** which anchor the placenta to the uterine lining. The uterine vessels open on to the spaces between the major villous stems. These lakes of blood are lined by maternal endothelium. Many other villi, carrying fetal blood vessels also occupy the blood-filled spaces between the major stem villi. The fetal blood is contained in the capillaries of the villi and separated from the maternal blood by fetal endothelium, mesenchyme and the trophoblast (syncytiotrophoblast outside and the incomplete cytotrophoblast inside). The fetal surface of the placenta is covered by the smooth transparent amnion, and the umbilical vessels can be seen ramifying and passing into the placental substance. At birth, the placenta is 15–20 cm in diameter, 3–4 cm thick and weighs approximately 500 g. The full-term fetus measures about 50 cm from crown to heel and weighs about 3 kg.

CHAPTER 3

THE VERTEBRAL COLUMN

This curved flexible pillar forms the central axis of the skeleton. It supports the weight of the head, trunk and upper limbs and transmits it through the pelvic girdle to the lower limbs. In the male it is about 70 cm long. It is composed of 33 bony segments, the vertebrae, united by cartilaginous discs and ligaments and within its canal it contains and protects the spinal cord.

The vertebrae are classified into five groups from above downwards, the cervical (7), thoracic (12), lumbar (5), sacral (5) and coccygeal (4). In the adult the sacral and coccygeal vertebrae fuse to form two bones, the sacrum and the coccyx.

A TYPICAL VERTEBRA

A typical vertebra has a body in front and a vertebral arch behind, together enclosing the vertebral foramen. The arch consists of paired anterior rounded pedicles and posterior flattened laminae. Transverse processes are attached in the region of union of the pedicles and laminae, and spinous processes to the union of the laminae. There are two superior and two inferior articular processes in contact with similar processes on adjacent vertebrae.

The **body** is short and cylindrical, slightly constricted in its middle and possessing flat upper and lower articular surfaces. Its posterior aspect is perforated by foramina for large basivertebral veins. The **pedicles** are short, thick, rounded processes extending backwards from the postero-lateral aspects of the body and are grooved above and below. With adjacent pedicles they bound intervertebral foramina which are traversed by the spinal nerves and vessels. The **laminae** are flat and fuse with each other posteriorly in the midline to form a backwardly projecting **spinous process**. The laminae of adjacent vertebrae overlap each other. The expanded tip of the spinous process may be palpable posteriorly in the midline. Superior and inferior pairs of **articular processes** arise near the junction of the pedicles and laminae. Each bears an articular facet for articulation with the adjacent vertebra. The stout **transverse processes** project laterally from the junction of the pedicles and laminae.

Regional Variations

Cervical, thoracic and lumbar groups of vertebrae are recognisable by characteristics which are most marked in their central members, whilst the vertebrae at each end of the group tend to resemble those of the adjacent region.

Cervical Region

A typical cervical vertebra (Fig. 3.1) has a small oval body, the superior articular surface of which bears lateral lips which articulate by small synovial joints with the reciprocally bevelled inferior articular surface of the vertebra above. The vertebral foramen is relatively large. Each short wide transverse process encloses a **foramen transversarium** and ends laterally as anterior and posterior tubercles. The articular processes are large and rounded. The superior articular surface faces backwards and upwards, the inferior in the opposite direction. The spine is bifid and placed deeply between the extensor muscles of the neck. The 1st, 2nd and 7th cervical vertebrae show some variations from this pattern.

FIG. 3.1
A typical cervical vertebra, superior aspect.

FIG. 3.2
The atlas, superior aspect.

The 1st cervical vertebra (the **atlas,** Fig. 3.2) is modified to allow free movement of the head. It consists of a ring of bone with neither body nor spine. The two bulky articular **lateral masses** are united by a shorter anterior and a longer posterior arch. The upper articular facets on the lateral masses are kidney-shaped, concave in their long axis and articulate with the occipital condyles. The lower articular facets are flat, circular and articulate with the 2nd cervical vertebra. Medially the masses bear a tubercle for the attachment of the transverse ligament of the atlas. The **anterior arch** has a small midline tubercle anteriorly for attachment of the anterior longitudinal ligament and bears posteriorly a facet for articulation with the dens of the axis. Its superior border gives attachment to the anterior atlanto-occipital membrane. The **posterior arch** bears a small midline tubercle for the attachment of the ligamentum nuchae. Its superior border is grooved on each side laterally by the vertebral artery and between the grooves gives attachment to the posterior atlanto-occipital membrane. The transverse processes are long, wide, possess no tubercles and their tips are palpable behind the angle of the mandible where they are crossed by the accessory nerve.

34

The 2nd cervical vertebra (the **axis,** Fig. 3.3) bears a conical projection, the **dens,** on the upper surface of its body. (This represents the body of the atlas.) It articulates with the back of the anterior arch of the atlas and is held in position by the transverse ligament of the atlas. The superior articular facets face upwards and are large and circular.

The 7th cervical vertebra (the **vertebra prominens**) has a long nonbifid spine which is distinctly palpable at the lower end of the nuchal furrow.

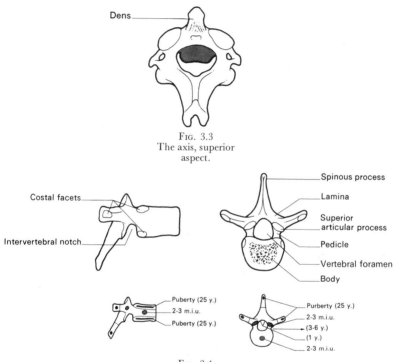

Fig. 3.3
The axis, superior
aspect.

Fig. 3.4
A typical thoracic vertebra, lateral and superior aspects.
Inset: ossification (m.i.u., months in utero; y., years).

Thoracic Region

A typical thoracic vertebra (Fig. 3.4) has a wedge-shaped body which is deeper posteriorly. The sides of each body articulate with paired ribs at a **superior** and a smaller **inferior costal facet** near the back of the upper and lower borders. The transverse processes are directed backwards and laterally, and their expanded ends bear articular facets for the tubercles of the corresponding ribs. The superior articular facets face backwards and laterally. The broad laminae and downward projecting spines overlap those of the vertebra below.

35

The bodies of the upper vertebra are smaller and narrower and their superior articular facets tend to face more superiorly. The bodies of the lower vertebrae are larger and broader, and their spines are more horizontal. The costal facets on the transverse processes are absent in the last two vertebrae. Each transverse process of the 12th thoracic vertebra bears an accessory process.

The body of the 1st thoracic vertebra has a larger upper facet for the 1st rib and a smaller inferior facet for the 2nd rib. The costal facets on the bodies of the 10th, 11th and 12th vertebrae are normally single and complete.

Lumbar Region

A typical lumbar vertebra (Fig. 3.5) possesses a large kidney-shaped body, wider from side to side than from before backwards. The bulky

Mamillary process — — Accessory process

Fig. 3.5
A typical lumbar vertebra,
superior aspect.

transverse processes project directly laterally, and posteriorly at their bases bear a small tubercle, the **accessory process.** The superior articular facets face backwards and medially and on the posterior surface of each process is a rounded **mamillary process.** The broad flat spinous process projects horizontally backwards.

The 5th lumbar vertebra is atypical—its body is wedge-shaped, being thicker anteriorly than posteriorly. Its transverse process is small and conical and arises from the side of the body and the pedicle. The forward facing inferior articular facet prevents it sliding anteriorly on the sloping upper surface of the sacrum.

The sacrum and coccyx are described on page 133.

JOINTS AND LIGAMENTS

The articular surfaces of the bodies of adjacent vertebrae are covered by a thin layer of hyaline cartilage and united by a thick fibro-cartilaginous **intervertebral disc.** The centre of the disc (**nucleus pulposus**) is gelatinous and is surrounded by a peripheral fibrous part, the **anulus fibrosus.** The disc acts as a shock absorber. It is normally under pressure and occasionally the semisolid nucleus herniates through a defect in the anulus and may press on the spinal cord or its nerves producing symptoms and signs of compression. The discs contribute about a quarter to the length of the column and are thicker in the cervical and lumbar regions. The vertebral bodies are also united by **anterior** and **posterior longitudinal ligaments.** The anterior ligament is a flat band extending from the occipital bone to the front of the sacrum. It is firmly attached to each vertebral body and disc. The posterior ligament is a broad band which extends from the sacral canal to the back of the body of the axis. It is also attached to each intervertebral disc.

Adjacent vertebral arches articulate by two plane synovial joints between paired articular processes. The joints possess a weak capsular ligament and additional support is provided by accessory ligaments:

(i) the **ligamenta flava** unite the adjacent laminae. They contain a large amount of yellow elastic tissue. They maintain the curvatures of the vertebral column, support the column when in the flexed position and help to restore it to the extended erect position.

(ii) the **supraspinous, interspinous** and **intertransverse ligaments.**

VARIATIONS

In the cervical region the vertebral bodies are also united by small synovial joints between the reciprocally lipped and bevelled lateral margins of their bodies.

The atlanto-occipital and atlanto-axial joints are modified to allow free movement of the head. X-ray pictures taken through the wide open mouth show these joints.

The **atlanto-occipital joints** are condyloid synovial joints between the convex occipital condyles and the concave upper surface of the lateral masses of the atlas. They possess weak capsular ligaments and two accessory ligaments, the **anterior** and **posterior atlanto-occipital membranes** which pass between the corresponding arch of the atlas and the margins of the foramen magnum.

The **atlanto-axial joints** comprise two lateral synovial plane joints between the lateral masses of the two vertebrae and a median synovial pivot between the dens and a ring formed by the anterior arch and the transverse ligament of the atlas. This latter has a weak capsular ligament and accessory ligaments, viz:

(i) the **membrana tectoria** is the upward continuation of the posterior longitudinal ligament. It ascends from the back of the body of the axis to the occipital bone just within the foramen magnum.

(ii) the **cruciate ligament** lies anterior to the membrana tectoria. It consists of the transverse ligament of the atlas passing between the lateral masses of the atlas, and a longitudinal ligament passing from the body of the axis to the anterior margin of the foramen magnum.

(iii) the **two alar ligaments** diverge from the upper part of the dens to the medial side of the occipital condyles.

(iv) the **apical ligament** is a thin ligament and lies anterior to the cruciate ligament. It ascends from the apex of the dens to the anterior margin of the foramen magnum.

FUNCTIONAL ASPECTS

CURVATURES AND MOBILITY: In the fetus the column is flexed throughout its length producing a primary curvature. After birth two secondary curvatures develop; extension of the cervical region is produced by the muscles raising the head, and extension of the lumbar region accompanies the adoption of the erect posture. The thoracic and sacral regions retain the primary curvature. The curves and intervertebral discs confer a certain resilience upon the column.

Movement: Whilst only limited movements between adjacent vertebrae are possible, these augment each other and the column as a whole will move extensively. Flexion is most marked in the cervical region, rotation in the thoracic, and extension and lateral flexion in the lumbar region. Flexion: rectus abdominis aided by the prevertebral muscles. When flexion occurs from the anatomical position, gravity is an important factor. Extension: by the long muscles of the back. Lateral flexion: sternocleido-mastoid and trapezius, the oblique abdominal wall muscles and quadratus lumborum. Rotation: sternocleidomastoid and internal and external oblique abdominal muscles. Movements of the head: the head can be rotated, flexed, extended and laterally flexed. Rotation occurs at the atlanto-axial joints and the other movements at the atlanto-occipital joints. Movement of the head is usually accompanied by synergic movements of the neck. Rotation: sternocleidomastoid, trapezius, splenius capitis and suboccipital muscles. Flexion: longus capitis and the muscles depressing the fixed mandible, aided by gravity. Extension: postvertebral muscles. Lateral flexion: sternocleidomastoid and trapezius.

Stability: This depends almost entirely on the muscles surrounding the column aided by the ligamenta flava, for neither bony nor ligamentous factors alone could withstand the large forces frequently acting on the column. The majority of fractures of the vertebral bodies do not produce instability of the vertebral column, as the strong ligaments connecting the vertebrae are not easily torn. If however some ligamenta flava and inter-spinous ligaments are ruptured the vertebral column is unstable and subsequent displacement may produce compression of the spinal cord and irreversible damage.

VERTEBRAL CANAL: This extends from the foramen magnum to the sacral hiatus. It is a bony-ligamentous canal and opens below on to the back of the lower sacral segments and the coccyx. The spinal cord ends about the level of the 2nd lumbar vertebra, the dural sac at the level of the 2nd sacral vertebra and the filum terminale is attached to the back of the coccyx. The supracristal plane, through the highest points of the iliac crests, cuts across the spine of the 4th lumbar vertebra. The umbilicus is about the level of the lower border of the body of the 3rd lumbar vertebra. The dural sac with its enclosed spinal cord, spinal nerves, and cerebrospinal fluid is separated from the bony-ligamentous wall by a fat-filled extradural space in which lie the emerging spinal nerves and the internal vertebral venous plexus.

BLOOD SUPPLY: The vertebral column is supplied by segmental spinal branches of the ascending cervical, vertebral, intercostal, lumbar and lateral sacral arteries. The veins drain to the external vertebral venous plexuses which communicate throughout their length with the internal vertebral venous plexus within the vertebral canal. The external vertebral venous plexus drains to the internal iliac, lumbar, azygos and vertebral veins. The internal vertebral venous plexuses communicate with pelvic plexuses below and intracranial venous sinuses above. The basivertebral veins carry blood from the red marrow of the vertebral bodies into the internal vertebral plexus.

THORAX

CHAPTER 4

THE THORACIC WALL AND DIAPHRAGM

The thorax has a bony-cartilaginous skeleton and contains the principal organs of respiration and circulation. Its walls are formed of 12 thoracic vertebrae posteriorly, a midline sternum anteriorly, and 12 pairs of ribs with costal cartilages and intercostal muscles laterally. It is conical in shape, possessing a narrow inlet superiorly and a wide outlet inferiorly.

The thoracic inlet is about 10 cm wide and 5 cm anteroposteriorly. It slopes downwards and forwards and is bounded by the 1st thoracic vertebra posteriorly, the superior border of the manubrium anteriorly and the 1st rib and costal cartilage laterally. It transmits the oesophagus, the trachea, the large vessels and nerves of the head and neck, and the vessels of the upper limbs. On each side is the apex of the lung, covered by the pleura.

The outlet also is widest from side to side. It is bounded by the 12th thoracic vertebra posteriorly, the 12th and 11th ribs laterally and the costal cartilages of the 10th, 9th, 8th and 7th ribs anteriorly. The costal margin ascends to meet the sternum, forming the infrasternal angle. The outlet is closed by the diaphragm which separates thoracic and abdominal cavities.

Sternum (Fig. 4.1)

The sternum is a flat bone forming the median part of the anterior thoracic wall. It has three parts, the manubrium, the body and the xiphoid process from above downwards. It is palpable throughout most of its length.

The **manubrium** is a thick plate of bone about 5 cm long, wider above than below. Its upper border bears a central jugular notch between two lateral facets for articulation with the medial ends of the clavicles. The lateral borders are marked above by a pit for the 1st costal cartilage and below by a half facet for the upper part of the 2nd costal cartilage. The narrow inferior border articulates with the body at the palpable **sternal angle.**

The **body** of the sternum is longer (10 cm) and thinner than the manubrium. It is formed of four pieces (sternebrae) whose lines of fusion are marked by three faint transverse ridges on the adult bone. The lateral border possesses a half facet for the 2nd costal cartilage and five shallow pits for the 3rd–7th cartilages. The body tapers inferiorly to articulate with the xiphoid process.

The **xiphoid process** is thin, flat, and irregularly shaped and is cartilaginous in early life. It lies in the rectus sheath and gives attachment to the diaphragm posteriorly and the rectus abdominis anteriorly.

FIG. 4.1

The sternum, anterior aspect. Inset: ossification (m.i.u.,
months in utero; y., years).

Ribs

The **ribs** articulate posteriorly with the thoracic vertebrae and
anteriorly with their costal cartilages. They form a large part of the
thoracic wall. There are usually 12 on each side but this number may
be increased by the development of a cervical or lumbar rib. The upper
seven articulate through their cartilages with the sternum and are known
as true ribs; the 8th–10th articulate through their cartilages with the
cartilage immediately above and are called false ribs; the 11th and 12th
have free anterior ends and are known as floating ribs.

A typical rib consists of a head, neck, tubercle and body from behind
forwards. The **head** bears two facets for articulation with adjacent
vertebrae, separated by a transverse crest which is attached to the
intervertebral disc.

The constricted **neck** is flattened anteroposteriorly and its surfaces
give attachment to the costotransverse ligaments. The **tubercle** lies posteriorly at the junction of the neck and body. It bears a medial facet
for articulation with the transverse process. The **body** is flattened in a
vertical plane and curved to conform to the chest wall. Its upper border
is rounded whilst its lower is sharp and limits the costal groove on its
internal surface. The body bends lateral to the tubercle at the **angle** which
marks the lateral limit of the attachment of the erector spinae muscles. The
anterior end of the rib possesses a small depression for the costal cartilage.

The 1st, 10th, 11th and 12th ribs are atypical.

The **1st rib** (Fig. 4.2) is short, wide and flattened in a horizontal
plane. It has superior and inferior surfaces, and medial and lateral

borders. Its head bears a single facet for articulation with the 1st thoracic vertebra and posteriorly its tubercle and angle coincide. The lower surface is smooth and lies on the pleura. A small **scalene tubercle** on its medial border marks the attachment of scalenus anterior. On the upper surface the tubercle separates an anterior groove for the subclavian vein and a posterior groove for the subclavian artery and the lower trunk of the brachial plexus. Scalenus medius is attached to a roughened area behind the artery. Anteriorly the upper surface gives attachment to subclavius muscle and the costoclavicular ligament. Between the pleura and the

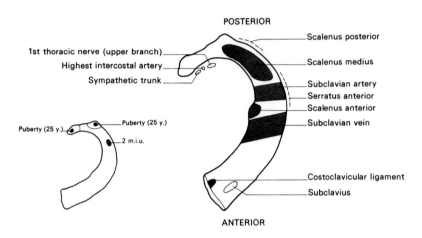

FIG. 4.2

The upper surface of the 1st rib, showing some of its muscular attachments and immediate relations. Inset: ossification (m.i.u., months in utero; y., years).

front of the neck of the rib (from medial to lateral) lie the sympathetic trunk, the superior intercostal artery and the large branch of the 1st thoracic nerve to the brachial plexus.

The heads of the 10th, 11th and 12th ribs bear a single articular facet. The 11th and 12th ribs are short and possess neither necks nor tubercles. The 12th also lacks an angle and a subcostal groove, and gives attachment to quadratus lumborum muscle and the lateral arcuate ligament of the diaphragm.

The **costal cartilages** are flexible bars of hyaline cartilage which contribute to the elasticity of the thoracic walls. They extend forwards from the anterior ends of the ribs. The 1st–7th articulate directly with the sternum, the 8th–10th with the lower borders of the preceding cartilages. The 11th and 12th possess free pointed ends which lie in the abdominal wall musculature.

Thoracic Vertebrae
(see page 35).

JOINTS OF THE THORACIC CAGE

These comprise the intervertebral, rib and sternal joints.

Intervertebral Joints
(see page 36).

Rib Joints
A typical rib articulates behind with the vertebral column in two places and anteriorly with its own costal cartilage.

Costovertebral joints: the two facets on the head of most ribs articulate with adjacent vertebrae at two synovial joints; the lower facet with its own vertebra and the upper with the vertebra above. The crest on the head is attached to the intervening disc by an intra-articular ligament. The capsule of these joints is strengthened by ligaments which run from the head of the rib to the vertebral bodies. The heads of the 1st, 10th, 11th and 12th ribs usually have only one facet and articulate with only one vertebra.

Costotransverse joints are synovial joints on the upper 10 ribs. The upper joint surfaces are reciprocally curved and the lower are more flattened. The capsular ligament is strengthened by accessory costotransverse ligaments. The lower two ribs are attached to the transverse processes only by ligaments.

The joints between the ribs and their costal cartilages (**costochondral**), and between the 1st costal cartilage and the sternum are primary cartilaginous joints. Joints between the 2nd–7th costal cartilages and the sternum and those between adjacent costal cartilages have a synovial cavity.

Sternal Joints
The manubriosternal joint is a secondary cartilaginous joint. The fibrocartilaginous disc allows a slight hinge movement of the body on the manubrium during inspiration. The xiphisternal joint is also of the secondary cartilaginous variety but usually becomes a bony union in later life.

Movements of the ribs (see page 50).

The Thoracic Cage
Note that:

(a) the vertebral column intrudes into the cage posteriorly, making the thoracic cavity kidney-shaped in transverse section;

(b) the ribs increase in length from the 1st to the 7th and thereafter become shorter;

(c) they lie at an angle of about 45° to the vertebral column, the obliquity increasing down to the 9th rib where it reaches its maximum;

(d) the anterior ends of the ribs fall increasingly short of the sternum and their costal cartilages are correspondingly lengthened;

(e) from the back it is seen that the rib angles lie nearer the midline superiorly.

The cage gives attachment to:

(a) some of the muscles supporting the weight of the upper limb—

serratus anterior, pectoralis major and minor, trapezius and latissimus dorsi;

(b) muscles of the abdominal wall, thereby helping to support the abdominal viscera;

(c) extensor muscles of the back as far laterally as the angles of the ribs;

(d) scalene muscles which help to raise the 1st ribs;

(e) diaphragm and intercostal muscles (see below).

THE INTERCOSTAL SPACES

These lie between the ribs and costal cartilages. They contain the external, internal and innermost intercostal muscles and the intercostal vessels and nerves. Deep to them lies the pleura.

The **external intercostal muscle** descends obliquely forwards from the lower border of the rib above to the upper border of the rib below. Anteriorly between the costal cartilages its fibres are replaced by a fibrous sheet, the external intercostal membrane.

The **internal intercostal muscle** lies deep to the external intercostal muscle. It descends obliquely backwards from the subcostal groove of the rib above to the upper border of the rib below. Posteriorly, behind the angle of the rib, its fibres are replaced by a fibrous sheet, the internal intercostal membrane.

The **innermost intercostal muscle** forms an incomplete sheet, lying between the ribs and the pleura. Posterior and lateral portions pass over and are attached to the inner surfaces of the ribs. Anteriorly a more distinct fan-like portion, the transversus thoracis muscle, spreads upwards from the back of the lower end of the sternum to the inner surfaces of the 2nd–6th costal cartilages.

ACTIONS: the intercostal muscles approximate the ribs. When the 1st rib is anchored by the scalene muscles, the approximation of the ribs raises the sternum and air is drawn into the lungs. The external intercostal may then be most active. When the lower ribs are anchored by the abdominal muscles, approximation of the ribs lowers the sternum and air is forced out of the lungs. The internal intercostal muscles may then be most active. Transversus thoracis depresses the upper costal cartilages. Contraction of the intercostal muscles also helps to maintain the rigidity of the chest wall, thus preventing the tissues between the ribs from being pushed out or pulled in by changes in the intrathoracic pressure produced mainly by action of the diaphragm.

NERVE SUPPLY: intercostal nerves.

The Intercostal Vessels and Nerves

These form a neurovascular bundle in which the vein is superior and the nerve inferior. The bundle passes forwards around the chest wall in the subcostal groove deep to the internal intercostal muscle and lying on the innermost intercostal muscle and the pleura.

The **intercostal arteries:** each space is supplied by a single posterior artery and paired anterior intercostal arteries. The lower two spaces have only posterior arteries.

The 1st and 2nd posterior intercostal arteries arise from the superior intercostal artery (a branch of the costocervical trunk). The remainder come from the descending thoracic aorta. They pass forwards in the space above the corresponding nerve, and give spinal branches, branches to the lateral chest wall and a small collateral branch which passes forwards in the space with a collateral branch of the nerve.

The anterior intercostal arteries of the upper six spaces are branches of the internal thoracic artery and the arteries of the next three spaces, of its terminal branch, the musculophrenic artery. They pass laterally to anastomose with the posterior artery and its collateral branch.

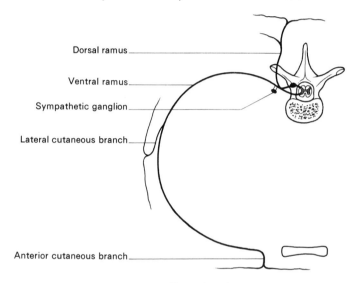

Dorsal ramus

Ventral ramus

Sympathetic ganglion

Lateral cutaneous branch

Anterior cutaneous branch

FIG. 4.3
The distribution of a typical intercostal nerve. Muscle branches are not shown.

The **internal thoracic artery** arises from the subclavian artery (p. 333) and descends just lateral to the sternal border to end in the 6th interspace by dividing into musculophrenic and superior epigastric arteries. Near its origin it is crossed over by the phrenic nerve and in the chest it lies between the costal cartilages superficially and the transversus thoracis and pleura deeply.

BRANCHES
(i) anterior intercostal arteries—to the upper six spaces.
(ii) perforating cutaneous branches—in the female these are larger and supply the breast.
(iii) **superior epigastric artery**—descends between the costal and xiphoid origins of the diaphragm into the rectus sheath and anastomoses with the inferior epigastric artery (branch of the external iliac artery). It supplies the contents of the rectus sheath.
(iv) **musculophrenic artery**—descends laterally behind the costal

47

margin, gives anterior intercostal branches to the 7th, 8th and 9th spaces and supplies the diaphragm and pericardium.

The **intercostal veins:** the intercostal spaces drain by two anterior veins and a single posterior intercostal vein. The anterior pass to the musculophrenic and internal thoracic veins; the posterior pass in an irregular manner to the brachiocephalic vein (1st space) and the azygos system of veins (the other spaces).

The **intercostal nerves** (Fig. 4.3): these are the ventral rami of the upper 11 thoracic spinal nerves. Each spinal nerve is attached to the spinal cord by ventral and dorsal roots. The latter possess a ganglion which is situated in the intervertebral foramen. Before emerging from the foramen the two roots unite and almost immediately divide into dorsal and ventral rami. The dorsal ramus supplies the extensor muscles of the back before ending in medial and lateral cutaneous branches which supply the skin of the back. The ventral rami form the intercostal nerves.

A typical intercostal nerve (3rd or 4th) passes laterally into the subcostal groove. It continues around the chest wall between internal intercostal muscle externally and the innermost intercostal muscles and pleura internally. At the anterior end of the space it turns forwards and pierces the internal intercostal muscle, the anterior intercostal membrane and pectoralis major to end as an anterior cutaneous branch.

BRANCHES

(i) collateral branch—arises near the angle of the rib and runs forwards with a similar branch of the artery below the parent trunk.

(ii) muscular branches.

(iii) lateral cutaneous nerve—also arises near the angle of the rib, pierces the intercostal muscles in the midaxillary line and ends up by dividing into anterior and posterior branches.

(iv) anterior cutaneous nerve—divides into a small medial and a larger lateral branch.

The 1st intercostal nerve has no lateral cutaneous branch but sends a large branch to the brachial plexus. The lateral branch of the 2nd and sometimes the 3rd intercostal nerve forms the intercostobrachial nerve which supplies the skin of the axilla. The 12th thoracic (subcostal) nerve runs forwards below the 12th rib to the anterior abdominal wall and supplies its muscles. (Its lateral cutaneous branch supplies the skin over the anterior superior iliac spine.)

Surgical access to a pleural cavity (thoracotomy) is gained by an incision which follows the line of a rib and enters the chest via the bed of the rib or via the intercostal space. An alternative approach to the mediastinum and heart is through a midline sternotomy dividing the sternum vertically.

Rib fractures may be accompanied by haemorrhage from intercostal vessels and the bleeding may be into the pleural cavity producing a haemothorax. Occasionally the underlying lung may be torn by a fractured rib and the air leak into the pleural cavity is known as a pneumothorax. Multiple rib fractures may allow a segment of the chest wall to become unstable thus interfering with the normal respiratory movements. The tidal respiratory volume may then be dangerously diminished.

THE DIAPHRAGM

This musculotendinous septum separates the abdominal and thoracic cavities. It has a central tendinous part and a peripheral muscular part. During quiet respiration, the central tendon moves little so that the position of the heart varies only slightly during the respiratory cycle.

ATTACHMENTS
Peripheral

(i) sternal part—from the back of the xiphoid process by two muscular slips.

(ii) costal part—from the inner surfaces of the lower six costal cartilages, interdigitating with transversus abdominis.

(iii) vertebral part—from the sides of the bodies of the upper lumbar vertebrae by two crura, and from the medial and lateral arcuate ligaments on each side. The **right crus** is attached to the bodies of the first three vertebrae and the **left crus** to the first two. The larger right crus passes forwards and to the left and surrounds the oesophageal opening. The **medial arcuate ligament** is the thickened upper edge of psoas fascia and passes over psoas from the body of the 1st lumbar vertebra to its transverse process. The **lateral arcuate ligament** is anterior to quadratus lumborum and passes from the transverse process of the 1st lumbar vertebra to the 12th rib.

There is often a gap between the vertebral and costal attachments and the pleura is then only separated by the perirenal tissues from the peritoneum

Central: the fibres are attached to the periphery of a trilobed central tendon.

ACTIONS: it is the principal muscle of inspiration. During contraction, the dome of the diaphragm descends and flattens, and the vertical diameter of the chest is increased. The abdominal wall is relaxed to accommodate the changed position of the liver. In expiration, the diaphragm relaxes. In expulsive efforts, e.g. micturition and defaecation, the intra-abdominal pressure is increased by simultaneous contraction of the diaphragm and abdominal wall muscles.

NERVE SUPPLY: the right and left halves are supplied by the corresponding phrenic nerves. The periphery receives additional sensory branches from intercostal nerves.

OPENINGS: there are three large openings in the diaphragm, from before backwards:

(i) for the inferior vena cava—in the central tendon to the right of the midline at the level of the 8th thoracic vertebra. It also transmits the right phrenic nerve.

(ii) for the oesophagus—in the muscle derived from the right crus, to the left of the midline at the level of the 10th thoracic vertebra. It also transmits the anterior and posterior gastric nerves, and oesophageal branches of the left gastric vessels.

(iii) for the aorta—between the crura of the diaphragm in front of the 12th thoracic vertebra. It also transmits the thoracic duct and the azygos vein.

The left phrenic nerve pierces the left dome of the diaphragm. The splanchnic nerves pierce the crus, the sympathetic trunk passes behind the medial arcuate ligament, the subcostal nerve and vessels pass behind the lateral arcuate ligament, and the superior epigastric vessels pass between sternal and costal attachments of the diaphragm.

RELATIONS: the heart and lungs within the pericardial and pleural sacs respectively lie on the upper surface. The fibrous pericardium is firmly adherent to the central tendon. Inferiorly on the right side are the liver, right kidney and suprarenal gland, and on the left the fundus of the stomach, spleen, left kidney and suprarenal gland.

DEVELOPMENT: see page 26.

RESPIRATION

The inspiratory and expiratory phases of respiration are produced by an alternating increase and decrease in the volume of the thoracic cavity. Many of the following details have been shown by X-ray examination.

INSPIRATION: the diaphragm contracts, descends, and increases the height of the cavity. The upper ribs are fixed by the scalene muscles and the remainder raised by the intercostal muscles. The manner in which the ribs move depends on the shape of their articulations with the transverse processes. An upper rib rotates around an axis passing along its neck, and its anterior end is elevated—this increases the anteroposterior and the transverse diameters of the chest. A lower rib is capable of gliding and rotation at the costotransverse joints. This permits movement around a vertical axis through the head, and increases the transverse diameter of the chest. In forced inspiration fixation of the shoulder girdle enables serratus anterior and the pectoralis muscles to raise the ribs.

EXPIRATION: this is produced mainly by elastic recoil of the costal cartilages and lung tissue. Simultaneous contraction of the abdominal wall muscles increases intra-abdominal pressure and forces the diaphragm upwards. This latter movement is exaggerated in forced expiration. (See also page 88.)

THE BREAST

In the male and prepubertal female this is a rudimentary organ. The adult female breast is a soft, hemispherical structure, situated on the front of the thorax and consisting of glandular tissue and a varying amount of fat. The gland lies in the superficial fascia. The fascia invests it and forms septa which divide the gland into lobules and attach it to the skin and the underlying deep fascia over pectoralis major. The base of the breast extends from the 2nd to the 6th rib and from the side of the sternum to near the midaxillary line. Its apex, the nipple, is surrounded by thin, pigmented skin, the areola. The size and shape of the breast is very variable.

BLOOD SUPPLY: branches of the internal thoracic, anterior intercostal and lateral thoracic arteries. The veins correspond to the arteries.

LYMPH DRAINAGE: lymph drains from the gland to a subcutaneous subareolar plexus and to a submammary plexus on pectoralis major. From these plexuses lymph drains laterally to the pectoral nodes, superiorly to the infraclavicular and lower deep cervical nodes, inferiorly via the subcutaneous plexus on the anterior abdominal wall to diaphragmatic nodes, and medially to the parasternal nodes and across the midline to communicate with plexuses of the breast of the opposite side. Complete removal of all the possible affected nodes in a patient with breast cancer is thus impracticable and radiotherapy to the regional lymph nodes is therefore often combined with surgery in an attempt to ablate all the neoplastic deposits.

HISTOLOGY: the breast has a framework of fatty connective tissue and is divided by fascial septa into 15–20 lobes of glandular tissue. Each lobe comprises clusters of alveoli whose ducts unite to form a lactiferous duct which passes towards the nipple. Deep to the nipple each duct dilates to form a lactiferous sinus from which a short straight part of the duct opens on to the nipple. The nipple and areola contain some smooth muscle and modified sebaceous glands (the areolar glands) but little fat.

The mammary glands are modified skin glands and develop from an ectodermal downgrowth. The resting (non-active) breast contains little glandular tissue. In pregnancy, however, the tissue undergoes marked proliferation and its blood supply increases prior to the onset of lactation.

CHAPTER 5

THE THORACIC CAVITY AND HEART

The thoracic cavity is divided into right and left pleural cavities by a central partition, the **mediastinum.** This irregular partition between the two pleural sacs is bounded behind by the vertebral column and in front by the sternum. Inferiorly it is limited by the diaphragm and above is continuous with the structures in the root of the neck. It contains the heart, larger vessels, oesophagus, trachea and lymph nodes, all embedded in loose areolar tissue. By careful positioning of the person and the use of radio-opaque media, many of the organs can be investigated radiologically.

THE HEART

The heart is the muscular pump of the circulation. It is composed of four chambers (two atria and two ventricles), which are demarcated on its surface by coronary and interventricular sulci. It lies suspended by the large vessels within the pericardial sac. The heart is the size of a clenched fist, weighs about 300 g and is the shape of a flattened cone, possessing a base and an apex. It lies obliquely across the lower mediastinum behind the sternum.

The base faces posteriorly; it is square in outline and is formed mainly of the left atrium, receiving the four pulmonary veins. The apex is at the left inferior extremity of the heart and is formed by the tip of the left ventricle. The anterior (sternocostal) surface is formed mainly by the right ventricle, separated on the right by the vertical coronary sulcus from the right atrium and on the left by the anterior interventricular sulcus from the left ventricle. The surface merges superiorly with the beginning of the aorta and pulmonary artery.

The inferior (diaphragmatic) surface is formed mainly of the right and left ventricles anteriorly and part of the right atrium posteriorly. The inferior vena cava enters the right atrium at the right posterior corner of this surface which rests on the central tendon of the diaphragm. The left surface is formed by the left ventricle and a small part of the left atrium. It is in contact with the left lung. The right surface is formed by the right atrium which receives the superior vena cava above and the inferior vena cava below. It is in contact with the right lung.

The Chambers of the Heart

The right chambers of the heart pump blood through the lungs, and the left through the systemic circulation.

The **right atrium** (Fig. 5.1) is a thin-walled narrow chamber. Between the superior and inferior venae cavae, it forms the right border of the heart. Superomedially a small projection, the **right auricle** overlaps the beginning of the ascending aorta. The posterior part of the wall behind the caval openings is smooth and separates the cavity from the left atrium. It is marked by a shallow oval depression, the **fossa ovalis,** bounded by a crescentic ridge, the **limbus** of the fossa ovalis. Anteriorly the wall is thicker and formed of parallel muscular ridges which pass transversely from the right auricle to a prominent vertical ridge, the **crista terminalis,** between the caval openings. The crista is marked by a slight groove, the sulcus terminalis, on the outer surface of the heart.

The superior caval orifice in the upper part of the cavity has no valve; to its left lies the cavity of the right auricle. The inferior caval orifice is guarded by a thin fold of endocardium anteriorly, the valve of the inferior

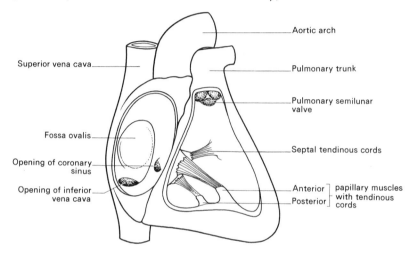

FIG. 5.1
Diagram showing the interior of the right atrium and the right ventricle.

vena cava. The atrioventricular orifice lies to the left of the inferior caval opening and between them is a smaller orifice, the opening of the coronary sinus, also with an endocardial flap guarding it.

The **right ventricle** (Fig. 5.1) is a thick-walled elongated chamber projecting forwards and to the left of the right atrium and forming part of the anterior and inferior surfaces of the heart. The interventricular septum separates the right from the left ventricle and bulges into the right cavity, making it crescentic in cross section. The walls of the cavity are covered by interlacing muscle bands except superiorly where the smooth-walled wide **infundibulum** leads to the pulmonary orifice. Near the apex a distinct muscle bundle, the septomarginal band, often crosses the cavity. The atrioventricular orifice lies postero-inferiorly. It is guarded by the **tricuspid valve** which possesses three thin cusps, each attached at its base to the fibrous ring surrounding the orifice. The cusps consist of a little fibrous tissue covered on both sides by endocardium. The atrial surfaces of the valve cusps are smooth. Their margins and ventricular surfaces are anchored to the ventricular walls by fine tendinous cords which arise directly from the septum or from two small conical **papillary muscles** situated on the anterior and inferior walls of the cavity. These muscles tighten the tendinous cords and prevent eversion of the cusps into the atrial cavity during ventricular contraction. The pulmonary orifice is a fibrous ring lying at the upper end of the smoother infundibulum. It is guarded by a valve possessing three semilunar valvules, one posterior and two anterior. In the middle of the free margin of each valvule is a thickened nodule.

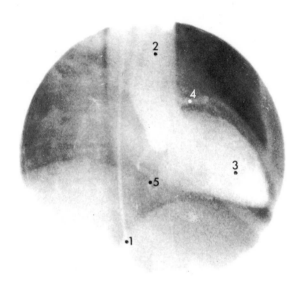

Fig. 5.2

Left ventriculogram. A catheter (1) was passed into a femoral artery, through the aorta and aortic valve, and into the left ventricle. Radiopaque material was then injected.

1. Catheter	4. Left coronary artery
2. Ascending aorta	5. Right coronary artery
3. Left ventricle	

The **left atrium,** a thin, smooth-walled, rectangular chamber, lies behind the right atrium and forms most of the base of the heart. Superiorly a small projection, the left **auricle** overlies the left side of the pulmonary trunk. The four pulmonary veins enter symmetrically on its posterior surface, two on each side; their orifices possess no valves. The left atrioventricular orifice lies in the anterior wall. The posterior wall of the atrium is separated by the oblique sinus of pericardium from the oesophagus, left bronchus and descending thoracic aorta.

The **left ventricle** extends forwards and to the left from the left atrium and lies mainly behind the right ventricle. It forms the apex, the left border and surface and part of the anterior and inferior surfaces of the heart (Fig. 5.2). Its walls are very thick and covered on the inside by muscular ridges except for a smooth area just below the aortic orifice, the **vestibule.** The conical cavity possesses two orifices, the left atrioventricular posteriorly and the aortic superiorly. The left atrioventricular orifice is guarded by the **mitral (bicuspid) valve,** the two cusps of which are attached to a fibrous ring surrounding the orifice. Their free margins and ventricular surfaces are anchored to papillary muscles on the ventricular wall by tendinous cords. The anterior cusp is the larger, lies between the aortic and mitral orifices, and blood flows over both its surfaces. The aortic orifice is a fibrous ring lying behind and to the right of the pulmonary orifice. It is guarded by a valve possessing three semilunar valvules (one anterior, two posterior) which are similar to those of the pulmonary valve.

The interventricular septum: the position of this is marked on the surface of the heart by the anterior and posterior interventricular sulci. The right ventricle, into which it bulges, lies anterior, the left ventricle posterior. The septum is very thick except for a thin membranous portion between the vestibule and the infundibulum.

BLOOD AND NERVE SUPPLY

Arteries (Fig. 5.3)

The **right coronary artery** arises from the anterior aortic sinus and passes forwards between the right auricle and the pulmonary trunk to gain the right coronary sulcus in which it runs, firstly descending the anterior surface and then crossing the inferior surface of the heart where it anastomoses with the left coronary artery (Fig. 5.4).

BRANCHES
(i) atrial and ventricular branches.
(ii) **marginal artery**—runs to the left towards the apex along the lower border of the heart.
(iii) **posterior interventricular artery**—runs along the posterior interventricular sulcus towards the apex where it anastomoses with the anterior interventricular artery.

The **left coronary artery** arises from the left posterior aortic sinus. It passes forward between the left auricle and the pulmonary trunk to gain the left coronary sulcus (Fig. 5.5).

BRANCHES
(i) **anterior interventricular artery**—descends in the anterior interventricular sulcus towards the apex, turns round the lower border and anastomoses with the posterior interventricular artery.
(ii) **circumflex artery**—runs to the left in the coronary sulcus and then passes behind to anastomose with the terminal branch of the right coronary artery. It gives off the **marginal artery** which runs along the left border of the heart.
(iii) atrial and ventricular branches.

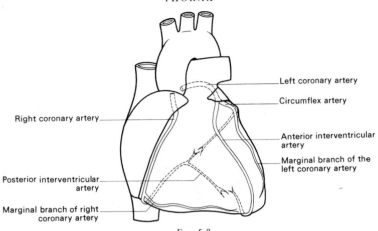

FIG. 5.3
The distribution of the coronary arteries.

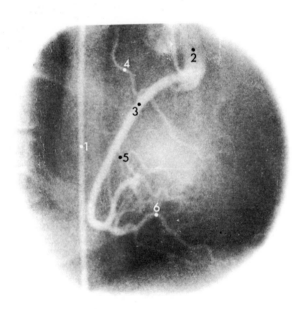

FIG. 5.4
Right coronary arteriogram—right oblique view. A catheter has been introduced into a femoral artery, passed up the aorta and into the origin of the coronary artery. Radiopaque material was then injected.

1. Catheter
2. Ascending aorta
3. Right coronary artery in anterior coronary sulcus

4. S.A node artery
5. Anterior ventricular branch
6. Posterior interventricular branch

Generally the right ventricle is supplied by the right coronary artery, the left ventricle by the left, the interventricular septum by both, and the atria in a variable manner. Although anastomoses between the two arteries are present in the coronary sulcus, near the apex and in the septum, sudden occlusion of a larger branch may result in ischaemia of an area of heart muscle. If the area affected includes the conducting system or is relatively large, death of the patient may occur. Lesser degrees of damage decrease the work capacity of the heart and ischaemic pain (angina) may be experienced on exertion.

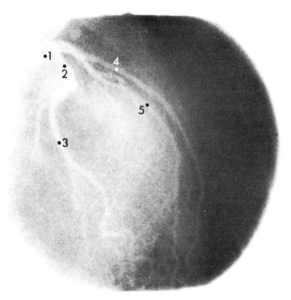

FIG. 5.5
Left coronary arteriogram, oblique view.

1. Left coronary artery
2. Circumflex artery in the coronary sulcus
3. Left marginal artery
4. Anterior interventricular artery
5. Diagonal artery

Veins (Fig. (5.6)

These drain mainly via the coronary sinus. The anterior cardiac veins and the venae cordis minimae open into the right atrium.

The **coronary sinus** is formed at the left border of the heart as a continuation of the great cardiac vein. It passes in the posterior coronary sulcus and enters the right atrium to the left of the orifice for the inferior vena cava. It is about 3 cm long.

TRIBUTARIES

(i) **great cardiac vein**—is a large vessel which drains both ventricles. (It ascends the anterior interventricular sulcus and turns around the left border of the heart to become the coronary sinus. A left marginal vein enters it.)

(ii) **middle cardiac vein**—lies in the posterior interventricular sulcus.

(iii) **small cardiac vein**—runs to the right along the lower border of the heart to reach the coronary sulcus and enter the right extremity of the sinus.

(iv) **left posterior ventricular vein**—runs up the back of the left ventricle and enters the coronary sinus.

(v) **oblique vein**—lies on the posterior wall of the left atrium. It is a remnant of the left superior vena cava.

Fig. 5.6
The venous drainage of the heart.

Anterior cardiac veins—several small veins which drain the anterior wall of the right ventricle and open into the right atrium.

Venae cordis minimae—are small veins draining much of the heart walls. They open into the cavities of the heart.

Lymph drainage: to the tracheobronchial lymph nodes.

Nerve supply: this is derived from the vagus and sympathetic fibres (upper thoracic segments) through the cardiac plexus (p. 81). The fibres are distributed with the coronary arteries. Parasympathetic ganglion cells are found on the heart walls. Sensory fibres subserving reflex activity pass in the vagus, and pain fibres pass into the spinal nerves (T1–T3). Many pain fibres traverse the sympathetic ganglia.

THE CONDUCTING SYSTEM OF THE HEART

This system is formed of specialised cardiac muscle cells which in man are difficult to distinguish histologically from cardiac muscle. It comprises the sinu-atrial (SA) node, the atrioventricular (AV) node, the AV bundle (of His), its right and left branches and a terminal subendocardial plexus

(Purkinje fibres). This system initiates the sequence of events comprising the cardiac cycle and controls its regularity.

The **SA node** (pacemaker) is a small vascular area of conducting tissue lying in the wall of the right atrium at the upper end of the sulcus terminalis and to the right of the superior caval opening. Impulses are conducted from it through the atrial wall to the **AV node** which is a similar nodule lying in the septal wall of the right atrium above the opening of the coronary sinus. The **AV bundle** arises from the node, descends across the membranous part of the interventricular septum and divides into right and left branches which are distributed to their respective ventricles. Some of the right branch traverses the septomarginal band to reach the anterior ventricular wall. The branches ramify and form the subendocardial plexus which is distributed to the papillary muscles and ventricular walls.

HISTOLOGY

The heart wall is composed of three layers; a thin outer epicardium (serous pericardium), a very thick muscular (myocardial) layer and a thin inner endocardium of cubical endothelial cells. The myocardial cells are embedded in areolar tissue. Except for the AV bundle there is no myocardial continuity between the atria and the ventricles; they are separated by a pair of fibrous rings encircling both atrioventricular orifices in a figure-of-eight fashion. To these rings the myocardial muscle fibres are attached and they encircle the heart chambers in complex spirals and whorls. Cardiac muscle consists of branching striated fibres with a central nucleus and transverse intercalated discs at points of union of branches.

THE PERICARDIUM (Fig. 5.7)

The pericardium is a fibroserous membrane containing the heart and the adjacent parts of the large vessels entering and leaving it. It consists of an outer fibrous pericardium and an inner serous pericardium.

The serous pericardium is a closed serous sac, invaginated by the heart, possessing visceral and parietal layers and enclosing a narrow pericardial cavity. Visceral pericardium covers the whole surface of the heart and is continuous with the parietal pericardium lining the inner surface of fibrous pericardium. The lines of reflection from the heart to the fibrous pericardium are shown in Figure 5.7. Its irregular form is related to the complex development of the heart. The serous pericardium is derived from the lining of the pericardial part of the coelomic cavity.

The fibrous pericardium forms a strong flask-shaped sac around the heart and serous pericardium. It blends inferiorly with the central tendon of the diaphragm, superiorly with the adventitia of the aorta, pulmonary trunk and superior vena cava, and posteriorly with that of the pulmonary veins.

DEVELOPMENT OF THE HEART AND PERICARDIUM

The embryonic heart develops from a vascular tube which hangs from the dorsal wall of the pericardial part of the coelomic sac. In its development two main processes are involved : (i) bending and differential growth, and (ii) division into right and left sides. (See page 27.)

BENDING AND DIFFERENTIAL GROWTH OF THE HEART TUBE

The heart is suspended from the dorsal wall of the embryo by a mesentery, the dorsal mesocardium. The caudal (venous) end of the heart tube receives the superior and inferior venae cavae and the common

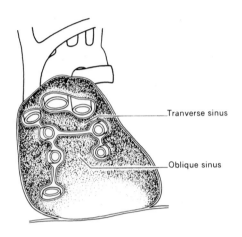

Tranverse sinus

Oblique sinus

FIG. 5.7
Diagram of the interior of the pericardium, viewed from in front, after removal
of the heart.

pulmonary vein. These vessels remain enclosed in a common sleeve of pericardium. The cephalic (arterial) end divides to form the aorta and pulmonary artery which similarly remain enclosed in a common sleeve of pericardium. The cephalic part of the tube elongates and descends, the arteries coming to lie in front of the veins. Simultaneously the middle of the dorsal mesocardium breaks down and forms a dorsal communication between the two sides of the pericardial cavity, the **transverse sinus** of the pericardium. This lies between the folded arterial and venous ends of the tube. In the adult the sinus lies behind the aorta and pulmonary artery, and in front of the superior vena cava and pulmonary veins.

The sleeve of pericardium surrounding the veins is stretched to form a ∩-shaped cul-de-sac (the **oblique sinus**) bounded by two pulmonary veins on the left and two pulmonary veins and the venae cavae on the right (Fig. 5.7). It is separated from the transverse sinus superiorly by a double layer of pericardium.

Four dilatations develop in the primitive heart, the sinus venosus at the venous end, then the atrium, the ventricle and the bulbus cordis (the latter leading into the truncus arteriosus). The atrium is continuous with the ventricle through a narrow atrioventricular canal.

DIVISION INTO RIGHT AND LEFT SIDES

Longitudinal partitions divide the atrium, ventricle and bulbus cordis into right and left atria, right and left ventricles and the pulmonary and aortic trunks respectively.

Division of the atrium and the atrioventricular canal: two small projections, the endocardial cushions, unite across the narrow atrioventricular canal dividing it into right and left portions. In the atrial cavity a septum (the septum primum) descends and fuses with the endocardial cushions; it becomes perforated in its upper part. A septum secundum grows down on the right side of the septum primum, overlapping the perforation. The oblique communication which persists between the two cavities is known as the **foramen ovale.** The septum primum acts in a valve-like manner, opening the foramen ovale and allowing blood to flow from the right to the left atrium but not in the reverse direction. The lower edge of the septum secundum forms the limbus ovalis of the adult.

Division of the ventricle and bulbus cordis: the ventricle is divided by the development of a septum which fuses with the endocardial cushions above. The cavity of the bulbus cordis is divided by a spiral septum into the pulmonary and aortic trunks. The ventricular septum and the septum of the bulbus cordis unite with each other in such a way that the right ventricle leads into the pulmonary artery and the left ventricle into the aorta.

In their growth the ventricles incorporate part of the bulbus cordis thus forming the smooth-walled infundibulum and vestibule. The left atrium incorporates the pulmonary veins and the right atrium the sinus venosus and venae cavae, thus forming the smooth-walled part of each cavity.

FETAL CIRCULATION

Oxygenated blood from the placenta passes through the liver in the ductus venosus and then into the inferior vena cava and right atrium. The angle between the superior and inferior venae cavae directs the placental blood through the foramen ovale into the left atrium. It then passes through the left ventricle into the aorta. Much of the blood goes to the head of the embryo to supply the developing brain. It returns to the heart in the superior vena cava and is directed into the right ventricle and then into the pulmonary artery. Blood in the pulmonary artery is shunted along the ductus arteriosus into the aorta, thus by-passing the lungs, and joins the aortic blood beyond the points of emergence of the cephalic blood flow. The blood in the thoracic and abdominal aorta passes to the rest of the body and much passes to the placenta in the umbilical arteries. The venous return from the body enters the inferior vena cava and mixes with the blood coming from the placenta through the umbilical vein and ductus venosus. At birth, the lungs take in air and there is a much greater flow of blood to the lungs with a subsequent increased venous return. This raises the pressure in the left atrium and so closes the foramen ovale. About the same time the ductus arteriosus and the ductus venosus also close, so establishing the adult pattern of circulation.

Cardiac abnormalities are among the most frequently encountered congenital defects and some are incompatible with independent life. One of the commonest abnormalities is a bicuspid aortic valve, this being usually without symptoms. The abnormalities such as a persistent patent ductus arteriosus, atrial septal defects (where the foramen ovale has failed to close) and ventricular defects may require surgical correction in childhood. Combined defects can also occur, the commonest consisting of a ventricular septal defect, pulmonary valvular stenosis (narrowing) and an aorta which communicates with both the right and left ventricular cavities.

CHAPTER 6

OTHER MEDIASTINAL STRUCTURES

THE LARGE ARTERIES

THE AORTA (Figs. 6.1, 6.3, 6.4)
The aorta is the main arterial trunk of the systemic circulation and in
the healthy state its walls contain a large amount of yellow elastic tissue.
It arises from the left ventricle and ascends for a short distance before
arching backwards over the root of the left lung and descending through
the thorax and abdomen. It is divided into an ascending part, an arch,
a descending thoracic part and an abdominal part.

Pleura
Oesophagus
Trachea
Right vagus nerve
Right phrenic nerve
Superior vena cava
Brachiocephalic artery

Thoracic duct
Recurrent laryngeal nerve
Left subclavian artery
Left vagus nerve
Left phrenic nerve
Left common carotid artery
Left brachiocephalic vein

FIG. 6.1
Diagrammatic representation of the structures seen on a
transverse section through the mediastinum at the level of the
upper border of the body of the 3rd thoracic vertebra.

Ascending aorta—this is a wide vessel about 5 cm long. It begins at
the aortic orifice and ascends to the right around the pulmonary trunk
as far as the level of the sternal angle. Above each of the semilunar folds
(valvules) of the aortic valve is a dilatation, an **aortic sinus.**

RELATIONS: it lies within the fibrous pericardium enclosed in a sheath
of serous pericardium which is common to it and the pulmonary trunk.
The lower part lies behind the infundibulum of the right ventricle and
the beginning of the pulmonary trunk and above this it is related to the
sternum. Posteriorly from below upwards are the left atrium, right
pulmonary artery and the right main bronchus. To the left lie the left
auricle and the pulmonary trunk; to the right, the right auricle and the
superior vena cava.

63

Branches: right and left coronary arteries arise from the sinuses (p. 55).

Arch of the aorta—this part of the aorta passes upwards behind the manubrium from the level of the sternal angle. It arches backwards and to the left over the root of the left lung and descends to reach the left side of the 4th thoracic vertebra.

Relations: to its left lie the mediastinal pleura and lung, the left phrenic nerve in front and vagus behind. To its right lie the superior vena cava with the right phrenic nerve on its right side, the trachea and left recurrent laryngeal nerve, the oesophagus and thoracic duct and then the 4th thoracic vertebra, from before backwards. Inferiorly it crosses, from before backwards, the bifurcation of the pulmonary trunk, the ligamentum arteriosum, and the left main bronchus. Superiorly are its three branches, crossed anteriorly by the left brachiocephalic vein. The arch is connected inferiorly to the left pulmonary artery by the ligamentum arteriosum, a fibrous remnant of the ductus arteriosus. The left recurrent laryngeal nerve passes posteriorly around the ligamentum and the arch. The superficial cardiac plexus lies anterior to the ligamentum and the deep plexus inferior to the arch.

Branches
(i) the **brachiocephalic artery** is the first branch of the arch. It arises behind the manubrium and ascends, passing backwards and to the right as far as the right sternoclavicular joint where it divides into right subclavian and right common carotid arteries.

Relations: anteriorly the left brachiocephalic vein and thymus separate it from the manubrium. Posteriorly lies the trachea. To its right lies the right brachiocephalic vein and the superior vena cava and to its left the left common carotid artery.

It has only terminal branches, the right subclavian (p. 331) and the right common carotid arteries (p. 333).
(ii) the **left common carotid artery** (p. 334).
(iii) the **left subclavian artery** (p. 331).

Descending aorta—this descends from the left side of the 4th thoracic vertebra inclining medially to the front of the 12th vertebra where it passes through the diaphragm to become the abdominal aorta (p. 127).

Relations: anteriorly, from above downwards, the root of the left lung, the left atrium separated by pericardium, the oesophagus and the diaphragm. Posteriorly it lies on the vertebral column and hemiazygos veins. Its left side is in contact with the left pleura and lung and its right with the oesophagus above and the right lung and pleura below. The thoracic duct and azygos vein lie to its right side.

Branches
(i) 3rd–11th posterior intercostal arteries and the subcostal artery (p. 46).
(ii) two or three bronchial arteries.
(iii) four or five oesophageal arteries.
(iv) mediastinal and diaphragmatic arteries.

THE PULMONARY TRUNK (Fig. 6.2, 6.4)

This wide vessel, about 5 cm long, begins at the pulmonary orifice, ascends posteriorly on the left side of the aortic trunk and ends by bifurcating into right and left pulmonary arteries in the concavity of the aortic arch. It lies in front of the transverse sinus and is contained within

Fig. 6.2

Pulmonary arteriogram. The catheter (1) has been introduced through the right basilic vein, passed through the right atrium and ventricle, and enters the pulmonary trunk through the pulmonary valve.

1. Catheter	3. Right pulmonary artery
2. Pulmonary trunk	4. Left pulmonary artery

a common sleeve of serous pericardium with the ascending aorta. The right and left coronary arteries and the two auricles surround its base and it is covered anteriorly and on its left by the left pleura and lung.

BRANCHES

(i) the **right pulmonary artery** passes to the hilus of the right lung behind the ascending aorta and superior vena cava, and in front of the oesophagus and right main bronchus.

(ii) the **left pulmonary artery** passes in front of the left bronchus and the descending aorta to the hilus of the left lung. It is connected by a short fibrous band, the ligamentum arteriosum, to the lower surface of the aortic arch.

In the lungs these arteries and their branches accompany the bronchi and bronchioles.

THE LARGE VEINS (Figs. 6.1, 6.3, 6.4)

The brachiocephalic veins are formed behind the sternoclavicular joints by the union of the corresponding internal jugular and subclavian veins. After a short course they unite to form the superior vena cava about the middle of the right border of the manubrium.

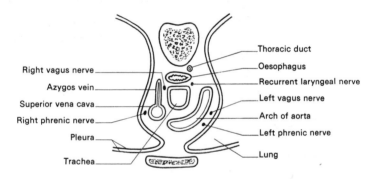

Right vagus nerve
Azygos vein
Superior vena cava
Right phrenic nerve
Pleura
Trachea

Thoracic duct
Oesophagus
Recurrent laryngeal nerve
Left vagus nerve
Arch of aorta
Left phrenic nerve
Lung

Fig. 6.3
Diagrammatic representation of the structures seen on a transverse section through the mediastinum at the level of the upper part of the body of the 4th thoracic vertebra and of the arch of the aorta.

The **right brachiocephalic vein** is about 3 cm long. It descends vertically behind the right border of the manubrium, anterolateral to the brachiocephalic artery. The right phrenic nerve descends along its lateral surface between it and the pleura.

The **left brachiocephalic vein** is about 6 cm long. It descends obliquely behind the manubrium crossing above the arch of the aorta and in front of its three large branches and the trachea. Thymic remnants may lie anteriorly.

TRIBUTARIES: corresponding to some branches of the subclavian artery, viz.:

(i) vertebral vein—drains neck muscles at the back and vertebral column.

(ii) inferior thyroid veins—usually unite in front of the trachea, and their common trunk enters the left brachiocephalic vein.

(iii) internal thoracic vein—drains anterior chest wall and diaphragm.

(iv) additionally, the thoracic duct enters the beginning of the left vein; the right lymph duct enters the beginning of the right vein. The left superior intercostal vein runs across the aortic arch to enter the left brachiocephalic vein.

The **superior vena cava**—a wide vessel about 7 cm long. It is formed by the union of the two brachiocephalic veins at the middle of the right border of the manubrium and descends vertically behind the manubrium and body of the sternum to enter the right atrium at the level of the 3rd right costal cartilage. It possesses no valves.

RELATIONS: in its lower half it is covered by the fibrous and serous pericardium. Anterior are the right lung and pleura, and the manubrium. Posterior is the right lung root. Medial are the ascending aorta and the brachiocephalic artery. Lateral are the right phrenic nerve and the pleura and lung. The azygos vein is its only tributary, entering it posteriorly.

The **pulmonary veins** are short wide vessels passing to the left atrium, usually two (upper and lower) from each lung. In the hilus of the lung they lie below and in front of the artery. On the right the upper passes behind the superior vena cava, the lower behind the right atrium. On the left both veins pass in front of the aorta.

The **azygos vein** is formed in the abdomen in front of the 2nd lumbar vertebra either as a branch of the inferior vena cava or by the union of the right subcostal and ascending lumbar veins. It leaves the abdomen through the aortic opening of the diaphragm. In the thorax it lies to the right of the aorta and thoracic duct and ascends on the right of the vertebral bodies covered by pleura. At the level of the 4th thoracic vertebra, it arches forwards over the hilus of the right lung to enter the superior vena cava. Above the hilus it lies between the lung and pleural sac laterally and the oesophagus and trachea medially.

TRIBUTARIES
(i) right ascending lumbar vein.
(ii) 4th–11th right posterior intercostal veins and subcostal vein.
(iii) right superior intercostal vein.
(iv) right bronchial veins.
(v) accessory hemiazygos and hemiazygos veins—these lie on the left side of the vertebral column and receive the 4th–11th left intercostal veins. They pass to the right in front of the mid-thoracic vertebrae to open separately into the azygos vein. The left ascending lumbar vein continues as the hemiazygos vein.

The **inferior vena cava** is a wide vessel which pierces the central tendon of the diaphragm and, after a short intrathoracic course, enters the lower part of the right atrium. (See also pages 49 and 129.)

OTHER STRUCTURES

THE PHRENIC NERVES (Figs. 6.1, 6.3, 6.4) See also page 338.

The right and left phrenic nerves descend through the thorax, in front of each lung root.

The **right phrenic nerve** enters the thorax on the lateral side of the right brachiocephalic vein and in its descent it lies on the pericardium covering the superior vena cava, the right atrium and the inferior vena cava. It passes through the caval opening in the diaphragm. Throughout its course it is covered laterally by mediastinal pleura.

The **left phrenic nerve** enters the thorax in front of the left subclavian artery, behind the left brachiocephalic vein. In its descent it crosses the aortic arch and the pericardium covering the left ventricle to reach and pierce the diaphragm. Throughout its course it is covered laterally by mediastinal pleura.

Both nerves supply the diaphragm and also give sensory branches to the mediastinal and diaphragmatic pleura, to the pericardium, and to the peritoneum.

THE VAGUS NERVES (Figs. 6.1, 6.3, 6.4) See also page 321.

The **right vagus nerve** enters the thorax posterolateral to the right brachiocephalic artery. It descends between the trachea medially, and

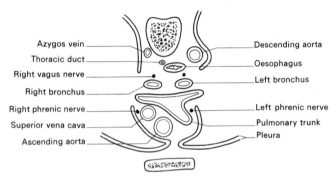

Azygos vein
Thoracic duct
Right vagus nerve
Right bronchus
Right phrenic nerve
Superior vena cava
Ascending aorta

Descending aorta
Oesophagus
Left bronchus
Left phrenic nerve
Pulmonary trunk
Pleura

FIG. 6.4

Diagrammatic representation of the structures seen on a transverse section through the mediastinum at the level of the lower border of the 5th thoracic vertebra.

the mediastinal pleura, the lung and the azygos vein laterally, to the back of the right main bronchus where it gives numerous branches to the pulmonary plexus before proceeding to the oesophageal plexus.

The **left vagus nerve** enters the thorax between the left common carotid and subclavian arteries, behind the left brachiocephalic vein. It descends inclining posteriorly across the left side of the aortic arch, giving off its recurrent laryngeal branch before passing medially behind the root of the lung to the oesophagus. The two vagi form the oesophageal plexus. From this plexus emerge anterior and posterior gastric nerves containing fibres of both vagi and sympathetic nerves. They descend through the oesophageal opening of the diaphragm. The anterior nerve supplies the front of the stomach, the duodenum, pancreas and liver; the posterior supplies the back of the stomach and gives branches which pass through the coeliac plexus to other abdominal viscera (Fig. 6.5).

BRANCHES

(i) left recurrent laryngeal nerve—winds around the ligamentum

arteriosum and aortic arch and then ascends between trachea and oeso-phagus into the neck (p. 322).
(ii) cardiac branches—to the cardiac plexus (p. 81).
(iii) branches to the pulmonary and oesophageal plexuses (p. 81).

THE THYMUS

This bilobed mass of lymphoid tissues lies in front of the trachea in the root of the neck and upper thorax. It is large at birth but atrophies after puberty. Variable in size, it may extend down beyond the aortic arch lying in front of the brachiocephalic veins and the left common carotid artery in the mediastinum. It is supplied by branches of the inferior thyroid and internal thoracic arteries and its veins drain to the internal thoracic and left brachiocephalic veins.

HISTOLOGY AND EMBRYOLOGY: it is lobulated and formed of numerous cells embedded in a reticular network of fine collagen fibres. In the outer denser cortex, lymphocytes are predominant: the inner medulla contains paler round cells, thymocytes, and nests of concentrically arranged cells —Hassall's corpuscles. It is derived from the 3rd pair of pharyngeal pouches, and parathyroid tissue may be embedded in it.

THE OESOPHAGUS (Figs. 6.1, 6.3, 6.4, 6.5.) See also page 95 and page 330.

The oesophagus descends through the thorax mainly to the left of the midline, curves forwards in its lower part away from the vertebral column and pierces the diaphragm at the level of the 10th thoracic vertebra.

RELATIONS: in the upper part of the mediastinum it lies between the vertebral column posteriorly and the trachea anteriorly; the left recurrent laryngeal nerve lies in the groove between it and the trachea. Below, it is separated from the vertebral column, from above downwards, by the thoracic duct, the hemiazygos veins, the right posterior intercostal arteries and the descending thoracic aorta. Anteriorly below the trachea, it is crossed by the left bronchus, and below this it is separated by pericardium from the left atrium. On the right it is covered with mediastinal pleura and the azygos vein arches forwards above the lung root. On the left it is separated from the mediastinal pleura above by the left subclavian artery, the thoracic duct, the aortic arch and descending aorta. Its lower part is in contact with the pleura.

THE TRACHEA AND BRONCHI (Figs. 6.1, 6.3, 6.4, 7.6, 7.7). See also page 329.

The trachea lies in the midline anterior to the oesophagus, the left recurrent laryngeal nerve ascending in the groove between them. Anteriorly it is crossed by the brachiocephalic artery and then by the left brachiocephalic vein. On its left lie the common carotid and subclavian arteries above and the aortic arch below. On its right are the mediastinal pleura, the right vagus nerve and the azygos vein.

The tracheal bifurcation is at the level of the sternal angle and the lower border of the 4th thoracic vertebra. It lies anterior to the oesophagus, behind and to the right of the bifurcation of the pulmonary trunk. It is separated from the right pulmonary artery by the deep part of the cardiac plexus and tracheobronchial lymph nodes.

The **extrapulmonary bronchi**: the main bronchus on each side arises

Fig. 6.5

Barium swallow. The patient has swallowed a mouthful of barium sulphate suspension just before these radiographs were taken. A–Anteroposterior view. B–Lateral view.

1. Impression of aortic arch
2. Oesophagogastric junction
3. Fundus of stomach
4. Trachea

5. Cardiac impression (left atrium)
6. Diaphragm
7. Oesophagogastric junction

at the bifurcation and descends passing laterally to enter the hilus of the lung where it divides to form the intrapulmonary bronchial tree.

The **right bronchus** is about 3 cm long. It is wider and somewhat more vertical than the left and foreign bodies therefore tend to enter it more frequently. The right upper lobe bronchus arises from it just before it enters the hilus.

RELATIONS: anteriorly the right pulmonary artery separates it from the pericardium and the superior vena cava. The arch of the azygos vein is above it and posteriorly lies the pulmonary plexus and the bronchial vessels.

The **left bronchus** is about 5 cm long.

RELATIONS: anteriorly the left pulmonary artery separates it from the left atrium. The arch of the aorta is above it, and posteriorly lies the pulmonary plexus and bronchial vessels which separate it from the oesophagus and descending thoracic aorta.

The structure of the extrapulmonary bronchi is similar to that of the trachea (p. 329).

Direct viewing of the trachea and proximal main bronchi is possible with a bronchoscope. Instillation of a radio-opaque contrast medium, Lipiodol, into the bronchi, permits X-rays to show the arrangement of the distal smaller bronchi (Figs. 7.6, 7.7). Bronchial cancer is one of the commonest malignant diseases and readily spreads to the tracheo-bronchial lymph nodes. It can produce early symptoms of bronchial obstruction.

CHAPTER 7

THE PLEURA AND LUNGS

THE PLEURA

Each pleural sac is a closed cavity lined by a serous membrane which is invaginated by a lung. Parietal pleura lines the outer walls of the cavity and visceral (pulmonary) pleura covers the lungs. The layers of pleura are continuous around the root of the lung and are separated only by a thin layer of serous fluid. The two layers of pleura can glide easily on each other but are prevented from separating by the **surface tension** of the serous

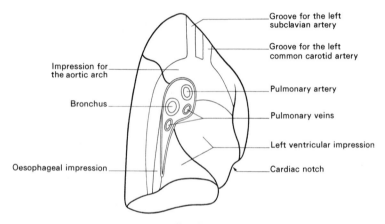

Groove for the left subclavian artery

Groove for the left common carotid artery

Impression for the aortic arch

Bronchus

Pulmonary artery

Pulmonary veins

Left ventricular impression

Oesophageal impression

Cardiac notch

FIG. 7.1

The medial surface of the left lung. Some of the principal structures in contact with the lung are shown.

fluid and the **negative pressure** in the closed cavity. As a result, when the diaphragm descends and the thoracic cage expands, the lung also has to expand and so air is drawn in from the trachea.

The pleura is a fibro-elastic membrane lined by squamous mesothelial cells. The parietal pleura lines the ribs, costal cartilages and the inter-costal spaces, the lateral surface of the mediastinum and the upper surface of the diaphragm. Superiorly it extends beyond the thoracic inlet into the neck to form the cervical **dome** of pleura. Inferiorly, around the margin of the diaphragm, it forms a narrow gutter, the **costodiaphragmatic recess.** Anteriorly, in front of the heart, the left costal and mediastinal surfaces are in contact forming the **costomediastinal recess.** The mediastinal pleura invests the main bronchi and pulmonary vessels as an overlarge collar and passes on to the surface of the lung to become pulmonary pleura. This completely covers the lung and extends into its interlobar fissures.

The extent of the pleural sacs on each side should be noted. On both sides the upper limit of the cervical pleura lies about 3 cm above the medial third of the clavicle. From here the lines of pleural reflections descend behind the sternoclavicular joints to meet in the midline at the level of the 2nd costal cartilages. At the 4th cartilage, the left pleura deviates laterally to descend along the lateral border of the sternum as far as the 6th cartilage, whereas the right pleura continues vertically downwards near the midline to the 6th cartilage. At the 6th costal cartilage

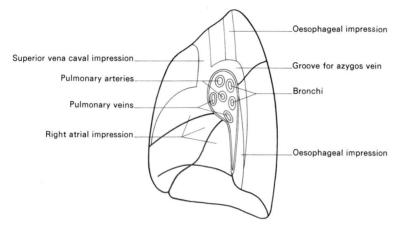

FIG. 7.2
The medial surface of the right lung. Some of the principal structures in contact with the lung are shown.

the lower border of both pleural reflections passes laterally just behind the costal margin to reach the 8th rib in the midclavicular line, the 10th rib in the midaxillary line and the 12th rib in the paravertebral line. The paravertebral line lies about 3 cm from the midline and corresponds to the tips of the transverse processes.

The pleura is supplied by blood from the tissues it covers. Pulmonary pleura has no pain fibres but the parietal pleura is richly supplied by the nerves in the subjacent tissues. Lymph from the pulmonary pleura passes to a superficial plexus in the lung and then to the hilar nodes. The parietal pleura drains to parasternal, diaphragmatic and posterior mediastinal nodes.

THE LUNGS (Figs. 7.1, 7.2, 7.3)

The lungs are the paired organs of respiration. Each lies in its pleural sac attached to the mediastinum at the hilus. The lung is spongy and elastic in texture and cone-shaped to conform to the contours of the

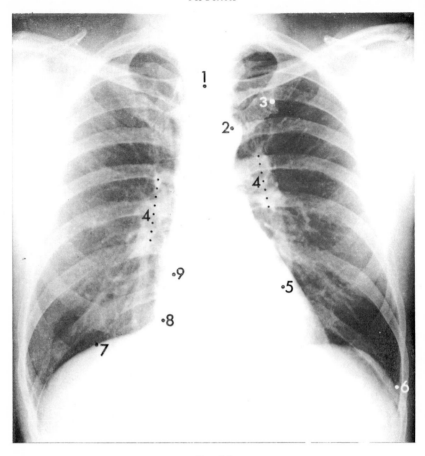

FIG. 7.3

Radiograph of the chest, using no contrast medium — anteroposterior view. The dense shadow occupying most of the upper abdomen is produced by the liver, which contains much blood. Many of the radiating streaks from the hilus of the lung are produced by the large blood vessels. Some hilar shadows may be caused by calcified lymph nodes. Shadows of the heart and large vessels are seen centrally.

1. Trachea	6. Left costodiaphragmatic recess
2. Aortic knuckle	7. Right dome of diaphragm
3. 1st costochondral junction	8. Inferior vena cava
4. Hilar shadows	9. Right atrium
5. Left ventricle	

thoracic cavity. The right lung weighs about 620 g and the left about 560 g. The lungs have a characteristic mottled appearance on X-ray films. The clear areas are lung tissue and the dense shadows at the hilus and radiating outwards are caused by hilar tissues (lymph nodes) and by blood vessels (Fig. 7.3).

Each lung has an **apex** in the root of the neck and a **base** resting on the diaphragm. The base is separated by a sharp inferior border from a lateral convex costal surface and a medial concave (mediastinal) surface. In the centre of this latter surface, the structures forming the root of the lung are seen to be surrounded by a collar of pleura. The concavity of the medial surface is accentuated on the left to accommodate the left ventricle of the heart. The anterior border on the left side is deeply indented by the heart to form the **cardiac notch.** The posterior border is rounded and lies in the paravertebral gutter.

The lungs are divided into lobes by fissures which extend deeply into their substance. An **oblique fissure** divides the left lung into an upper and a lower lobe; oblique and horizontal fissures divide the right lung into upper, middle and lower lobes. The oblique fissure of both lungs may be marked by a line curving around the chest wall from the spine of the 3rd thoracic vertebra to the 6th costochondral junction. The **horizontal fissure** is marked by a horizontal line passing laterally to the oblique line from the 4th right costal cartilage.

The **lower lobes** of both lungs lie below and behind the oblique fissure and comprise most of the posterior and inferior borders and parts of the medial and costal surfaces. The **upper lobe** of the left lung lies above and in front of the oblique fissure and comprises the apex, substantial portions of the mediastinal and costal surfaces and the whole of the anterior border including the cardiac notch. The equivalent part of the right lung is divided by the horizontal fissure into a large upper lobe and wedge-shaped anteriorly placed smaller **middle lobe.** A thin antero-inferior part of the left upper lobe, adjacent to the cardiac notch, is known as the lingula and represents the middle lobe. Variation exists in this lobar pattern. Fissures, especially the horizontal, may be incomplete or absent, and occasionally additional lobes are present.

The **hilus** of each lung contains a main bronchus, pulmonary artery, two pulmonary veins, the pulmonary plexus, and lymph nodes, all surrounded by the collar of pleura whose narrow inferior extension is known as the pulmonary ligament. On both sides the bronchus lies behind the pulmonary artery, and the two pulmonary veins lie antero-inferior to both other structures.

The Intrapulmonary Bronchi and Bronchopulmonary Segments

The right upper lobe bronchus arises from the right main bronchus just before the hilus, and soon after entering the lung substance it divides into three segmental bronchi. The middle lobe bronchus arises from the right bronchus just below the upper lobe bronchus and divides into two segmental bronchi. The continuation of the right bronchus passes to the lower lobe and divides into five segmental bronchi.

The left upper lobe bronchus arises from the main bronchus within the lung and divides into five segmental bronchi, two passing to the lingula. The continuation of the left bronchus passes to the lower lobe and divides into five segmental branches. Each segmental bronchus is distributed to a functionally independent unit of lung tissue—a **bronchopulmonary segment.** There are three segments in each upper lobe and two in the right middle lobe which are equivalent to the two in the lingula of the left lung. The five segments in the right lower lobe are more or less equivalent to those in the left lower lobe.

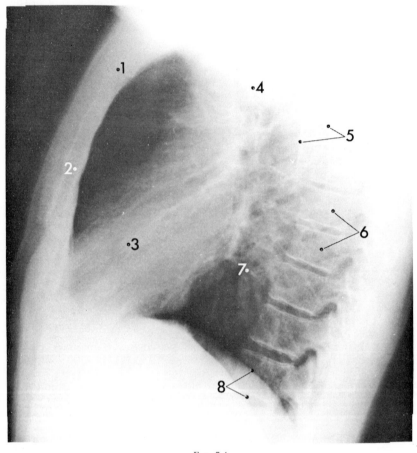

FIG. 7.4

Radiograph of the chest—lateral view. Note the large space between the heart and the sternum in front, and between the heart and the vertebral bodies behind.

1. Manubriosternal joint	5. Borders of scapulae
2. Sternum	6. Vertebral bodies
3. Cardiac shadow	7. Retrocardiac space
4. Trachea	8. Domes of diaphragm

RELATIONS

Parietal relations: the borders of the lungs closely follow the lines of pleural reflection on the chest wall except below where the inferior border of the lung lies approximately two intercostal spaces above the inferior limit of the pleura and in front where the anterior border of the left lung in the region of the cardiac notch lies about 3 cm lateral to the pleural reflection in this region. The costal surface is related to the thoracic wall. The base is separated by the diaphragm from the right lobe of the liver on the right side and the left lobe of the liver, stomach and spleen on the left. The apex is covered by the dome of pleura which lines the supra-

FIG. 7.5

Tomogram of chest through hilar region showing soft tissue shadows, anteroposterior view. By the technique of tomography, it is possible to obtain a radiograph of an 'isolated layer' of the body.

1. Right main bronchus	4. Left pulmonary artery
2. Right pulmonary artery	5. Left main bronchus
3. Right pulmonary veins	6. Left pulmonary vein

pleural membrane, a fibrous sheet extending from the transverse process of the 7th cervical vertebra to the inner border of the 1st rib. The subclavian vessels arch over the apex above the pleura and membrane. Posteriorly the branch of the 1st thoracic nerve to the brachial plexus, the superior intercostal artery, the sympathetic trunk and the pleura separate the apex of the lung from the neck of the 1st rib.

The medial relations of the two lungs differ (Figs. 7.1, 7.2, 7.3).

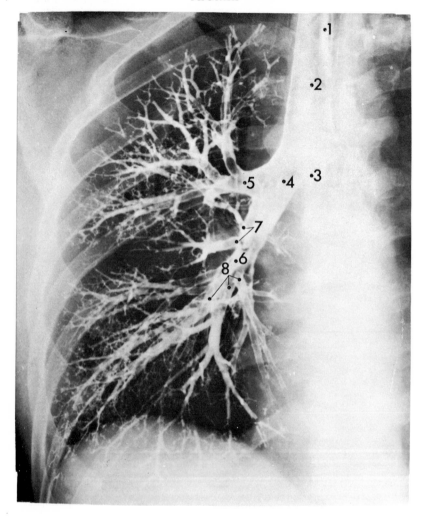

FIG. 7.6

Bronchogram of right lung, anteroposterior view. A radiopaque substance is introduced into the lung along a catheter inserted into the trachea.

1. Intubation catheter
2. Trachea
3. Carina
4. Right main bronchus

5. Right upper lobe bronchus
6. Right middle lobe bronchus
7. Right apical lower lobe bronchi
8. Right basal lower lobe bronchi

On the left: there is a large concavity antero-inferiorly for the left ventricle of the heart. It is continuous superiorly with a groove for the aortic arch which passes in front of and above the hilus. Above the groove

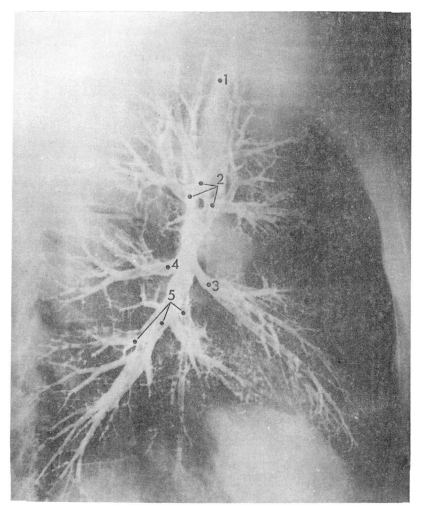

FIG. 7.7
Bronchogram of right lung, lateral view.

1. Trachea
2. Right upper lobe bronchi
3. Right middle lobe bronchus

4. Right apical lower lobe bronchus
5. Right basal lower lobe bronchi

the surface is in contact with the left brachiocephalic vein, left common carotid and left subclavian arteries, and the oesophagus.

On the right: there is a shallow concavity in front of the hilus for the right atrium. This is continuous above with a groove for the superior vena cava and with a short one below for the inferior vena cava. The azygos vein grooves the lung as it arches forwards above the hilus. The oesophagus, which lies near the posterior border, is in contact throughout its length save where the azygos vein separates it from the lung. Between the superior vena cava and the oesophagus superiorly is the trachea.

BLOOD SUPPLY: lung tissue is supplied by the bronchial branches of the descending thoracic aorta. The bronchial veins drain to the azygos or accessory hemiazygos veins. Poorly oxygenated blood is conveyed to the lung alveoli by the pulmonary artery whose branches correspond to and accompany the bronchial tree. The terminal branches end in a capillary network within the alveolar walls. Venous tributaries from the network return with the bronchi to upper and lower pulmonary veins.

LYMPH DRAINAGE: this is via a superficial subpleural lymph plexus and a deep plexus of vessels accompanying the bronchi. Both groups drain through hilar (bronchopulmonary) lymph nodes to tracheobronchial nodes around the bifurcation of the trachea and thence to mediastinal lymph trunks.

NERVE SUPPLY: sympathetic from the upper thoracic segments and parasympathetic from the vagus, both pass through the pulmonary plexus. Sensory fibres pass mainly in the vagus.

HISTOLOGY: the walls of intrapulmonary bronchi, lined by respiratory epithelium, are formed of fibrous tissue and smooth muscle, and contain rings of hyaline cartilage. The bronchi divide and redivide until their diameter is less than 1 mm after which they are known as bronchioles, the walls of which lack mucous glands and cartilaginous rings. The bronchioles subdivide to form respiratory bronchioles whose walls, lined by nonciliated columnar epithelium, contain smooth muscle. Each respiratory bronchiole opens into a number of alveolar ducts from which arise alveolar sacs whose walls possess the terminal respiratory saccules, the alveoli. Alveolar walls are lined by simple squamous epithelium.

EMBRYOLOGY: the lungs develop from a single ventral pharyngeal outgrowth which bifurcates. The lung buds enlarge into the coelomic pericardioperitoneal canals (see pages 24 and 29).

X-rays of the chest allow accurate localisation of disease of the lung, in addition to defining abnormal collections of air or fluid in the pleural space. The use of radiopaque contrast substances greatly facilitates localisation of the lesion (Figs. 7.6, 7.7). Excision of a segment, a lobe or a whole lung can be undertaken. A knowledge of the pattern of division of the bronchi helps when a part of the lung has to be drained of pus.

CHAPTER 8

THE AUTONOMIC NERVOUS SYSTEM AND

LYMPH DRAINAGE

AUTONOMIC NERVOUS SYSTEM

The autonomic nerve supply of the thoracic viscera is derived from the collateral plexuses, viz.: cardiac, pulmonary and the oesophageal plexuses. These plexuses receive sympathetic contributions from the cervical and thoracic sympathetic trunks and parasympathetic contributions from the vagi (p. 69).

The Collateral Plexuses

The **cardiac plexus:** the superficial (ventral) part lies in front of the ligamentum arteriosum; the deep (dorsal) part in front of the bifurcation of the trachea. They communicate with each other and functionally are a single unit, receiving branches from each of the cervical sympathetic ganglia, the upper thoracic ganglia, and parasympathetic cardiac branches from both vagi. Branches pass with the coronary arteries to supply heart muscle, coronary arteries, the conducting system of the heart, and some branches pass to the pulmonary plexus.

The **pulmonary plexus** lies in front of and behind the lung roots. It receives branches from the upper four thoracic sympathetic ganglia and from both vagi. It supplies the lung substance and visceral pleura.

The **oesophageal plexus** is a network surrounding the lower oesophagus. It receives branches from the upper thoracic sympathetic ganglia and from both vagi. It supplies the oesophagus and forms anterior and posterior vagal trunks which pass with the oesophagus into the abdomen as anterior and posterior gastric nerves (p. 164).

The Thoracic Sympathetic Trunk

Each ganglionated trunk lies alongside the vertebral column in front of the necks of the ribs. It continues superiorly into the cervical sympathetic trunk and inferiorly into the lumbar. It usually possesses 12 ganglia, one corresponding to each thoracic nerve, but often the 1st is fused with the inferior cervical ganglion to form a large **stellate ganglion** above the neck of the 1st rib. Each ganglion is attached to its spinal nerve by a white (preganglionic) and a grey (postganglionic) ramus.

BRANCHES
(i) rami communicantes.
(ii) the upper four ganglia give branches to the cardiac, pulmonary and oesophageal plexuses.
(iii) the greater, lesser and least **splanchnic nerves:** the greater arises from the 5th–9th ganglia; the lesser from the 10th–11th and the least (renal nerve) from the 12th. They descend over the posterior thoracic wall

81

medial to the sympathetic chain and enter the abdomen by piercing the corresponding crus of the diaphragm to reach the abdominal plexuses. Their fibres synapse in the coeliac and other pre-aortic ganglia.

Each cervical sympathetic ganglion gives branches to the cardiac plexuses which pass into the thorax alongside the large vessels in the neck (p. 339).

The vagi are described on page 68.

LYMPH DRAINAGE

The vessels may be divided into those draining the chest wall and those draining the thoracic viscera.

The **chest wall** drains by superficial and deep vessels. The superficial drain, together with those of the breast, to the central and pectoral groups of axillary lymph nodes. The vessels draining the deep part of the wall pass to three groups of nodes:

(i) **parasternal nodes**—lie alongside the internal thoracic artery. Their efferents pass to the mediastinal lymph trunk.

(ii) **intercostal nodes**—lie at the posterior end of the intercostal spaces. Their efferents pass to the right lymph duct and the thoracic duct.

(iii) **diaphragmatic nodes**—lie on the upper surface of the diaphragm. Their efferents drain to the parasternal and posterior mediastinal nodes and communicate through the diaphragm with the vessels draining the upper surface of the liver.

The **thoracic viscera** drain to three main groups of nodes:

(i) **anterior mediastinal nodes**—lie in front of the brachiocephalic veins and drain the thymus and anterior pericardium. Their efferents join those of the tracheobronchial nodes.

(ii) **tracheobronchial nodes**—lie alongside the trachea and bronchi and drain the lungs, bronchi, trachea and heart. Their efferents join with vessels from the anterior mediastinal nodes to form the bronchomediastinal lymph trunk. On the right side the trunk ascends alongside the trachea to join the right lymph duct, and on the left to join the thoracic duct.

(iii) the **posterior mediastinal nodes**—lie alongside the oesophagus behind the pericardium. They drain the oesophagus and posterior pericardium. Their efferents pass to the thoracic duct.

The thoracic duct and the smaller right lymph duct are the final vessels along which lymph passes before entering the bloodstream.

The Thoracic Duct

This is about 45 cm long. It arises in the abdomen from the cisterna chyli (p. 162) and enters the thorax through the aortic opening of the diaphragm to the right of the aorta. It ascends in front of the vertebral column on the left of the azygos vein and behind the oesophagus. In front of the 5th thoracic vertebra it passes to the left behind the oesophagus and continues its ascent to the level of the 7th cervical vertebra where it arches laterally behind the carotid sheath and then forwards in front of the subclavian artery to enter the beginning of the left brachiocephalic vein.

TRIBUTARIES drain all the body below the diaphragm and the left half above the diaphragm and, in addition, the posterior part of the right chest wall. It usually receives the united left jugular and subclavian lymph trunks and the left mediastinal lymph trunk.

The Right Lymph Duct

This is a short vessel which is often absent. It is formed in the neck by the union of the jugular, subclavian and bronchomediastinal lymph trunks. It enters the beginning of the right brachiocephalic vein and drains lymph from the right upper limb, the right side of the head, neck and the thorax, with the exception noted above.

ABDOMEN AND PELVIS

THE ABDOMEN AND PERITONEUM

The abdomen is that part of the trunk between the diaphragm and pelvis. For descriptive purposes the anterior abdominal wall is divided into nine regions by two horizontal and two vertical planes. The horizontal planes are the transpyloric (midway between the jugular notch and the crest of the pubis), and the transtubercular (through the tubercles of the iliac crests). The vertical planes are the right and left lateral which pass through the midinguinal points (between anterior superior iliac spine and symphysis pubis). The regions so formed are—centrally, from above downwards, the epigastric, the umbilical and the pubic. On each side of there are the hypochondriac, lateral and inguinal regions. The transpyloric plane is coincident with the level of the tip of the 9th costal cartilage anteriorly and the body of the 1st lumbar vertebra posteriorly. The subcostal plane (through the lowest part of the costal margin) is sometimes used instead of the transpyloric plane.

Skeleton: vertebrae—see page 36; sacrum—see page 133; ribs—see page 43; pelvis—see pages 131 and 136.

ANTERIOR ABDOMINAL WALL

The skin of the anterior abdominal wall is supplied by the 6th thoracic to 1st lumbar spinal nerves. T6 supplies the epigastric region. T10 the umbilical region and L1 the groin. The superficial fascia is in two layers. The more superficial is fatty and continuous with the superficial fascia of the thorax and thigh; the deeper is membranous and best developed in the lower abdomen. It is attached inferiorly to the iliac crest, the fascia lata of the thigh and the pubic tubercle. It is continued in front of the symphysis pubis, below and between the two pubic tubercles, and is attached to the inferior ischiopubic rami and the posterior border of the perineal membrane. (See page 152 for relations of this fascia in the perineum.)

Laterally, the anterior abdominal wall consists of three sheet-like muscles in separate layers, an outer external oblique, a middle internal oblique and an inner transversus abdominis. Anteriorly they become aponeurotic, fuse and form the sheath around rectus abdominis.

External Oblique

ATTACHMENTS
Superior—from the outer surfaces at the lower eight ribs, interdigitating with serratus anterior and latissimus dorsi.

Inferior—the fleshy posterior fibres pass downwards to the anterior half of the iliac crest. The muscle has a free posterior border. Anteriorly, the fibres become aponeurotic, pass medially and downwards, in front of the rectus abdominis to be attached to the xiphoid process, the linea alba and the front of the body of the pubis. The pubic crest forms the base of a triangular deficiency in the aponeurosis, the **superficial inguinal ring.** The apex of the deficiency points laterally and its thickened borders form the lateral and medial crura. Between the pubic tubercle and the anterior superior iliac spine the free lower border of the aponeurosis is known as the **inguinal ligament.** This free lower border turns backwards and inwards on itself and gives attachment laterally to internal oblique and transversus abdominis. Its medial 2 cm is expanded and is attached to the pectineal line on the pubis. It forms the pectineal part of the inguinal ligament (lacunar ligament) which, with the inguinal ligament proper, forms the gutter-like floor of the inguinal canal. Below the inguinal ligament, the aponeurosis is continuous with the fascia lata of the thigh.

Internal Oblique

ATTACHMENTS
Lateral—in a continuous line from the thoracolumbar fascia, the anterior two-thirds of the iliac crest and the lateral two-thirds of the inguinal ligament.

Medial—the vertical posterior fibres ascend to the costal margin. Most of the fibres pass upwards and medially and form an aponeurosis which splits around the upper part of rectus abdominis and reaches the linea alba. In the lower abdomen the fibres pass in front of rectus abdominis and leave a free edge posteriorly known as the arcuate line. The fibres from the inguinal ligament arch medially over the spermatic cord, uniting with the transversus abdominis aponeurosis to form the **conjoint tendon** (inguinal falx) which passes anterior to the lower part of the rectus abdominis to reach the crest and medial part of the pectineal line of the pubis.

Transversus Abdominis

ATTACHMENTS
Lateral—in a continuous line from the inner surfaces of the lower six costal cartilages (interdigitating with the diaphragm), the thoracolumbar fascia, the anterior two-thirds of the iliac crest and the lateral one-third of the inguinal ligament.

Medial—the horizontal upper fibres become aponeurotic lateral to the rectus abdominis muscle and reinforce the posterior wall of its sheath from the xiphoid to the arcuate line. Below this the aponeurosis blends with the internal oblique aponeurosis to form the conjoint tendon.

Deep to transversus abdominis lie the transversalis fascia and peritoneum.

Rectus Abdominis

Each muscle lies ventrally alongside the midline enclosed in a fibrous sheath. It is formed of vertically running fibres and is wider above than below.

ATTACHMENTS

Superior—the anterior surface of the 5th, 6th and 7th costal cartilages and the xiphoid process.

Inferior—the pubic crest and the front of the pubic symphysis.

There are two or three horizontal tendinous intersections in the muscle which are attached to the anterior layer of the sheath.

The **rectus sheath** is formed by the aponeuroses of the three flat abdominal muscles which join in the midline to form a strong fibrous raphé, the **linea alba.** Above the costal margin the posterior wall of the sheath is absent and the anterior wall is formed by the external oblique aponeurosis. Between the costal margin and a point midway between the umbilicus and the pubic symphysis, the internal oblique aponeurosis splits to enclose the muscle and is reinforced anteriorly by the external oblique and posteriorly by the transversus abdominis. The lower free edge of the posterior wall forms the **arcuate line.** Inferior to it the rectus muscle lies on the transversalis fascia and peritoneum and the anterior wall is formed by all three aponeuroses. The sheath contains (i) rectus abdominis, (ii) superior and inferior epigastric vessels (which anastomose in the sheath), (iii) the 7th–11th intercostal and subcostal nerves, (iv) lymph vessels.

ACTIONS

The muscles form an elastic wall that both supports the abdominal viscera and yet allows changes in their size and position during diaphragmatic movements. They assist in respiration and in expulsive efforts such as defaecation, micturition, parturition and vomiting. The muscles of both sides act together in flexing the trunk; their unilateral action produces lateral flexion of the trunk and the oblique muscles can produce trunk rotation.

NERVE SUPPLY

The lower five intercostal nerves and the subcostal nerve. The three lateral muscles are also supplied by the 1st lumbar nerve.

BLOOD SUPPLY

The anterior abdominal wall receives its blood supply from the superior and inferior epigastric, the intercostal and subcostal arteries, and branches of the femoral artery. The veins correspond to the arteries.

Surgical access to the abdomen is gained through a variety of incisions. Surgeons operating on the gall bladder, stomach, duodenum and spleen frequently use either midline (through the linea alba) or paramedian incisions. The latter are made vertically about 2 cm from the midline through the anterior rectus sheath and, after the rectus abdominis muscle has been retracted laterally (see Fig. 9.1), through the posterior rectus sheath and peritoneum. Oblique muscle splitting incisions in the right iliac regions through external and internal obliques and transversus abdominis muscles provide access to the appendix. Longer oblique muscle cutting incisions allow access to the right colon or, on the left side, to the sigmoid colon and rectum. Lower paramedian incisions provide similar access to the latter structures. Pelvic organs can be approached through a low transverse incision through the anterior rectus sheath and peritoneum. The rectus

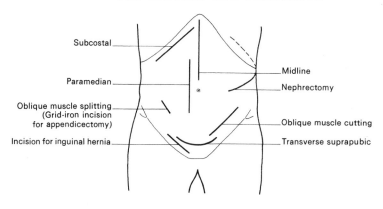

Subcostal

Paramedian

Oblique muscle splitting
(Grid-iron incision
for appendicectomy)

Incision for inguinal hernia

Midline

Nephrectomy

Oblique muscle cutting

Transverse suprapubic

FIG. 9.1
Diagram showing the position of some of the more common surgical incisions through the
anterior abdominal wall.

muscles may be divided transversely but it is usually sufficient to retract
them laterally.

THE INGUINAL CANAL

This is an oblique passage through the anterior abdominal wall. It
extends from the **deep inguinal ring,** a deficiency in the transversalis
fascia just above the midpoint of the inguinal ligament, to the **superficial
inguinal ring,** a deficiency in the external oblique aponeurosis, lying just
above the pubic tubercle. The canal is about 4 cm long and possesses
anterior and posterior walls and a floor.

Anterior wall—formed throughout by the external oblique aponeurosis and reinforced laterally by the internal oblique.

Posterior wall—formed by the transversalis fascia throughout and
reinforced by the conjoint tendon medially. The inferior epigastric artery
ascends in this wall, medial to the deep ring.

Floor—the grooved upper surface of the inguinal ligament and its
medial pectineal (lacunar) part.

The spermatic cord in the male and the round ligament of the uterus
in the female traverse the canal.

The Spermatic Cord

The testis in its descent from the lumbar region and through the
inguinal canal brings its own vessels and nerves with it. A prolongation
of peritoneum, the **processus vaginalis,** precedes the testis down the
fetal inguinal canal and is later obliterated. The spermatic cord gains three
coverings from the layers through which it passes:

(i) internal spermatic fascia—from the transversalis fascia,
(ii) cremasteric fascia and muscle—from internal oblique,

(iii) external spermatic fascia—from external oblique.

It contains three nerves, three arteries, lymph vessels and three other structures. Namely:

  (i) the genital branch of the genitofemoral nerve, the ilio-inguinal nerve and sympathetic nerves,

  (ii) the testicular artery (from the aorta), the cremasteric artery (from the inferior epigastric artery), and the artery to the ductus deferens (from the inferior vesical artery),

(iii) lymphatic vessels draining to the para-aortic lymph nodes,

(iv) the pampiniform plexus of veins, the ductus deferens, and the remains of the processus vaginalis.

Inguinal herniae—an indirect inguinal hernia passes through the deep ring and the whole length of the canal, possibly in a patent processus vaginalis. A direct inguinal hernia enters only the lower part of the canal by pushing through a weakened posterior wall. (A hernia is a protrusion of an organ or tissue through its normal containing wall.)

Undescended testis—usually the testis has descended through the inguinal canal into the scrotum by the time of birth, but it may be retarded or impeded along the line of descent and so remain undescended. It may pass through the external inguinal ring but fail to enter the scrotum and end up in an ectopic position.

THE TESTIS AND EPIDIDYMIS

The two testes are oval glandular organs. Each is suspended in the scrotum by the spermatic cord and is about 4 cm long and 2·5 cm in diameter. It has upper and lower poles. The epididymis, with the ductus deferens on the medial side, is applied to its posterolateral aspect. The other aspects of the gland and the sides of the epididymis are covered by the visceral layer of a closed serous sac, the **tunica vaginalis,** the lower end of the processus vaginalis. The tunica vaginalis, testis, epididymis and ductus deferens are surrounded by extensions of the spermatic cord coverings, namely (i) internal spermatic fascia, (ii) cremaster muscle and cremasteric fascia, (iii) external spermatic fascia, and (iv) superficial fascia which contains some smooth muscle, the dartos, and scrotal skin. Each testis is separated from its fellow by the median scrotal septum. Vessels and nerves enter the gland posteriorly at its lower pole.

The epididymis is a tightly coiled tube about 6 m long applied to the posterolateral surface of the testis. It consists of an enlarged upper extremity (the head), a body and a tapering lower extremity (the tail). The head is attached to the upper pole of the testis by the efferent ducts of the testis. The lumen of the tube is continuous with these efferent ducts above and with the ductus deferens below (see page 150).

BLOOD SUPPLY

The testicular artery and to a lesser extent, the artery to the ductus. Venous blood drains via the pampiniform plexus to the right and left testicular veins. The right drains into the inferior vena cava and the left into the left renal vein.

NERVE SUPPLY

Sympathetic fibres, which originate in the 10th thoracic segment pass to the gland along the testicular artery. Afferent fibres enter the spinal cord in spinal nerves, the genitofemoral and ilio-inguinal nerves.

LYMPH DRAINAGE

Lymph vessels pass with the arteries to para-aortic nodes.

HISTOLOGY: the testis is covered by thin mesothelium (the tunica vaginalis), continuous with the peritoneum in the embryo. Under this is a dense fibrous coat, the **tunica albuginea** which is thickened posteriorly to form the mediastinum testis. From the mediastinum incomplete septa radiate into the gland and divide it into 200–400 compartments, each of which contains two to four convoluted **seminiferous tubules.** These tubules open into the plexiform **rete testis** in the mediastinum and about 20 **efferent ducts** pass from the rete to the head of the epididymis where they become convoluted prior to forming the duct of the epididymis. The seminiferous tubules consist of a thin basement membrane and, after puberty, contain developing spermatozoa. Scattered groups of interstitial cells are present between the tubules. The efferent ducts and the duct of the epididymis have muscular walls and are lined by ciliated columnar and pseudostratified epithelium respectively. The ductus deferens has muscular walls and the lining is much folded and mostly nonciliated.

EMBRYOLOGY: the testis develops from the coelomic mesothelium of the posterior abdominal wall and is attached by its lower pole to a mesodermal mass, the gubernaculum. During development, the testis, preceded by the gubernaculum, descends and passes through the inguinal canal. At birth it lies in the scrotum. A tubular process of peritoneum the processus vaginalis, passes into the scrotum with the descending testis. Its neck is usually obliterated at the time of birth. The developing testis is associated with the mesonephros and mesonephric duct. Tubules of the former become efferent ducts and the head of the epididymis. The duct becomes the ductus deferens.

PERITONEAL CAVITY

PERITONEUM

Peritoneum is a thin serous membrane (mesothelium) enclosing the peritoneal cavity. The part lining the abdominal walls is known as parietal and that covering the viscera as visceral peritoneum. The visceral and parietal layers are separated by a small amount of serous fluid. Viscera invaginate the sac to a varying extent. Some are almost completely invested in peritoneum and carry with them double layers known as mesenteries, ligaments, folds or omenta. Others are incompletely invested and have bare areas in contact with the abdominal walls. This invagination of the viscera decreases the size and increases the complexity of the peritoneal cavity.

ARRANGEMENT (Figs. 9.2, 9.3)

Near the midline and between the umbilicus and the oesophagus, a double layer of peritoneum passes back from the diaphragm and separates to enclose the liver. Anteriorly these two layers are in apposition and form the **falciform ligament**. Superiorly the right layer is pulled from the diaphragm to form the coronary and right triangular ligaments and it encloses much of the bare area of the liver. The left layer forms the left triangular ligament. On the visceral surface of the liver, the two layers reunite along the fissure for the ligamentum venosum and the porta hepatis to form the **lesser omentum**. The two layers of the lesser omentum pass back to the oesophagus, the stomach and the beginning

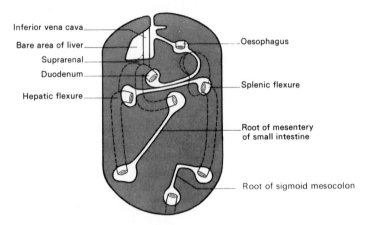

Inferior vena cava

Bare area of liver

Suprarenal

Duodenum

Hepatic flexure

Oesophagus

Splenic flexure

Root of mesentery of small intestine

Root of sigmoid mesocolon

FIG. 9.2
Diagrammatic lay-out of the lines of attachment to the posterior abdominal wall of the peritoneal mesenteries of the alimentary tract.

of the duodenum, and separate to enclose the three structures. The layers come together again along the greater curvature of the stomach. The peritoneum is attached to the posterior abdominal wall from the descending (2nd) part of the duodenum, along the anterior border of the pancreas, the anterior surface of the left kidney and the under surface of the diaphragm as far as the oesophageal opening. Between these attachments and the greater curvature of the stomach, the **greater omentum** hangs down in a lax double fold in front of the transverse colon and meso-colon, and small intestine. Between the stomach and the anterior surface of the left kidney, the peritoneum encloses the spleen and so is divided into gastrosplenic (gastrolienal) and lienorenal ligaments. The four peritoneal layers of the greater omental fold fuse with each other and become adherent to the upper surface of the transverse mesocolon, so that the transverse colon appears to be enclosed within the layers of the greater omentum (Fig. 9.3A).

The transverse mesocolon is attached to the posterior abdominal wall horizontally across the descending (2nd) part of the duodenum, the anterior border of the pancreas and the anterior surface of the left kidney. The parietal peritoneum covering the posterior abdominal wall below the transverse mesocolon also covers the horizontal (3rd) part of the duodenum and the anterior surfaces of the ascending and descending colons, as these structures lie on the posterior abdominal wall. Peritoneum forms a mesentery for the sigmoid colon. This is attached along a ∧-shaped line

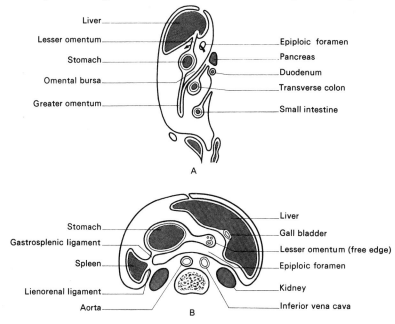

Liver
Lesser omentum
Stomach
Omental bursa
Greater omentum

Epiploic foramen
Pancreas
Duodenum
Transverse colon
Small intestine

A

Stomach
Gastrosplenic ligament
Spleen
Lienorenal ligament
Aorta

Liver
Gall bladder
Lesser omentum (free edge)
Epiploic foramen
Kidney
Inferior vena cava

B

Fig. 9.3

Diagrammatic lay-out of the peritoneum; A, in a sagittal section to the left of the epiploic foramen; B, in a horizontal section through the epiploic foramen.

whose apex lies over the left sacro-iliac joint. This same parietal peritoneum forms a mesentery for the jejunum and ileum which is attached to the posterior abdominal wall along a line joining the duodenojejunal flexure and the ileocolic junction.

The **omental bursa** (lesser sac) of peritoneum is a diverticulum of the peritoneal cavity lying behind the stomach and in front of the posterior abdominal wall. Its opening, the epiploic foramen, is directed to the right, and is bounded by the liver superiorly, the inferior vena cava posteriorly, the duodenum inferiorly and the free edge of the lesser omentum anteriorly (Fig. 9.3B). The omental bursa extends downwards into the greater omentum, to the left as far as the hilus of the spleen and superiorly into a recess between the liver (caudate lobe) and the diaphragm. Its anterior and posterior relations are shown in Figure 9.3.

The abdominal peritoneum extends down into the pelvis to cover the pelvic walls and the upper surfaces of the viscera. It covers the superior surface of the bladder. In the male it covers the upper end of the seminal vesicles and dips down into the rectovesical fossa, whence it ascends on to the front and sides of the rectum. In the female, peritoneum covers the anterior and posterior surfaces of the uterus and uterine tubes. The peritoneal fold over each tube extends to the pelvic walls and is known as the **broad ligament** of the uterus. It separates a shallow uterovesical pouch in front (which is present between the uterus and bladder) from a deeper recto-uterine pouch posteriorly (pouch of Douglas). This latter pouch has the rectum behind and the uterus and upper part of the vagina in front.

EMBRYOLOGY (see also pp. 26 and 30)

A knowledge of the following basic facts is essential in the understanding of the peritoneal arrangements. The primitive alimentary tract is attached to the posterior abdominal wall by a dorsal mesentery. Ventrally there is a mesentery only in the foregut region and it is attached to the anterior abdominal wall above the umbilicus. The caudal end of the foregut, which later forms part of the duodenum, comes to lie on the posterior abdominal wall and loses its dorsal mesentery. The midgut migrates into the body stalk (umbilical cord) and increases greatly the length of its dorsal mesentery. On its subsequent return to the abdominal cavity the midgut loop rotates so that the distal part of the loop (future ascending and transverse colon) comes to lie to the right of and across the proximal part (future duodenum and small intestine). The stomach, jejunum, ileum, transverse and sigmoid colons retain their mesenteries; the duodenum, ascending and descending colons lose their mesenteries and lie on the posterior abdominal wall covered only anteriorly by peritoneum.

The primitive stomach rotates, its left surface becoming anterior. The spleen develops in the left side of its dorsal mesentery and in doing so divides this mesentery into gastrosplenic and lienorenal ligaments. Below the greater curvature of the stomach the dorsal mesentery increases in size and forms a double fold—the greater omentum—in front of the transverse colon and mesocolon.

The liver develops in the ventral mesentery which provides its peritoneal covering. This part of the mesentery also forms the falciform ligament which connects the liver to the anterior abdominal wall, and the lesser omentum which connects the liver to the lesser curvature of the stomach. The liver grows towards the right causing the lesser omentum and stomach to trap behind them a pouch of the peritoneum called the omental bursa.

Incomplete healing of an infection of the peritoneal cavity may lead to abscess formation in its recesses. In the lower abdomen infection may localise in the rectovesical or recto-uterine pouch and so cause a pelvic abscess. In the upper abdomen abscesses may develop in the right and left subphrenic spaces, (on each side of the falciform ligament), the right subhepatic space (between the liver and the right kidney, and less commonly in the omental bursa (lesser sac) of the peritoneum. (See page 114.)

CHAPTER 10

THE ABDOMINAL ALIMENTARY TRACT

THE ABDOMINAL OESOPHAGUS

This is about 3 cm long. It enters the abdomen on the left of the midline through fibres of the right crus posterior to the central tendon of the diaphragm and becomes continuous with the stomach at the **cardiac orifice.** It lies between the diaphragm and the left lobe of the liver and is covered anterolaterally by peritoneum. Gastric vessels and vagal nerves lie in its walls. (See also pages 69 and 164.) Reflux of gastric contents is normally prevented by the lower oesophageal sphincter and the oblique angle of entry of the oesophagus into the stomach. If reflux does occur, inflammation of the lower oesophagus and subsequent stricture formation may result. Not infrequently, the oesophageal opening in the diaphragm becomes incompetent and a part of the stomach is allowed to slide into the mediastinum. This condition, known as a hiatus hernia, also predisposes to the reflux of gastric contents.

THE STOMACH (Fig. 10.1)

This is a dilatation of the alimentary canal between the oesophagus and the duodenum. Although variable in size, shape and position, it is usually J-shaped and situated in the left hypochondrium and epigastrium, its lower part extending to the level of the umbilicus. But it may be shorter and more horizontal (steerhorn stomach) or longer, drooping into the pelvis (fishhook stomach). Differences in the size, shape and motility and rate of emptying of the stomach can be demonstrated by X-rays after a barium meal. The pattern of the mucosal folds can also be seen and irregularities detected. The air in the fundus can often be seen on a plain X-ray film. Changes in position and posture of the subject and states of nervous tension will alter markedly the appearance of the stomach. The activity of the pyloric sphincter is also very obvious.

The stomach is divided into a fundus, a body and a pyloric portion. It possesses anterior and posterior surfaces, both covered by peritoneum, and lesser (right) and greater (left) curvatures. The **fundus** is that part above the level of the oesophageal opening (cardiac orifice). The **body** extends from the fundus to the **angular notch** (the most dependent part of the lesser curvature) and the pyloric portion from the notch to the pyloric sphincter (pylorus) which separates the stomach from the duodenum. The pyloric part is subdivided into a proximal dilated **pyloric antrum** and a distal tubular **pyloric canal.** The **lesser curvature** is the upper right border and extends from the right of the oesophagus to the pylorus; to it is attached the lesser omentum. The angular notch is near its lower end. The **greater curvature** extends from the left of the oesophagus around the fundus to the pylorus, forming the left border of the stomach. It gives attachment to the gastrosplenic ligament and the greater omentum.

95

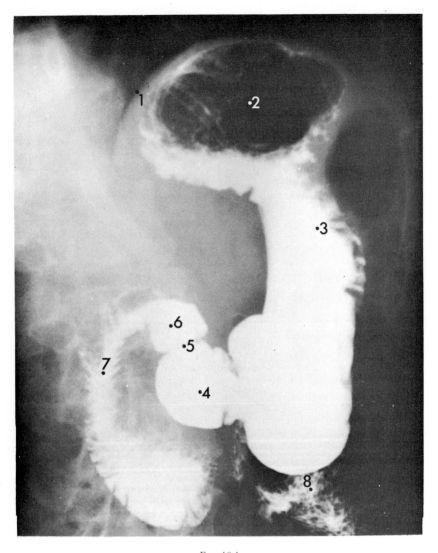

FIG. 10.1

Radiograph of stomach. The barium meal has outlined the stomach and some has entered the duodenum and jejunum.

1. Left dome of diaphragm
2. Gas in fundus
3. Body
4. Pyloric antrum
5. Pylorus
6. Duodenal cap
7. Descending part of duodenum
8. Jejunum

RELATIONS

Anterior—the left lobe of the liver, diaphragm and anterior abdominal wall.

Posterior (stomach bed)—the omental bursa separates it from the diaphragm above, the pancreas, splenic artery, spleen, the left kidney and

FIG. 10.2

The arterial supply (above) and the venous drainage (below) of the stomach and the duodenum.

suprarenal gland from right to left across the middle, and the transverse mesocolon and colon below.

Superior—the lesser omentum and the gastric vessels.

Inferior—the greater omentum and the gastro-epiploic vessels.

BLOOD SUPPLY: the left and right gastric arteries supply the lesser curvature and adjacent surfaces; the left and right gastro-epiploic arteries supply the greater curvature, and the short gastric branches from the splenic artery supply the fundus. All these arteries are derived from the coeliac trunk (p. 106). All the blood from the stomach passes to the portal vein. The right and left gastric veins enter it directly, the right gastro-epiploic vein

97

drains to the superior mesenteric vein and the left gastro-epiploic vein and the short gastric veins drain to the splenic vein (Fig. 10.2).

LYMPH DRAINAGE: all lymph passes to the coeliac group of pre-aortic nodes. It flows from the lesser curvature via nodes along the left gastric artery which communicate with nodes at the porta hepatis; from the fundus, lymph drains to nodes along the splenic artery; from the rest of the greater curvature lymph passes to nodes around the gastro-epiploic, splenic and hepatic arteries.

HISTOLOGY: the stomach wall has four coats:

(a) *mucous*—this is lined with columnar epithelium and limited externally by the muscularis mucosae. Three types of glands are found.

(i) cardiac glands—mucus secreting with long ducts found around the cardiac orifice.

(ii) gastric glands—short ducts and long straight alveoli lined with peptic (enzyme secreting) and oxyntic (acid secreting) cells, and some mucous cells are found in the fundus and body.

(iii) pyloric glands—mucus and gastrin secreting with long ducts and short coiled alveoli.

(b) *submucous*.

(c) *muscular*—three layers of fibres: innermost oblique, middle circular (which is thickest at the pyloric sphincter) and outer longitudinal.

(d) *serous*—peritoneal coat.

The Pylorus

This sphincter is a thickening of the circular muscle coat and is found usually at the level of the upper border of the 1st lumbar vertebra. The sphincter regulates the flow of material between the stomach and the duodenum. Its position is marked on the anterior abdominal wall about 3 cm to the right of the midline on the transpyloric plane.

Gastric ulcers are usually situated along the lesser curve, particularly in the region of the angular notch. Cancer of the stomach is not uncommon in older people. The diagnosis of all gastric and duodenal disease is aided by a barium meal (Fig. 10.1). The oesophagus, stomach and duodenum may also be directly visualised by a gastroscope.

SMALL INTESTINE

This narrow tube extends from the stomach to the colon. Its length (about 5 m) depends on the state of tone of its muscle wall. It consists of the duodenum, jejunum and ileum.

THE DUODENUM (Fig. 10.3)

This lies on the posterior abdominal wall in the epigastric and umbilical regions. It is about 25 cm long, extends from the pylorus to the duodenojejunal flexure and embraces the head of the pancreas in a C-shaped curve which is open to the left. Near the pylorus and the duodenojejunal flexure, the surface is completely covered by peritoneum; the remainder of the tube is retroperitoneal and relatively immobile. For descriptive purposes it is divided into four parts which can be visualised with X-rays. The part seen adjacent to the pylorus is called the duodenal cap.

The 1st part (5 cm long) passes from the pylorus upwards, backwards and to the right, and then turns downwards to join the 2nd part (8 cm long) which descends to the right side of the 3rd lumbar vertebra. The 3rd part (10 cm long) passes to the left across the posterior abdominal wall and turns upwards to become the 4th part (3 cm long) which ascends to the duodenojejunal flexure on the left side of the 2nd lumbar vertebra.

FIG. 10.3

Diagram indicating some of the principal structures in the upper part of the posterior abdominal wall. (The pancreas is stippled.)

RELATIONS

Superior (1st) part, the first 2 cm, has similar peritoneal relations to the stomach. The lesser omentum passes from the upper border and the greater omentum from the lower. Posteriorly the omental bursa separates it from the pancreas, and anteriorly it is separated from the fundus of the gall bladder and the liver by the greater sac. The rest is retroperitoneal. Superiorly is the opening into the omental bursa and the free border of the lesser omentum; posteriorly is the common bile duct, portal vein and gastroduodenal artery. Inferiorly it rests on the pancreas, and anteriorly the greater sac separates it from the liver and the neck of the gall bladder.

Descending (2nd) part is crossed anteriorly by the attachment of the transverse mesocolon, and posteriorly it is in contact with the right suprarenal gland, the hilus of the right kidney and the right psoas. Above the transverse colon and mesocolon it is in contact with the liver, and below with coils of small intestine. On its left lies the head of the pancreas, the bile duct and the pancreaticoduodenal vessels. The duodenal papilla, a common opening for the pancreatic and bile ducts, opens about halfway down its posteromedial wall.

Horizontal (3rd) part lies below the head and uncinate process of the pancreas and crosses, from right to left, the right ureter and right psoas, the gonadal vessels, the inferior vena cava and the aorta. It is crossed

FIG. 10.4
Barium follow-through. Barium has passed through the pylorus and now fills the duodenum and small intestine.

1. Stomach   2. Jejunum   3. Loops of ileum

anteriorly by the superior mesenteric vessels and the root of the mesentery of the small intestine, and covered anteriorly and inferiorly by coils of small intestine.

100

Ascending (4th) part lies to the left of the vertebral column on the left psoas. The inferior mesenteric vein, the left ureter and the lower pole of the left kidney lie on its left side. The pancreas is medial to it and it is related anteriorly to the root of the mesentery and the coils of small intestine.

HISTOLOGY: the duodenum has a similar basic structure to that of the stomach but the mucous membrane shows numerous villi and some of the glands (duodenal mucous glands) extend through the muscularis mucosae into the submucous layer.

Duodenal ulcers are a common affliction and the vast majority occur in the superior part of the duodenum. When posteriorly situated, penetration by the ulcer may cause bleeding from the gastroduodenal artery or erosion into the head of the pancreas. Anterior ulcers are more frequently complicated by perforation into the general peritoneal cavity.

The Duodenojejunal Flexure
This lies on the left of the 2nd lumbar vertebra and faces downwards and to the left, sometimes supported by a muscular slip, the suspensory muscle of the duodenum which comes from the right crus of the diaphragm. Small peritoneal recesses are sometimes found behind the left side of the 4th part of the duodenum and behind the adjacent part of the inferior mesenteric vein.

THE JEJUNUM AND ILEUM (Fig. 10.4).
These are the proximal and distal parts of the coiled small intestine, extending from the duodenum to the colon. They are suspended from the posterior abdominal wall by a mesentery and are situated below the transverse colon mainly in the central abdomen but parts may extend into the pelvis. They are covered with peritoneum except at their mesenteric attachment. The jejunum is wider and thicker-walled than the ileum; its mucous membrane is thrown into circular folds with many villi but it has fewer aggregations of lymphoid tissue in its wall and less fat in its mesentery than the ileum. The arrangement of blood vessels varies between the jejunum and ileum.

RELATIONS: the shorter jejunum lies above and to the left of the ileum. The root of the mesentery passes downwards from the left side of the 2nd lumbar vertebra to the right sacro-iliac joint crossing in turn the left psoas, aorta, inferior vena cava, right gonadal vessels, right psoas and ureter (Figs. 9.2 and 10.3).

THE LARGE INTESTINE (Fig. 10.5)

This extends from the ileocaecal junction to the anus and is about 1·5 m long. It consists of the caecum, the appendix, the ascending, transverse, descending and sigmoid colons, the rectum and the anal canal. The longitudinal muscle of the caecum and colon is restricted to three bands, **taeniae coli,** which are shorter than the rest of the wall and cause it to be sacculated. Fatty tags, **appendices epiploicae,** project outwards from the wall of the large intestine. The mucous membrane has no villi but mucous cells are numerous.

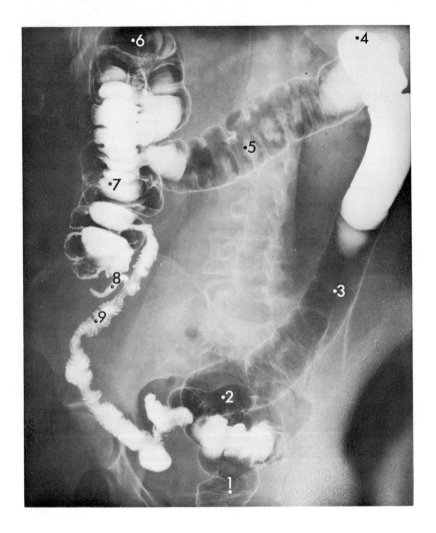

FIG. 10.5
Radiograph after partial evacuation following a barium enema. The radiopaque material
outlines first the rectum and colon and passes into the terminal ileum. Note the relatively
high position of the hepatic flexure.

1. Rectum	6. Hepatic flexure
2. Sigmoid colon	7. Ascending colon
3. Descending colon	8. Appendix
4. Splenic flexure	9. Reflux into terminal ileum
5. Transverse colon	

102

FIG. 10.6

Radiograph taken with patient lying on the right side after air and barium have been introduced into the colon. Note the position of the heavier barium and the horizontal fluid-line.

1. Rectum	5. Transverse colon
2. Sigmoid colon	6. Hepatic flexure
3. Descending colon	7. Ascending colon
4. Splenic flexure	8. Caecum

THE CAECUM

This blind sac (about 8 cm wide and 8 cm long) is continuous with the ascending colon. It is situated in the right iliac fossa, completely invested in peritoneum. The taeniae coli converge on the appendix which is attached to the posteromedial wall. The **ileocaecal orifice,** an oval slit, opens on its medial wall and is surrounded by a thickening of the ileal circular muscle coat, the ileocaecal sphincter.

RELATIONS: it lies on iliacus and psoas and the lateral cutaneous nerve of the thigh; anteriorly is the small intestine and the anterior abdominal wall. The femoral nerve and external iliac vessels lie on its left side.

THE VERMIFORM APPENDIX

This narrow diverticulum (about 8 cm long) arises from the postero-medial aspect of the caecum about 3 cm below the ileocaecal orifice. It is clothed in peritoneum which connects it by a mesentery, the meso-appendix, to the terminal ileum. The appendicular artery lies within this fold. Aggregations of lymphoid tissue are found in the wall and may replace the muscle coat in places. The appendix lies most commonly behind the caecum or within the pelvis. It is very mobile and its relations are variable. Inflammation of the appendix is a common condition and it may lead to peritonitis.

THE ASCENDING COLON

This lies in the right lumbar region and extends from the ileocaecal orifice to the under surface of the right lobe of the liver where it turns to the left, forming the **right colic (hepatic) flexure.** It is about 15 cm long; peritoneum covers it anteriorly and on both sides and fixes it to the posterior abdominal wall, thus forming a **paracolic gutter** along its right side. At the upper end, this gutter leads into a subphrenic space.

RELATIONS: posteriorly it lies on iliacus, quadratus lumborum and the lower pole of the right kidney. Its peritoneal surfaces are in contact with coils of small intestine.

THE TRANSVERSE COLON

This extends upwards from the right to the **left colic (splenic) flexure** across the abdomen suspended by the transverse mesocolon. It is about 50 cm long.

RELATIONS: initially it lies directly on the descending part of the duodenum and the head of the pancreas, but in its subsequent course it is attached by its mesentery to the body of the pancreas and is related anterosuperiorly to the liver, gall bladder, stomach, greater omentum and spleen. Posteriorly it lies on the descending part of the duodenum, head of the pancreas, small intestine and the left kidney.

THE DESCENDING COLON (Fig. 10.6)

This is the narrowest part of the colon. It lies in the left lumbar region and extends from the left colic flexure to the pelvic brim where it continues as the sigmoid colon. It is about 30 cm long. Peritoneum covers it anteriorly and on both sides, fixing it to the posterior abdominal wall and forming a **paracolic gutter** on its left side. The left colic flexure lies higher than the right and is attached to the diaphragm by a fold of peritoneum, the phrenicocolic ligament.

FIG. 10.7

Selective coeliac arteriogram. The catheter (1) has been introduced into the right femoral artery and passed through the iliac arteries and aorta into the origin of the coeliac trunk. (Renal pelvises and ureters are also seen because the contrast medium is excreted by the kidneys.)

1. Catheter	5. Hepatic artery
2. Coeliac trunk	6. Gastroduodenal artery
3. Splenic artery	7. Right gastro-epiploic artery
4. Left gastric artery	

RELATIONS: posteriorly it lies on the lower pole of the left kidney and the diaphragm, quadratus lumborum, iliacus and psoas. Its peritoneal surfaces are in contact with coils of small intestine.

THE SIGMOID COLON

This lies in the left iliac region and extends from the pelvic brim to the front of the 3rd sacral segment where it becomes continuous with the rectum. Its length (usually about 40 cm) and position are variable.

It is attached to a ∧-shaped mesentery, the sigmoid mesocolon (Fig. 9.2), to the pelvic wall. The apex of the ∧ overlies the left ureter anterior to the bifurcation of the left common iliac artery and the sacro-iliac joint.

RELATIONS: posteriorly it lies on the left ureter and common iliac vessels, superiorly it is covered by coils of small intestine and inferiorly it lies on the bladder in the male or the uterus and bladder in the female.

The rectum and anal canal are described on page 139.

ARTERIAL SUPPLY OF THE GASTRO-INTESTINAL TRACT

This is from the coeliac, the superior mesenteric and the inferior mesenteric arteries, each arising from the front of the aorta and supplying respectively the abdominal foregut, the midgut and the hindgut.

THE COELIAC TRUNK (Figs. 10.2 and 10.7)

This short trunk arises just above the pancreas. It passes anteriorly for 2 cm and divides into left gastric, hepatic and splenic arteries. It is surrounded by the coeliac plexus of nerves and the coeliac group of lymph nodes.

Left Gastric Artery

This passes upwards and to the left behind the omental bursa to the oesophagus where it turns into the lesser omentum. It anastomoses with the right gastric artery on the lesser curvature of the stomach and supplies the lower third of the oesophagus and some of the stomach.

Hepatic Artery

This passes to the right towards the superior part of the duodenum and then turns into the lesser omentum in which it ascends in front of the portal vein. It divides into right and left terminal branches at the porta hepatis.

BRANCHES

(i) **right gastric artery**—runs along the lesser curvature of the stomach to anastomose with the left gastric artery in the lesser omentum.

(ii) **gastroduodenal artery**—descends behind the duodenum and divides into the **right gastro-epiploic** and **superior pancreatico-duodenal arteries.** The former passes along the greater curvature to anastomose with the left gastro-epiploic; the latter descends in the groove between the duodenum and the head of the pancreas, and supplies both these structures.

(iii) **right** and **left hepatic arteries**—ramify in the liver; the right gives a small **cystic artery** to the gall bladder. Variations in the pattern of these vessels are important in surgery of the gall bladder.

Splenic Artery

This runs a tortuous course to the left along the upper border of the pancreas and passes in the lienorenal ligament to the hilus of the spleen where it divides into terminal branches. It lies behind the omental bursa and crosses the left crus of the diaphragm, left psoas and the left suprarenal gland and kidney.

BRANCHES

(i) **pancreatic arteries**—several.

(ii) **short gastric arteries**—several, pass in the gastrosplenic ligament to the fundus of the stomach.

FIG. 10.8

Selective superior mesenteric arteriogram. The catheter (1) has been introduced through the right femoral artery and passed through the iliac arteries and aorta into the origin of the superior mesenteric artery. An atypical hepatic artery, present in 30 per cent of cases, is shown.

1. Catheter	4. Ileocolic artery
2. Middle colic artery	5. Jejunal and ileal branches
3. Right colic artery	6. Atypical hepatic branch

(iii) **left gastro-epiploic artery**—runs in the gastrosplenic ligament to the greater curvature of the stomach and anastomoses with the right gastro-epiploic artery.

THE SUPERIOR MESENTERIC ARTERY (Figs. 10.3, 10.8)

This arises just below the coeliac trunk, descends to the right behind the body and over the uncinate process of the pancreas. It crosses the horizontal part of the duodenum and enters the root of the mesentery. In the mesentery it supplies the small intestine and ends in the right iliac fossa by dividing into ileocolic and right colic arteries.

RELATIONS: its origin is surrounded by the superior mesenteric plexus of nerves and pre-aortic lymph nodes, and lies behind the pancreas and splenic vein. It passes downwards on the left renal vein, the uncinate process and the horizontal part of the duodenum, covered above by the body of the pancreas and below by the peritoneum. Its vein lies on its right side. Within the mesentery, accompanied by veins, lymph vessels and nerves, it crosses over in turn the inferior vena cava, the right psoas, the right ureter and the gonadal vessels.

BRANCHES

(i) **inferior pancreaticoduodenal artery**—runs to the right between the pancreas and the duodenum to anastomose with the superior pancreaticoduodenal artery. It supplies the pancreas and duodenum.

(ii) **jejunal and ileal arteries**—15–20 in number, arise from the left side of the artery within the mesentery. By repeated divisions and side-to-side anastomoses two to five tiers of arterial arcades are formed whose terminal branches enter the small intestine.

(iii) **ileocolic artery**—descends to the right and divides into ascending and descending branches; the former supplies the lower part of the ascending colon and anastomoses with the right colic artery; the latter gives anterior and posterior caecal branches. The appendicular artery is a branch of the posterior caecal artery.

(iv) **right colic artery**—descends to the right behind the peritoneum of the posterior abdominal wall, across the right psoas and ureter, and divides into ascending and descending branches. It supplies the ascending colon and anastomoses with the ileocolic and middle colic arteries.

(v) **middle colic artery**—passes upwards on the body of the pancreas to reach the mesocolon within which its branches supply the right two-thirds of the transverse colon.

THE INFERIOR MESENTERIC ARTERY (Figs. 10.3, 10.9)

This arises inferior to the duodenum and descends to the left across the posterior abdominal wall. It continues beyond the brim of the pelvis as the superior rectal artery.

RELATIONS: it is covered by the peritoneum of the posterior abdominal wall and crosses the left psoas and the left common iliac vessels. Its vein and the left ureter are on its left side.

BRANCHES

(i) **left colic artery**—ascends to the left across the left psoas and ureter as far as the left colic flexure. Its branches supply the transverse and descending colons and anastomose with the middle colic and sigmoid arteries.

(ii) **sigmoid arteries**—enter the sigmoid mesocolon to supply the sigmoid colon and the lower descending colon.

(iii) **superior rectal artery**—is the continuation of the inferior mesenteric artery in the pelvis. It descends in the lower part of the sigmoid mesocolon to reach the back of the rectum. It supplies the rectum and proximal

Fig. 10.9

Selective inferior mesenteric arteriogram. The catheter (1) has been introduced through the right femoral artery and passed up the iliac arteries and aorta into the origin of the inferior mesenteric artery. Radiopaque material from a previous injection is excreted by the kidney and produces a typical IVP appearance (Fig. 12.1).

1. Catheter
2. Inferior mesenteric artery
3. Left colic artery

4. Sigmoid arteries
5. Marginal artery
6. Superior rectal artery

two-thirds of the anal canal and anastomoses with the inferior rectal branch of the internal pudendal artery.

The terminal arteries supplying the gut form a continuous anastomotic arcade along the mesenteric border of the small intestine and the concavity of the large intestine.

109

VENOUS DRAINAGE OF THE GASTRO-INTESTINAL TRACT
(The hepatic portal system)

THE PORTAL VEIN (Figs. 10.2 and 10.3)

The gastro-intestinal tract from the lower end of the oesophagus to the upper part of the anal canal, the spleen, pancreas and gall bladder drain into the liver via the portal vein which is formed by the union of the splenic and superior mesenteric veins behind the neck of the pancreas. It ascends in the free edge of the lesser omentum to the porta hepatis where it divides into right and left branches.

RELATIONS: at its origin it lies in front of the inferior vena cava, behind the neck of the pancreas, and below and then behind the superior part of the duodenum. In the free edge of the lesser omentum it lies behind the hepatic artery on the left, and the common bile duct on the right, and is separated from the inferior vena cava by the opening into the omental bursa.

TRIBUTARIES

(i) **right** and **left gastric veins**—draining the lesser curvature of the stomach.

(ii) **superior pancreaticoduodenal vein.**

(iii) **para-umbilical veins**—pass in the falciform ligament to the left branch of the portal vein.

THE SUPERIOR MESENTERIC VEIN (Fig. 10.3)

This is formed in the mesentery in the right iliac fossa. It ascends on the right of its artery to the root of the mesentery and crosses anterior to the horizontal part of the duodenum and uncinate process of the pancreas to join the splenic vein behind the neck of the pancreas. Its tributaries correspond to the branches of its artery and it also receives the right gastro-epiploic vein.

THE SPLENIC VEIN (Fig. 10.3)

This is formed in the hilus of the spleen by the union of tributaries from the organ, the left gastro-epiploic and short gastric veins. It passes to the right behind the tail and body of the pancreas to join the superior mesenteric vein behind the neck of the pancreas.

RELATIONS: within the lienorenal ligament it is accompanied by its artery and the tail of the pancreas, and it crosses the left kidney, the left psoas and the aorta. The splenic artery lies above it.

TRIBUTARIES

(i) **short gastric veins**—draining the fundus of the stomach.

(ii) **left gastro-epiploic vein**—draining the left side of the greater curvature. Both these veins lie in the gastrosplenic ligament.

(iii) **inferior mesenteric vein**—the continuation of the superior rectal vein above the pelvic brim. It ascends on the posterior abdominal wall, to the left of its artery and of the duodenojejunal flexure. It passes behind the body of the pancreas and enters the splenic vein.

(iv) numerous **pancreatic veins** entering along its course.

Portal-Systemic Anastomoses

The portal system may anastomose with the systemic venous system in the following situations:

(i) the lower end of the oesophagus—between the left gastric and the azygos veins.

(ii) the lower part of the anal canal—between the superior and inferior rectal veins.

(iii) the umbilical region of the anterior abdominal wall—between the epigastric veins and the para-umbilical veins in the falciform ligament of the liver.

(iv) the bare areas of the gastro-intestinal tract and its related organs, e.g. veins between the bare area of the liver and the diaphragm. When the portal vein is obstructed by a thrombus, or the venous flow through the liver is impeded by fibrosis (cirrhosis), these portal–systemic communications enlarge. Severe haemorrhage may then occur especially from the dilated lower oesophageal veins (varices).

LYMPH DRAINAGE OF THE INTESTINAL TRACT

The intestinal mucosa is richly supplied with lymph vessels which drain via submucosal and subserous plexuses to nodes on the surface of the viscus. These drain into intermediate groups of nodes arranged along arteries (in the mesentery or on the abdominal wall) which in turn drain to one of three groups of **pre-aortic nodes** arranged about the origins of the coeliac, superior and inferior mesenteric arteries.

The **inferior mesenteric group** drains the distal one third of the transverse colon, the descending and the sigmoid colon and the upper part of the rectum.

The **superior mesenteric group** drains the distal half of the duodenum, the jejunum, ileum, caecum and appendix, and the ascending and proximal transverse colon.

The **coeliac group** drains the stomach and proximal duodenum, the liver, spleen and pancreas. It also drains the superior and inferior mesenteric groups of nodes. Efferent vessels pass to the cisterna chyli (p. 162).

HISTOLOGY OF THE INTESTINAL TRACT

The walls of the intestinal tract possess three coats: an inner mucous membrane, a muscular layer and an outer serous (peritoneal) layer.

The mucous membrane contains numerous lymph nodules. It is divided by the muscularis mucosae, a layer of smooth muscle, into the mucosa and the submucosa. The mucosa is lined by columnar epithelium with numerous goblet cells. It is invaginated to form simple intestinal glands and in the small intestine forms numerous finger-like projections, the villi, which contain blood and lymph vessels. The submucosa consists of loose areolar tissue containing blood vessels and the submucous (Meissner's) nerve plexus.

The muscular coat is in two layers, an inner circular and an outer longitudinal between which lies the myenteric (Auerbach's) nerve plexus.

111

The serous (peritoneal) layer is lined by flattened mesothelium derived from the lining of the coelomic cavity of the embryo.

REGIONAL VARIATIONS

The duodenum has mucous glands (Brunner's) whose coiled pits extend into the submucosa.

The jejunum and ileum: the villi of the jejunum are longer and more numerous than those of the ileum. The lymph tissue of the ileum is aggregated to form well-marked nodules (Peyer's patches).

The appendix has a mucous membrane containing many large lymphoid follicles.

The large intestine has no villi. Intestinal glands are well developed and contain many goblet cells. The longitudinal muscle layer as far as the rectum forms three discrete bundles of fibres, the taeniae coli, and the remaining intervening wall is sacculated.

EMBRYOLOGY: some aspects of the development of the gut and its rotation are described on page 94.

CHAPTER 11

THE LIVER, SPLEEN AND PANCREAS

THE LIVER (Figs. 11.1, 11.2)

This is the largest organ in the body and weighs about 1.5 kg. It lies under the diaphragm mainly in the right hypochondrium and is wedge-shaped, possessing rounded diaphragmatic, and visceral (inferior) surfaces. A normal liver may occasionally be palpated just below the right costal margin on deep inspiration.

FIG. 11.1
The liver, posterior and visceral aspects

The flattened **visceral surface** is set obliquely and faces downwards, backwards and to the left. It is divided into a right and a smaller left lobe by a continuous **interlobar fissure** which contains the ligamentum venosum above and the ligamentum teres below. The ligamentum venosum is the remnant of the ductus venosus which, in the fetus, joins the umbilical vein to the inferior vena cava and by-passes the liver. The ligamentum teres is the obliterated umbilical vein. In the adult, both ligaments are attached to the left branch of the portal vein. The right lobe contains the small **quadrate lobe** in front and the **caudate lobe** behind. The **porta hepatis** is a transverse sulcus through which pass the portal vein, hepatic artery, bile duct and lymph vessels. The caudate lobe lies between the interlobular fissure and the inferior vena cava, above the porta hepatis, and communicates with the right lobe proper by the **caudate process,** a narrow strip of tissue between the inferior vena cava and the porta hepatis. The quadrate lobe lies between the interlobar fissure and the gall bladder, and below the porta hepatis.

113

The liver is largely covered by peritoneum. It is connected to the stomach by the lesser omentum, the two layers of which are attached to the liver around the porta hepatis and along the fissure for the ligamentum venosum. The liver is attached to the anterior abdominal wall and the diaphragm by four peritoneal folds:

(i) the **falciform ligament** is sickle-shaped and extends from the

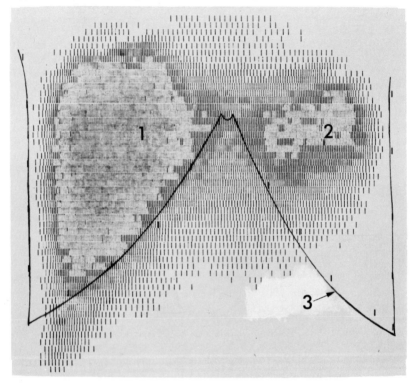

Fig. 11.2

Liver scan: the increased radio-activity is indicated by the closer packing of the short vertical lines.

1. Liver   3. Costal margin
2. Spleen

diaphragm and anterior abdominal wall above the umbilicus to the anterior and superior surfaces of the liver where its attachments demarcate the right and left lobes. Its inferior free border contains the ligamentum teres which can be traced across the visceral surface to the porta hepatis. The ligament separates the right and left subphrenic spaces (peritoneal pouches) and is the remains of the ventral mesentery.

(ii) the **coronary ligament** has upper and lower layers and connects the posterior surface of the right lobe to the diaphragm. Between these two layers the liver is not covered with peritoneum and is in direct contact with the diaphragm (the bare area).

(iii) the **right triangular ligament** is the right extremity of the coronary ligament where its upper and lower layers are in continuity.

(iv) the **left triangular ligament** similarly is at the left extremity and connects the posterior surface of the left lobe to the diaphragm. Because of the surface tension between the visceral and parietal layers of peritoneum, and of the vessels passing from the liver to the diaphragm, the liver moves in respiration. This is utilised in certain forms of artificial respiration (the rocking method).

RELATIONS: the liver is separated by the diaphragm from the heart and pericardium, lungs, pleura, and chest wall. The bare area of the posterior part of the diaphragmatic surface is also related to the inferior vena cava and the right suprarenal gland.

Visceral surface: the left lobe is in contact with the abdominal oesophagus, the fundus and body of the stomach, and the lesser omentum, the latter separating it from the pancreas. The gall bladder lies in a shallow fossa along the right margin of the quadrate lobe: it is usually in direct contact with the liver and its inferior surface is covered by peritoneum. The quadrate lobe and gall bladder are related to the superior part of the duodenum superiorly and to the transverse colon inferiorly. The caudate lobe is separated by the upper recess of the omental bursa from the diaphragm, and the caudate process forms the upper boundary of the opening into the omental bursa. The right lobe proper is separated from the right colic flexure inferiorly and the right kidney superiorly by the subhepatic (hepatorenal) peritoneal space (pouch) which communicates with the right medial paracolic gutter and with the omental bursa (lesser sac).

BLOOD SUPPLY: the hepatic artery and portal vein divide at the porta hepatis into right and left branches from which interlobular vessels ramify through the liver tissue. Blood drains by several hepatic veins to the inferior vena cava.

NERVE SUPPLY: from both vagi via the anterior gastric nerve and sympathetic fibres via the coeliac plexus.

LYMPH DRAINAGE: by superficial and deep plexuses. The superficial plexus on the diaphragmatic surface drains through the diaphragm to the anterior mediastinal nodes and on the viceral surface drains to nodes around the porta hepatis. The deep plexus drains either with the hepatic veins and the inferior vena cava to the posterior mediastinal nodes or with the portal vein to nodes around the porta hepatis.

HISTOLOGY: the liver has a fibrous capsule which is invaginated at the porta by the portal vein, hepatic artery and hepatic ducts to form sheaths around these structures in their intrahepatic course. The liver parenchyma is arranged as closely packed lobules about 1 mm in diameter. Each is composed of radiating double plates of liver cells separated by a vascular sinusoidal network. The sinusoids have an incomplete endothelial lining of which some cells are macrophagic (reticulo-endothelial) in function. This

network receives blood from interlobular branches of the hepatic artery
and portal vein and drains to a central (intralobular) vein from which
sublobular collecting vessels convey blood to the hepatic veins. Bile formed
by the liver cells is discharged into the bile canaliculi within the layers of
the cell plates. From the canaliculi, interlobular ducts pass to the right and
left hepatic ducts.

FIG. 11.3

Cholecystogram. Radiopaque material is excreted by the liver and concentrated by the
gall bladder. The extrahepatic biliary system is outlined (AFM 10: photograph was taken
10 minutes after fatty meal).

1. Gall bladder	5. Site of biliary ampulla
2. Cystic duct	6. Duodenum (descending part)
3. Common hepatic duct	7. 11th rib
4. Bile duct	

EMBRYOLOGY: the liver arises as a ventral outgrowth of the foregut
into the ventral mesentery and later it becomes embedded in the septum
transversum from which its capsule develops. The liver bud lies between
the two vitelline veins which enter into a sinusoidal network between the
developing plates of liver cells. (See also page 30.)

THE EXTRAHEPATIC BILIARY SYSTEM (Figs. 11.3 and 11.4)

This conveys bile from the liver to the duodenum. It consists of the
right and left hepatic ducts, the common hepatic duct, the gall bladder
and cystic duct, and the bile duct.

The **common hepatic duct** is formed by the union of the right and left **hepatic ducts** in the porta hepatis. It descends in the free edge of the lesser omentum and is soon joined by the **cystic duct** from the gall bladder to form the bile duct.

The **bile duct** is 8 cm long and extends from the junction of the cystic and common hepatic ducts to the duodenal papilla. It descends in the free edge of the lesser omentum, then behind the superior part of the duodenum and the head of the pancreas.

RELATIONS: in the lesser omentum the portal vein is posterior and separates it from the opening of the omental bursa. The hepatic artery lies on its left side. Behind the duodenum it is anterior to the portal vein and accompanied by the gastroduodenal artery on its left side. Behind the head of the pancreas it lies on the inferior vena cava and turns to the right to open, in common with the main pancreatic duct, into the **ampulla.** It enters the descending part of the duodenum at the apex of the **duodenal papilla** 10 cm beyond the pylorus. The opening into the ampulla is surrounded by a sphincter of smooth muscle.

The **gall bladder** is a pear-shaped sac lying in the right hypochondrium on the visceral surface of the right lobe of the liver. It has a fundus, body and neck. Its fundus and inferior surfaces are usually covered by peritoneum.

RELATIONS: the fundus extends beyond the inferior border of the liver, is in contact with the anterior abdominal wall deep to the tip of the 9th right costal cartilage, and lies on the beginning of the transverse colon. The body passes upwards towards the porta hepatis and overlies the descending part of the duodenum. The neck is sinuous and is continuous with the cystic duct which descends in the lesser omentum. It overlies the superior part of the duodenum.

VESSELS: the cystic artery, most commonly a branch of the right hepatic artery, supplies the gall bladder, and an accompanying vein drains into the portal vein. Blood from most of the extrahepatic biliary system drains directly into the liver. Lymph drains via nodes in the porta hepatis to the coeliac group of pre-aortic nodes.

The gall bladder, in common with the rest of the biliary tract, is lined by columnar epithelium with numerous mucus-secreting cells. Macroscopically, its mucous membrane shows a honeycombed appearance and is thrown into numerous folds (rugae). There is a constant spiral fold, the spiral valve, in the neck which probably prevents kinking of the duct.

The gall bladder concentrates and stores bile and adds mucus to it. Some radiopaque dyes are excreted by the liver and concentrated by the normal gall bladder. Irregularities of function and anomalous positions of the organ may be detected by X-ray examination (Fig. 11.3).

THE SPLEEN (Fig. 10.3)

This large lymphoid organ is situated deeply in the left hypochondrium where it lies obliquely beneath the 9th, 10th and 11th ribs. It is about 3 cm thick, 8 cm wide and 13 cm long and weighs about 200 g.

The spleen has posterior and anterior ends, inferior and superior (notched) borders, diaphragmatic and visceral surfaces, the latter bearing the hilus.

RELATIONS: the diaphragm separates the diaphragmatic surface from the left pleural sac, the lung and the 9th to the 11th ribs. The visceral surface is related to the stomach anteriorly, the left kidney and suprarenal

FIG.11.4

Biliary Tree. Radiopaque material has been introduced by the T-shaped tube which had been left in place temporarily after an operation at which the gall bladder was removed. The cystic duct was ligated close to the common hepatic duct.

1. T-tube
2. Right hepatic duct
3. Left hepatic duct
4. Common hepatic duct

5. Bile duct
6. Site of biliary ampulla
7. Duodenum

gland posteriorly, and the splenic flexure of the colon inferiorly. The tail of the pancreas, which lies in the lienorenal ligament, reaches as far as the hilus. The anterior end reaches the midaxillary line and lies on the phrenicocolic ligament, a fold of peritoneum passing from the diaphragm to the left colic flexure.

The organ is invested in peritoneum and suspended at its hilus by two peritoneal folds, the lienorenal and the gastrosplenic ligaments. These folds contain the splenic vessels and their branches and form the lateral limit of the omental bursa.

BLOOD AND NERVE SUPPLY: the splenic artery and vein, and branches of the coeliac plexus.

LYMPH DRAINAGE: along the splenic artery via the suprapancreatic nodes to the coeliac group of pre-aortic nodes.

HISTOLOGY: it is largely covered by peritoneum and has a fibrous capsule from which trabeculae extend into the organ to form a framework around the lymphoid tissue. The larger vessels run along the trabeculae. The arteries then pass through lymph nodules (white pulp) before dilating to form sinusoids in the diffuse internodular tissue (red pulp). The sinusoids drain via collecting veins into larger trabecular veins.

EMBRYOLOGY: the spleen develops on the left side of the dorsal mesentery of the stomach. It is mesodermal in origin, and later incorporates vascular and lymphatic elements. The spleen functions as part of the macrophage (reticulo-endothelial) and haemopoietic systems and also possibly as a vascular storage organ.

In its deep situation the spleen is usually well protected from injury but severe blows over the left lower chest may rupture the organ, particularly if the overlying ribs are fractured. Severe intraperitoneal haemorrhage then results and the spleen will need to be removed. An enlarged spleen is more easily damaged because it is more fragile.

THE PANCREAS (Fig. 10.3)

This is both an endocrine and an exocrine gland. It is about 15 cm long, lobulated and weighs about 80 g. It is retroperitoneal and extends across the posterior abdominal wall from the curve of the duodenum to the hilus at the spleen. The pancreas has a head with an uncinate process, a neck, a body and a tail.

The **head** is the expanded right extremity of the gland bearing inferiorly an **uncinate process** which passes to the left. The **body** is triangular in section and has anterior, inferior and posterior surfaces; it is connected to the head by a constricted **neck.** The **tail** is the narrowed left extremity and lies in the lienorenal ligament.

RELATIONS

(i) the head is embraced by the curve of the duodenum. Anteriorly from above downwards it is covered by the pylorus, the transverse colon and coils of small intestine. Posteriorly, the head lies on the inferior vena cava, the right renal vessels and the bile duct. The uncinate process lies on the left renal vein and the aorta, and is crossed anteriorly by the superior mesenteric vessels.

(ii) the neck lies between the pylorus and gastroduodenal artery anteriorly, and the beginning of the portal vein posteriorly.

(iii) the body—the coeliac artery lies above it and the hepatic and splenic arteries run along its upper border. Its anterior surface, covered by peritoneum of the omental bursa, is related to stomach and lesser omentum. Its inferior surface, covered by peritoneum of the greater sac, is related to the duodenojejunal flexure and coils of jejunum. The transverse meso-colon is attached to the border between the anterior and inferior surfaces. From right to left, the body lies on the aorta and superior mesenteric artery, the left crus of the diaphragm, the left renal vessels, the left suprarenal gland and the hilus and anterior surface of the left kidney. The splenic vein lies behind it throughout its length and is joined by the inferior mesenteric vein.

(iv) the tail lies with the splenic vessels between the two layers of the lienorenal ligament and reaches the hilus of the spleen.

The **pancreatic duct** traverses the length of the gland from left to right, draining the smaller interlobular ducts. In the head it descends to join the bile duct in the ampulla and opens into the descending part of the duodenum. The accessory pancreatic duct drains the lower part of the head and the uncinate process and may open separately into the duo-denum about 3 cm proximal to the main duct. These ducts usually communicate.

BLOOD SUPPLY: branches of the splenic and superior and inferior pancreaticoduodenal arteries. The veins from the body and tail join the splenic vein, and the pancreaticoduodenal veins pass to the superior mesenteric vein or portal vein.

NERVE SUPPLY: from the splanchnic nerves and the vagi via the coeliac plexus.

LYMPH DRAINAGE: via the suprapancreatic nodes alongside the splenic artery to the coeliac group of pre-aortic nodes.

HISTOLOGY: serous alveoli and their associated ducts give the gland its lobulated appearance. The ducts are lined with columnar epithelium. Scattered among the alveoli are clumps of closely packed paler staining cells, the islets (of Langerhans), which produce insulin and glucagon. The islets contain a mixture of acidophilic and basophilic cells.

The pancreatic enzymes produced by the alveoli play an important role in digestion, and the hormones produced by the islet tissue regulate the level of the blood sugar.

EMBRYOLOGY: the pancreas develops from the foregut. A ventral bud arises in common with the liver outgrowth from the duodenum and a dorsal bud arises proximal to it. Differential growth and rotation of the duodenum bring the buds together dorsally and fusion occurs. The pancreatic duct is formed from the ducts of both buds; the accessory from the dorsal duct only.

CHAPTER 12

THE KIDNEYS, SUPRARENAL GLANDS AND POSTERIOR ABDOMINAL WALL

THE KIDNEYS (Figs. 10.3, 12.1)

The two kidneys lie on the posterior abdominal wall on either side of the vertebral column. Their hila are about the level of the transpyloric plane. Each is about 10 cm long, 5 cm wide, 3 cm thick and weighs about 100 g. Each has upper and lower poles, anterior and posterior surfaces, a lateral convex border and a medial border whose concavity with the hilus, gives the kidney its characteristic shape. Each is obliquely set so that its upper pole is nearer the midline than its lower. The right kidney is slightly lower than the left because of the bulk of the liver on the right side. The kidneys are embedded in a mass of perirenal fat which is enclosed by part of the fascia transversalis (perirenal fascia). Superiorly the kidney is separated from the suprarenal gland by a layer of this fascia. Inferiorly the two layers remain separate as far as the iliac fossa; laterally they fuse but medially remain separate. The deeper layer passes behind the large vessels and fuses with the anterior longitudinal ligament in front of the vertebral column. The more superficial (anterior) layer passes medially to fuse with its fellow of the opposite side in front of the aorta.

RELATIONS: the posterior relations are similar on the two sides—the diaphragm separates the upper pole from the costodiaphragmatic recess of pleura and the 11th and 12th ribs. Below this the kidney lies on psoas, quadratus lumborum and transversus abdominis from medial to lateral. Quadratus lumborum is crossed by the subcostal nerve and vessels and the ilio-hypogastric and ilio-inguinal nerves.

Anterior relations of the **left kidney**—the suprarenal gland lies on its upper medial aspect, the spleen on its upper lateral aspect and the stomach between these two areas. The tail of the pancreas and the splenic vessels cross the hilus and body, and the lower pole is in contact with coils of jejunum medially and the left colic flexure laterally.

Anterior relations of the **right kidney**—its upper pole is capped by the suprarenal gland. The hilus is covered by the descending part of the duodenum and the lower pole by the right colic flexure laterally and the jejunum medially. The remainder of the surface is related to the visceral surface of the liver. At the **hilus** of each kidney the renal vein, artery and the pelvis of the ureter (its dilated upper end) lie in that order, from before backwards. A branch of the renal artery often passes posterior to the pelvis of the ureter. The pelvis of the ureter passes through the hilus into a narrow space, the renal **sinus,** where it divides into two large branches, the **major calyces.** Each of these divides into three or four **minor calyces,** into which project **pyramids** of renal tissue, the **papillae.** The calyces and renal vessels within the renal sinus are embedded in fat.

FIG. 12.1

Intravenous pyelogram (IVP). Radiopaque material is introduced by an intravenous injection and is excreted by the kidneys. The urinary tracts are outlined, including the substance of the kidneys. The 'clock' indicates the time which has elapsed since the injection was made.

1. Lower pole of right kidney
2. Lateral margin of kidney
3. Minor calyx
4. Major calyx

5. Pelvis of left ureter
6. Left and right ureters
7. Urinary bladder

BLOOD SUPPLY: each renal artery rises from the aorta and divides into branches near the hilus (Fig. 12.2). Venous tributaries unite to form the single wide renal veins which drain into the inferior vena cava.

NERVE SUPPLY: sympathetic nerves originate in the 12th thoracic and 1st lumbar segments, pass through the coeliac ganglia and along the renal artery to the organ. The parasympathetic nerves are derived from the vagi.

LYMPH DRAINAGE: into the para-aortic nodes around the origin of the renal arteries.

HISTOLOGY: each kidney consists of a **medulla** (formed of the pyramids) and a **cortex** which is both outside and between the pyramids. In the latter situation the cortex forms the renal **columns** through which pass the renal vessels. The histological and functional unit of the kidney is the nephron (renal tubule) composed of a glomerular (Bowman's) capsule, a proximal convoluted tubule, a loop of Henle, a distal convoluted tubule and a collecting duct. The cup-like glomerular capsule lies in the cortex around a tuft of capillaries, the glomerulus, and leads into the proximal convoluted tubule. The loop of Henle descends into the medulla nearly as far as the apex of the pyramid and then returns to the cortex and continues as the distal convoluted tubule. The distal tubules join the collecting ducts which pass through the medulla and open on the surface of a renal papilla into a minor calyx. The glomerular capsule is lined by thin specialised epithelium; cubical epithelium lines the proximal and distal convoluted tubule (the former has a brush border). The loop of Henle is lined by simple squamous and the collecting ducts by columnar epithelium.

THE URETERS

These are narrow muscular tubes 25 cm long which convey urine from the kidneys to the bladder. The dilated upper end, the **pelvis,** holds about 8 ml. The upper half of the ureter lies on the posterior abdominal wall and the remainder is within the pelvis.

RELATIONS: the abdominal course of the ureters is similar in male and female but the relations of the two sides differ. In the pelvis the course is different in each sex but similar on each side.

Abdominal part—the **right** ureter descends on psoas and crosses the genitofemoral nerve. Anteriorly, it is crossed by the descending part of the duodenum, the right colic, the ileocolic and gonadal vessels, and the root of the mesentery. Elsewhere it is covered by and adherent to peritoneum. The **left** ureter descends on psoas and crosses the genitofemoral nerve. It is crossed by the left colic and gonadal vessels, the root of the sigmoid mesocolon. Elsewhere it is covered by and adherent to peritoneum.

Pelvic part—in the **male** it crosses the common iliac vessels in front of the sacro-iliac joint and descends on the pelvic wall to the ischial spine before turning forwards and medially above levator ani. The ductus deferens crosses it superiorly from lateral to medial near the ischial spine. In the **female,** the ureter descends in a similar manner as far as the ischial spine where it turns forwards and medially under the root of the broad ligament. Here it is crossed superiorly by the uterine artery and lies in close relation with the lateral fornix of the vagina just before entering the bladder.

BLOOD SUPPLY: by a longitudinal anastomosis between renal, gonadal and inferior vesical arteries, supplemented by vessels from the parietal peritoneum. The veins drain into the renal, gonadal and internal iliac veins.

NERVE SUPPLY: sympathetic fibres originating in the upper lumbar segments. Sensory nerves enter the lower thoracic and upper lumbar segments of the cord.

LYMPH DRAINAGE: to para-aortic and internal iliac groups of nodes.

EMBRYOLOGY of kidney and ureter: in the fetus excretory tissue is bilaterally represented by two mesodermal masses, the mesonephros and a more caudal metanephros. The ureter, calyces and collecting ducts develop from a bud of the mesonephric duct. The remainder of the kidney is derived from the metanephric cap which surmounts the ureteric bud. (See also page 26.)

RADIOLOGY: Injection of radiopaque contrast media, intravenously or through a ureteric catheter, shows up the outline of the calyces, pelvis, ureter and bladder (see Figs. 12.1 and 12.2).

THE SUPRARENAL (ADRENAL) GLANDS (Fig. 10.3)

These two endocrine glands are situated on the upper poles of the kidneys. Each is enclosed in a sheath continuous with the perirenal fascia and weighs about 5 g. They are asymmetrical. The right gland is pyramidal in shape and lies in front of the right crus of the diaphragm behind the inferior vena cava and the bare area of the liver. The left gland is crescentic and its lower (medial) end reaches the hilus of the kidney. It lies in front of the left crus of the diaphragm, and behind the splenic vessels and the pancreas. It forms part of the stomach bed. The two glands are separated by the coeliac plexus lying on the front of the aorta.

BLOOD SUPPLY: by suprarenal arteries from the phrenic and renal arteries and the aorta. A large vein drains into the inferior vena cava on the right side and to the renal vein on the left side.

NERVE SUPPLY: preganglionic fibres from the splanchnic nerves end in the suprarenal medulla.

HISTOLOGY: the gland has an outer cortex and an inner medulla. The cortex is yellow and convoluted, and consists of polyhedral lipoid-filled cells arranged in three layers:
(i) outer, zona glomerulosa—cells arranged in clusters.
(ii) middle, zona fasciculata—cells in radially arranged columns.
(iii) inner zona reticulata—cells irregularly arranged.
The medulla is more vascular and contains perivascular collections of large ovoid chromaffin cells.

EMBRYOLOGY: the cortex develops from coelomic mesothelium and the medulla from the ectodermal cells of the neural crest.

FUNCTION: the cortex and medulla are independent endocrine glands. Cortical hormones are concerned with salt transport, electrolyte balance, blood pressure regulation as well as general metabolism and sexual development. The anterior lobe of the pituitary gland plays a large part in the control of cortical hormones. The medulla is controlled by the sympathetic nervous system and secretes adrenaline and noradrenaline.

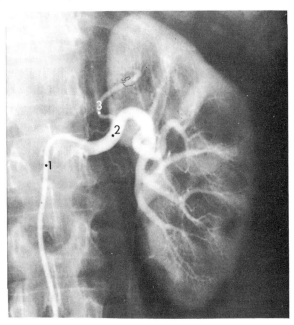

FIG. 12.2

Left selective renal arteriogram. The catheter (1) has been introduced through the right femoral artery and passed via the iliac vessels and aorta into the origin of the renal artery. The main branches of the artery are shown and the kidney is outlined by the radiopaque material in the glomeruli and other small vessels.

1. Catheter   2. Renal artery   3. Suprarenal artery

THE POSTERIOR ABDOMINAL WALL

This consists of the five lumbar vertebrae (see page 36), muscles, fascia and their related structures.

MUSCLES AND FASCIA

Psoas Major

ATTACHMENTS

Vertebral

(i) from the five intervertebral discs above each of the lumbar vertebrae and the adjacent vertebral bodies.

(ii) the lumbar transverse processes.

125

(iii) fibrous arches which cross the concave sides of the lumbar vertebral bodies.

Femoral—the lesser trochanter.

ACTIONS

(i) flexion and medial rotation of the femur.

(ii) flexion of the trunk.

NERVE SUPPLY: branches from 2nd and 3rd lumbar nerves.

Occasionally psoas minor can be seen as a thin band on the surface of psoas major. It arises from the intervertebral disc above the 1st lumbar vertebra and descends to be attached to the iliopubic eminence.

Quadratus Lumborum

ATTACHMENTS

Inferior—the iliolumbar ligament and the adjacent part of the iliac crest.

Superior—inferior border of the 12th rib.

Along its medial edge, fibres are attached to the transverse processes of the lumbar vertebrae.

ACTIONS: fixation of the 12th rib thus facilitating contraction of the diaphragm. It is also a lateral flexor of the trunk.

NERVE SUPPLY: branches from the 12th thoracic and the upper four lumbar nerves.

The Thoracolumbar Fascia

This encloses the muscles of the posterior abdominal wall and consists of three layers which fuse at the lateral border of these muscles to be continuous with the internal oblique and the transversus abdominis. The stronger posterior layer covers erector spinae and is reinforced by the aponeurosis of latissimus dorsi. Medially it is attached to the lumbar and sacral spines. Superiorly it is continuous over the postvertebral muscles and becomes the deep fascia of the back and neck.

The middle layer lies between erector spinae and quadratus lumborum. It is attached medially to the tips of the lumbar transverse processes and extends vertically between the iliac crest and the 12th rib. The thin anterior layer covers quadratus lumborum, separating it from psoas and peritoneum. It is attached medially to the front of the lumbar transverse processes and passes from the iliac crest to the 12th rib. Superiorly it is thickened to form the lateral arcuate ligament.

The Psoas Fascia

This forms a thick sheath over psoas and extends into the thigh. It is thickened superiorly to form the medial arcuate ligament.

NERVES

These comprise the subcostal nerve and the upper branches of the lumbosacral plexus.

The **subcostal nerve** is the anterior primary ramus of the 12th thoracic nerve. It enters the abdomen under the lateral arcuate ligament and lies on quadratus lumborum behind the kidney. It supplies the muscles of the posterior abdominal wall, and the skin and peritoneum in the suprapubic region.

The lumbar part of the **lumbosacral plexus** is formed in the substance of psoas by the anterior primary rami of the first four lumbar nerves.

BRANCHES

(i) and (ii) **iliohypogastric** and **ilio-inguinal nerves**—pass laterally around the posterior abdominal wall. The former supplies the skin around the superficial inguinal ring and the latter passes through the inguinal canal. They supply the skin and the lateral muscles of the anterior abdominal wall, and the skin over the pubis and external genitalia.

(iii) **genitofemoral nerve**—descends on the surface of psoas; the genital branch traverses the inguinal canal and the femoral branch passes behind the inguinal ligament and enters the thigh. The nerve supplies the skin covering the genitalia and the femoral triangle.

(iv) **lateral femoral cutaneous nerve**—this descends on iliacus to enter the thigh deep to the lateral end of the inguinal ligament. It supplies the parietal peritoneum of the iliac fossa and the skin over the lateral aspect of the thigh.

(v) **femoral nerve** (from the posterior divisions of the 2nd, 3rd and 4th lumbar nerves)—descends in the groove between iliacus and psoas and passes deep to the inguinal ligament and enters the thigh on the lateral side of the femoral artery (see also page 226). In the abdomen it supplies iliacus.

(vi) **obturator nerve** (from the anterior divisions of the 2nd, 3rd and 4th lumbar nerves)—descends medial to psoas and runs along the lateral pelvic wall to the obturator groove through which it passes and reaches the thigh. In the pelvis it passes between the internal iliac vessels and the lateral pelvic wall above the obturator artery. In the female it lies lateral to the ovary. It has no branches in the pelvis; its branches in the thigh are described on page 221.

(vii) **lumbosacral trunk** (4th and 5th lumbar nerves)—descends medial to psoas over the lateral part of the sacrum and joins the sacral part of the lumbosacral plexus (see page 162).

THE ABDOMINAL AORTA (Fig. 10.3)

The abdominal aorta is the continuation of the thoracic aorta and enters the abdomen in front of the 12th thoracic vertebra. It descends on the posterior abdominal wall slightly to the left of the midline and ends on the body of the 4th lumbar vertebra by bifurcating into the two common iliac arteries.

RELATIONS: the aorta is surrounded by networks of autonomic nerves and ganglia, and lymph vessels and nodes. The cisterna chyli lies between it and the right crus of the diaphragm. Posteriorly, it lies on the bodies of the upper four lumbar vertebrae, intervertebral discs and the left lumbar veins. On its right side lies the inferior vena cava, separated from it superiorly by the right crus of the diaphragm and the cisterna chyli. On its left side lie the left sympathetic trunk and from above downwards the left crus of the diaphragm, the pancreas, the ascending part of the duodenum and coils of small intestine. Anteriorly it is covered from above downwards by the peritoneum of the omental bursa, the pancreas and splenic vein, the left renal vein, the horizontal part of the duodenum and coils of small intestine. The stomach, transverse colon, greater and lesser omenta lie more superficially, in front of the omental bursa.

BRANCHES

(a) midline (unpaired)—to the alimentary tract, i.e. coeliac, superior and inferior mesenteric arteries.

(b) intermediate (paired)—to the gonads, kidneys and suprarenal glands.

(c) parietal (paired)—to the abdominal walls, i.e. phrenic and lumbar arteries.

(d) caudal (unpaired)—median sacral.

Unpaired

(i) those arteries supplying the abdominal alimentary tract and its derivatives; they arise from the front of the aorta (see page 106) coeliac trunk, superior mesenteric artery, inferior mesenteric artery.

(ii) **median sacral artery**—arises from the back of the aorta at the bifurcation and descends into the pelvis to supply the lower part of the rectum and the front of the sacrum.

Paired

(i) **inferior phrenic arteries**—are the 1st branches of the aorta, they supply the crura of the diaphragm and the suprarenal glands.

(ii) **suprarenal arteries.**

(iii) **renal arteries**—arise at the level of the 2nd lumbar vertebra and pass laterally to divide into terminal branches at the hilus of the kidney. The shorter left artery crosses the left crus of the diaphragm and psoas behind the body of the pancreas. The right artery crosses the right crus and psoas behind the head of the pancreas and the inferior vena cava. Each artery supplies the neighbouring part of the ureter and the suprarenal gland.

(iv) **testicular arteries**—arise at the level of the 3rd lumbar vertebra and descend obliquely across the posterior abdominal wall, around the pelvic brim to the deep inguinal rings. Each passes through the inguinal canal in the spermatic cord to reach and supply a testis.

RELATIONS: in the abdomen the arteries cross psoas and the ureter and the right artery first crosses the inferior vena cava. They are covered by peritoneum and crossed by colic vessels. Along the pelvic brim each lies above the external iliac vessels. It also supplies part of the ureter.

The **ovarian arteries** have a similar course in the abdomen but at the pelvic brim descend across the external iliac vessels and pass into the suspensory ligaments to reach and supply the ovaries. Each artery also supplies the ureter and anastomoses with the uterine artery in the broad ligament.

(v) **lumbar arteries**—the four pairs pass backwards around the upper four vertebral bodies deep to psoas to supply the vertebral column, the spinal cord and the posterior abdominal wall.

EMBRYOLOGY: the main embryonic vessels comprise a single ventral aorta which arises from the truncus arteriosus and communicates through pharyngeal arch arteries with paired dorsal aortae descending on either side of the midline. The 4th left pharyngeal arch artery forms the arch of the aorta, and the fused dorsal aortae form the descending thoracic and then the abdominal aorta.

Degenerative arterial disease produces some loss of elasticity of the wall of the aorta or its branches. A common consequence is thinning of the wall and dilatation of the vessel. The swelling thus produced is known as an aneurysm and is liable to rupture.

THE INFERIOR VENA CAVA (Fig. 10.3)

This is formed in front of the body of the 5th lumbar vertebra by the union of the two common iliac veins. It ascends on the posterior abdominal wall to the right of the midline as far as the caval opening in the central tendon of the diaphragm, through which it passes at the level of the 8th thoracic vertebra. After a short intrathoracic course, it opens into the right atrium.

RELATIONS: inferiorly the inferior vena cava lies on the right psoas, sympathetic trunk and the lower two lumbar vertebrae, and superiorly on the right crus of the diaphragm, separated from it by the right renal, suprarenal and inferior phrenic arteries and the right suprarenal gland. Anteriorly, it is covered from below upwards by the right common iliac artery, the posterior parietal peritoneum and the root of the mesentery of the small intestine, the right gonadal artery, the horizontal part of the duodenum, the head of the pancreas and the bile duct, the superior part of the duodenum, the opening into the omental bursa and the posterior surface of the liver in which it is embedded. The aorta is in contact with its left side, the right ureter lies on its right and it is intimately related to the neighbouring lymph and autonomic plexuses.

TRIBUTARIES
(i) lower two lumbar veins.
(ii) right gonadal vein.
(iii) renal veins—are formed in the hilus of the kidney and they lie anterior to their arteries. The right vein, about 3 cm long, lies behind the descending part of the duodenum; the left, about 8 cm long, lies behind the body of the pancreas, crosses the aorta and receives the left suprarenal and left gonadal veins.
(iv) right suprarenal vein.
(v) hepatic veins—convey portal and systemic blood from the liver and comprise two or three large trunks and a variable number of small vessels. They have no extrahepatic course.
(vi) phrenic veins.

EMBRYOLOGY: the inferior vena cava has a composite origin (see Fig. 2.5 and page 29).

(*a*) The part below the right renal vein develops from the right supra-cardinal vein.

(*b*) The part between the renal vein and the liver develops from the right subcardinal vein and its anastomosis with the right supracardinal vein.

(*c*) The remaining part develops from an anastomosis between the right subcardinal vein and the hepatic veins.

In the region of the kidneys, the right and left subcardinal veins anastomose and this communication remains as the left renal vein.

CHAPTER 13

THE PELVIS

The bony pelvis comprises the two hip bones, the sacrum and the coccyx. Anteriorly the hip bones articulate with each other at the symphysis pubis; posteriorly the sacrum articulates with both hip bones at the sacro-iliac joints. Through this bony girdle the weight of the trunk is transmitted to the lower limbs.

Hip (Innominate) Bone (Fig. 13.1)

This large, irregularly shaped bone consists of three parts, the ilium above, ischium below and pubis in front. In the child, they meet in a Y-shaped epiphyseal cartilage at the **acetabulum,** a cup-shaped fossa which articulates with the head of the femur. The fossa is prominently situated on the lateral aspect of the bone. By late puberty the three parts of the hip bone have fused together. The ilium expands upwards in a fan-like manner whilst below, the pubis and ischium unite to enclose the obturator foramen and form part of the wall of the lesser pelvis.

The **ilium** forms about two-fifths of the acetabulum and expands superiorly into a fluted, flattened plate, the **ala,** for muscular attachments. It has lateral (gluteal) and medial (pelvic) surfaces which are separated by the **iliac crest** superiorly and anterior and posterior borders. The gluteal surface gives attachment to muscles of the lower limb (p. 212).

The medial surface is divided into a posterior sacropelvic surface and an anterior iliac fossa. On the **sacropelvic surface** is the **auricular area** for the sacrum and behind this is a roughened area, the **iliac tuberosity** for the interosseous sacro-iliac ligaments. Between the **iliopubic eminence,** which marks the junction of the ilium and pubis, and the articular surface the bone is thickened to form the iliac part of the **arcuate line.**

The short anterior border of the ilium bears two small projections; the subcutaneous **anterior superior iliac spine** giving attachment to sartorius and the lateral end of the inguinal ligament, and the **anterior inferior iliac spine** to which are attached rectus femoris and the ilio-femoral ligament. The posterior border also bears two projections, the subcutaneous **posterior superior iliac spine** and the **posterior inferior iliac spine.** The border gives attachment to the upper part of the sacrotuberous ligament. The inferior spine lies just above the **greater sciatic notch,** a deep indentation lying below and behind the ilium. It is largely filled by piriformis.

The **iliac crest,** the curved subcutaneous upper margin of the ilium, extends from the anterior to the posterior superior iliac spine. Its outward convexity is accentuated by a lateral prominence, the **iliac tubercle,** 5 cm from the anterior spine. The crest is strong and gives attachment to

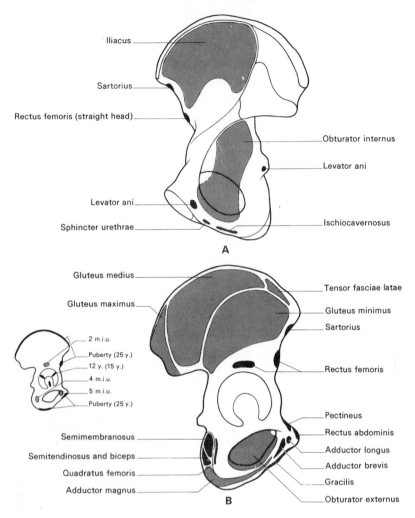

Iliacus

Sartorius

Rectus femoris (straight head)

Obturator internus

Levator ani

Levator ani

Sphincter urethrae

Ischiocavernosus

A

Gluteus medius

Gluteus maximus

Tensor fasciae latae

Gluteus minimus

Sartorius

2 m.i.u.

Puberty (25 y.)

12 y. (15 y.)

4 m.i.u.

5 m.i.u.

Puberty (25 y.)

Rectus femoris

Pectineus

Semimembranosus

Semitendinosus and biceps

Quadratus femoris

Adductor magnus

Rectus abdominis

Adductor longus

Adductor brevis

Gracilis

Obturator externus

B

Fig. 13.1

The hip bone; A, medial (internal) and B, lateral (external) surfaces.
Inset: ossification (m.i.u., months in utero; y., years).

muscles of the lateral and posterior abdominal walls, and to gluteus maximus of the buttock at the back.

The **ischium** forms the postero-inferior part of the hip bone. It consists of a body and a ramus. The **body** has femoral, dorsal and pelvic surfaces, and anterior and posterior borders. It forms two fifths of the acetabulum and inferiorly expands to form the **ischial tuberosity.** The roughened tuberosity gives attachment to the hamstrings and adductor

132

magnus muscles and to the sacrotuberous ligament. The femoral surface of the body of the ischium faces downwards and gives attachment to obturator externus. The dorsal surface lies above the ischial tuberosity and is crossed by the sciatic nerve, piriformis and obturator internus. The smooth pelvic surface gives attachment to obturator internus. The anterior border gives attachment to the obturator membrane. The posterior border is continuous with that of the ilium and bears a conical **ischial spine** which separates the greater sciatic notch superiorly from the **lesser sciatic notch** inferiorly. It gives attachment to levator ani and the sacrospinous ligament, and is crossed by the internal pudendal vessels, the pudendal nerve and the nerve to obturator internus. The **ischial ramus** passes forwards from the ischial tuberosity to join the inferior pubic ramus and form the **ischiopubic ramus.** It bounds the obturator foramen inferiorly and gives attachment to the adductor muscles of the thigh.

The **pubis** has a body and superior and inferior pubic rami, and helps to bound the obturator foramen. Its **body** has outer and inner (pelvic) surfaces and a superior border, the pubic crest. The outer surface gives attachment to adductor longus. The smooth pelvic surface is related to the bladder and gives attachment to levator ani. The oval **symphyseal surface** is covered with hyaline cartilage and joined to its fellow by a fibrocartilaginous disc and ligaments.

The thick palpable **pubic crest** gives attachment from within outwards to rectus abdominis, the conjoint tendon and the aponeurosis of external oblique. Laterally it projects to form the **pubic tubercle** to which is attached the medial end of the inguinal ligament. The **superior ramus** fuses with the ilium at the **iliopubic eminence** and forms about one-fifth of the acetabulum. It bears two ridges which diverge from the pubic tubercle. The sharp upper ridge, the **pectineal line,** passes laterally to become continuous with the iliac part of the **arcuate line;** it forms part of the pelvic brim and gives attachment to part of the inguinal ligament and pectineus. The lower and anterior ridge, the **obturator crest,** passes to the acetabulum and overlies the obturator groove on the inferior surface of the ramus. Between the two ridges pectineus is attached. The pelvic surface of the ramus is smooth and related to the bladder. The **inferior pubic ramus** descends to fuse with the ischial ramus and form the conjoined ischiopubic ramus. Its inferior border meets its fellow of the opposite side to form the **pubic arch.** Its femoral surface is roughened and gives attachment to the adductor muscles of the thigh; its pelvic surface in the male has an everted area for the attachment of a crus of the penis.

Sacrum (Fig. 13.2)
This is formed of five fused sacral vertebrae. It is triangular in shape and possesses a base superiorly, an apex inferiorly, and dorsal, pelvic, and two lateral surfaces. It is divided by paired rows of foramina on the dorsal and pelvic surfaces into a median portion which comprises the fused bodies of the vertebrae and a pair of lateral masses, formed of the fused costal elements and transverse processes. The pelvic and dorsal **sacral foramina** communicate by corresponding intervertebral fora-

mina with the central sacral canal. They convey the ventral and dorsal rami of the sacral nerves. The **base** is directed upwards and forwards, and is formed of the upper surface of the 1st sacral vertebra. Centrally, there is an oval articular facet on the upper surface of the body for the disc separating it from the 5th lumbar vertebra. The projecting anterior margin is known as the **promontory.** Behind the body is the upper opening of the sacral canal. On each side of the opening project

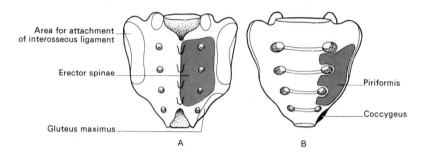

Fig. 13.2
The sacrum; A, dorsal (posterior) and B, pelvic (anterior) surfaces.

the **superior articular processes.** Lateral to the body are the fan-shaped lateral parts. The small **apex** articulates with the coccyx. The pelvic surface is concave and its median part is marked by four transverse ridges which end at the pelvic sacral foramina. The smooth lateral mass here gives attachment to piriformis. The upper part of the pelvic surface is in contact with peritoneum and the lower part with the rectum. The dorsal surface is convex and irregular. In the midline where it roofs the sacral canal it bears a **median sacral crest** and laterally two less prominent intermediate sacral crests: the latter are continuous inferiorly with the **sacral cornua** which articulate with the coccyx. Each row of dorsal sacral foramina lies between the intermediate crest and an irregular lateral sacral crest with its transverse tubercles. The posterior wall of the sacral canal is deficient inferiorly between the cornua, forming the **sacral hiatus** which is closed by fibrous tissue. The **sacral canal** is triangular in section and contains the cauda equina and cerebrospinal fluid within the meninges, and extradurally the internal vertebral venous plexus, spinal nerves and fat. The dorsal surface gives attachment to parts of erector spinae and to the thoracolumbar fascia.

The lateral surface bears a roughened **auricular surface** for the ilium, above and behind which is a pitted area for the attachment of the strong interosseous sacro-iliac ligaments.

The **coccyx** is small, triangular and is formed by the fusion of four coccygeal vertebrae. The 1st may be separate and articulates superiorly with the apex of the sacrum. It gives attachment to the sacrotuberous and sacrospinous ligaments and coccygeus, levator ani and gluteus maximus muscles.

JOINTS AND LIGAMENTS OF THE PELVIC GIRDLE

The Sacro-Iliac Joint

This is a synovial joint of the plane variety, between the irregular auricular surfaces of the sacrum and ilium.

LIGAMENTS

(*a*) Capsule: is attached to the articular margins.

(*b*) Capsular thickenings:

(i) **ventral sacro-iliac ligament**—a short, flat band strengthening the anterior part of the capsule.

(ii) **interosseous sacro-iliac ligament**—is very strong and consists of stout fibres uniting the pitted areas above and behind the auricular surfaces of both bones.

(iii) **dorsal sacro-iliac ligament**—lies superficial to the interosseous ligament and extends from the posterior superior iliac spine to the lateral tubercles of the sacrum. It is very strong.

(*c*) Accessory ligaments:

(i) **sacrotuberous ligament**—is a strong thick band, narrower in the middle than at each end, which extends from the posterior iliac spines, the transverse tubercles and the lateral crest of the sacrum, and the coccyx to the ischial tuberosity.

(ii) **sacrospinous ligament**—converges from the lateral border of the sacrum and coccyx to the ischial spine. Coccygeus lies on its pelvic surface.

These two ligaments form the posterior boundaries of the greater and lesser sciatic foramina respectively,

(iii) **iliolumbar ligament**—extends from the transverse process of the 5th lumbar vertebra to the posterior part of the iliac crest.

INTRACAPSULAR STRUCTURES: synovial membrane lines the non-articular surfaces of the joint. In adults the cavity may be partly obliterated by fibrous adhesions between the joint surfaces.

FUNCTIONAL ASPECTS: movement is limited to slight gliding and rotation by the reciprocal irregularities of the articular surfaces. Stability is maintained almost entirely by ligaments. The weight of the trunk transmitted through the vertebral column tends to rotate the sacral promontory towards the symphysis. This forward rotation is checked by the sacrospinous and sacrotuberous ligaments. Forward gliding movements are opposed by the interosseous and dorsal sacro-iliac ligaments. Hormonal influences in late pregnancy produce softening of the ligaments and increased mobility. The joint is supplied by the lateral sacral vessels and the 4th and 5th lumbar nerves.

RELATIONS: *dorsal*—erector spinae and gluteus maximus; *ventral*—lumbosacral trunk, obturator nerve, psoas, the bifurcation of the common iliac vessels, and the ureter; *inferior*—piriformis and superior gluteal vessels and nerve.

The Sacrococcygeal Joint

This is a secondary cartilaginous joint, the two bones being connected by a fibrocartilaginous intervertebral disc and by some small sacrococcygeal ligaments. There is considerable mobility which is increased in late pregnancy and the joint may be dislocated.

The Symphysis Pubis

This is a secondary cartilaginous joint between the symphyseal surfaces of the two pubic bones. The surfaces are covered by hyaline cartilage and are united by a fibrocartilaginous disc. The joint is strengthened on all surfaces by interpubic ligaments. The inferior ligament is thick and forms the anterior border of the pubic arch. Little separation of the pubic bones is possible except during late pregnancy.

The Articulated Pelvis

In the erect posture, the pelvis lies obliquely so that the anterior superior iliac spines and the top of the pubic symphysis lie in the same vertical plane.

The pelvis is divided into greater and lesser parts by an imaginary plane through the pelvic brim which is bounded by the arcuate lines anteriorly and laterally, and the promontory of the sacrum posteriorly. The **greater pelvis** is the expanded part above the pelvic brim which forms the lower part of the abdominal cavity. The **lesser pelvis** lies below the pelvic brim. In the female it forms the birth canal and, since its dimensions are not much greater than those of a fetal head, it is a space of much obstetric importance. It has an inlet, cavity, and outlet.

The **inlet** is the pelvic brim. In the male it is heart-shaped but in the female it is round or oval and its transverse diameter (13 cm) is greater than its anteroposterior diameter (11 cm). The **cavity** is a short curved canal, the posterior wall being about three times as long as the anterior wall. It is bounded by the lesser pelvic surfaces of the hip bones, the sacrum and the sacrospinous and sacrotuberous ligaments. The **outlet** is diamond-shaped, extending from the lower border of the pubic symphysis to the coccyx and bounded laterally by the ischiopubic rami and the sacrotuberous ligaments. In the female the anteroposterior diameter of the outlet (the conjugate, 13 cm) is greater than the transverse (12 cm).

It should be noted that the maximum diameter of the inlet is transverse and of the outlet, anteroposterior. The large diameters of the fetal head (anteroposterior) normally occupy the widest diameter of the part of the pelvis within which the head is lying. Therefore, in normal labour the head undergoes partial rotation during descent.

Sexual differences are more evident in the pelvis than in other bones. In the **male** the pelvis is rougher, thicker and heavier; the brim is heart-shaped rather than round or oval; the cavity is longer and the outlet narrower. In addition, the ischiopubic ramus is everted (due to attachment of the crus), the acetabular fossa is larger, the greater sciatic notch forms a more acute angle and the subpubic angle is less than 90° (in the female it is greater than 90°). Finally, the auricular surface of the sacrum extends over three vertebrae in the male, and in the female only over two vertebrae.

Fractures of the pelvis are commonly the result of crush injuries. Their most serious consequences are the associated soft tissue injuries. Bladder and urethral injuries are associated with pubic fractures and major vessel (common and internal iliac) damage with sacro-iliac fractures and dislocations.

MUSCLES AND FASCIA OF THE PELVIS (Fig. 13.3)

The **pelvic walls** are lined by a layer of muscles which, in turn, is covered by pelvic fascia. The muscles are iliacus lying in the iliac fossa, and obturator internus and piriformis on the walls of the lesser pelvis.

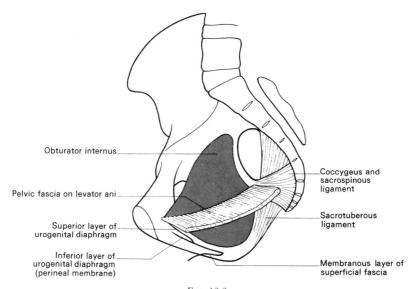

FIG. 13.3

Diagram of the lateral pelvic wall showing some of the muscular, ligamentous and fascial attachments. Below levator ani is the ischiorectal fossa.

Iliacus

ATTACHMENTS

Pelvic—the upper two-thirds of the iliac fossa.

Femoral—the fibres converge and pass under the inguinal ligament lateral to psoas with which it forms a common tendon. The tendon is attached to the lesser trochanter and to the area just below.

ACTIONS

(i) flexion of the trunk on the thigh,

(ii) flexion and medial rotation of the femur on the trunk.

NERVE SUPPLY: femoral nerve.

The **fascia iliacus** covers the iliacus muscle and is continued over psoas (p. 126) and into the thigh.

Obturator Internus

ATTACHMENTS
Pelvic—pelvic surface of the obturator membrane and the adjacent bone.

Femoral—the fibres converge on the lesser sciatic foramen and groove the ischium as they turn laterally to leave the pelvis. Its tendon passes to the medial surface of the greater trochanter.

ACTION: lateral rotation of the femur.

NERVE SUPPLY: nerve to obturator internus, a branch of the sacral plexus.

Piriformis

ATTACHMENTS
Sacral—the lateral part of the pelvic surface of the sacrum.

Femoral—it passes laterally through the greater sciatic foramen to the upper border of the greater trochanter.

ACTION: lateral rotation of the femur.

NERVE SUPPLY: direct branches from the sacral plexus.

The **pelvic floor** is a fibromuscular diaphragm separating the pelvic cavity above from the perineum and ischiorectal fossae below. It is formed by the two levator ani muscles anteriorly and the two coccygei muscles posteriorly.

Levator Ani

This is a broad thin muscle.

ATTACHMENTS
Lateral
(i) the back of the body of the pubis.
(ii) the pelvic surface of the ischial spine.
(iii) the fascia covering obturator internus between these two points.
Medial
The fibres descend to the midline and there meet fibres of the opposite side in a raphé. The anterior fibres pass backwards around the prostate or vagina to the fibrous perineal body. The middle fibres pass backwards and downwards around the rectum to the fibrous anococcygeal body. Some of these fibres blend with the anal sphincter muscles. The posterior fibres pass to the coccyx and a midline raphé between it and the anococcygeal body.

ACTIONS: it provides muscular support for the pelvic viscera, particularly when intra-abdominal pressure is raised as in defaecation, micturition and parturition, and it reinforces the rectal and urethral sphincters.

The gutter-like arrangement of the two muscles rotates the fetal head into the anterposterior plane as it descends through the pelvis.

NERVE SUPPLY: branches of the 3rd and 4th sacral nerves and of the pudendal nerve.

Coccygeus

This triangular muscle passes from the ischial spine to the sides of the lower sacrum and coccyx. Its actions are complementary to those of levator ani. It is supplied by branches from the 3rd and 4th sacral nerves.

The **pelvic fascia** covers all the walls and the surfaces of all viscera lying in the pelvic cavity. It is divided into parietal and visceral parts. The parietal fascia covers the walls and floor of the pelvic cavity. It is thick over obturator internus where it gives attachment to levator ani and is continuous superiorly with the fascia iliacus and the transversalis fascia. On levator ani the fascia is necessarily thin and expansile. Note that spinal nerves lie external to it and the pelvic vessels internal.

The visceral fascia is continuous with the parietal and covers the bladder, uterus and rectum. Thickenings around the lower parts of these viscera form ligaments which pass to the pelvic walls; they are considered with their respective organs.

THE RECTUM AND ANAL CANAL (Figs. 10.5, 10.6, 13.4, 13.6)

The **rectum** is the part of the alimentary tract extending from the sigmoid colon to the anal canal. It lies in the posterior part of the pelvis and is about 12 cm long. It begins in front of the 3rd sacral vertebra and curves forwards, usually making a prominent loop to the left, as far as the tip of the coccyx. Inferiorly it widens to form the rectal **ampulla.** It has no mesentery—its upper one-third is covered by peritoneum on its front and sides, the middle one-third on its front only and its lower one-third is embedded in pelvic fascia.

RELATIONS: laterally in its upper part it is in contact with coils of intestines, both are covered by peritoneum. Below this it is related to levator ani and coccygeus, and to the rectal vessels. Posteriorly the superior rectal artery, the 3rd, 4th and 5th sacral nerves, the sympathetic trunk, and lateral and median sacral vessels separate it from the lower part of the sacrum, the coccyx and the anococcygeal body in the midline, and from the lower part of piriformis, coccygeus and levator ani on each side. Anteriorly in both sexes the upper two-thirds forms the posterior wall of a peritoneal pouch, the rectovesical in the male and the recto-uterine in the female. Deep to the pouch in the male are the seminal vesicles, ducti deferentia, the bladder and the prostate gland. In the female in its lower one-third it is in contact with the posterior wall of the vagina and uterus.

The **anal canal** is the terminal part of the alimentary tract. It descends as the continuation of the rectum but turns posteriorly through the pelvic floor to open externally at the anus. It is about 4 cm long. Posteriorly it is related to the anococcygeal body; laterally, levator ani partly separates it from the ischiorectal fossa; and anteriorly the perineal body separates it in the female, from the lower end of the vagina, and in the male, from the bulb of the penis and the prostate gland. The anal canal is surrounded by internal and external anal sphincter muscles.

The **internal sphincter,** an involuntary muscle, is a continuation of the circular muscle coat of the rectum. It surrounds the upper two-thirds

139

of the anal canal and is innervated by the pelvic plexus. Sympathetic stimulation contracts the muscle.

The **external sphincter** encircles the lower two-thirds of the anal canal and is arranged in deep, superficial and subcutaneous parts (from above downwards). It is supplied by the inferior rectal nerves.

(i) The deep part surrounds the middle part of the anal canal. It has no bony attachment but is reinforced by the fibres of levator ani. Functionally this is an essential part of the anal sphincter.

(ii) The superficial part surrounds the lower part of the anal canal. It is attached to the anococcygeal body posteriorly and the perineal body anteriorly.

(iii) The subcutaneous part is a thick ring of muscle surrounding the anal orifice.

BLOOD SUPPLY: the superior, middle and inferior rectal arteries. The veins form communicating plexuses in the submucous coat and in the outer subserous coat of the rectum. These plexuses drain via the superior rectal vein to the portal vein and via the middle and inferior rectal veins to the internal iliac vein. The plexuses form an important portal-systemic anastomosis (p. 111). The submucous venous plexuses in the rectum and anal canal commonly enlarge later in life and in pregnancy, producing varicosities near the anal orifice known as piles. Bleeding may occur from such veins.

LYMPH DRAINAGE: the rectum and upper two-thirds of the anal canal—to the internal and common iliac nodes, the sacral nodes and along the superior rectal arteries to the pre-aortic nodes; the lower one-third of the anal canal—to upper superficial inguinal nodes. Cancer of the rectum commonly spreads via the lymph vessels; thus surgical attempts at cure must include removal of the appropriate lymph nodes. For similar reasons the surgical treatment of the less common cancer of the anal canal may demand removal of the inguinal nodes.

NERVE SUPPLY: the rectum and upper part of the anal canal— sympathetic nerves derived from aortic and pelvic plexuses contract the circular muscle and the internal sphincter; parasympathetic nerves from the pelvic splanchnic nerves 'empty' the viscus. The lower one-third of the anal canal and the external sphincter are supplied by the inferior rectal nerves and the perineal branch of the 4th sacral nerves.

HISTOLOGY: like the rest of the large intestine, the rectum and upper part of the anal canal have serous, muscular, submucous and mucous coats. The serous (peritoneal) coat is absent inferiorly; the muscular coat comprises a complete outer longitudinal and an inner circular layer; the submucous coat contains many veins embedded in fine areolar tissue; the mucous membrane is thick, lined with columnar epithelium and contains numerous mucous glands and aggregations of lymphoid tissue. The mucous membrane of the upper two-thirds of the anal canal forms marked longitudinal folds, known as anal columns, which in the newborn are connected inferiorly by horizontal crescentic folds, the anal valvules. The lower one-third of the anal canal is lined by stratified squamous epithelium. The muscle of the external anal sphincter is striated.

EMBRYOLOGY: the rectum and upper two-thirds of the anal canal are derived from the cloaca: the lower one-third of the canal and the external anal sphincter from the wall of an ectodermal pouch, the proctodeum. The separating membrane usually breaks down before birth. This dual development accounts for the differences in the blood supply, lymphatic drainage, nerve supply and histology between these two parts.

DEFAECATION

Faeces entering the rectum give rise to a desire to defaecate. Defaecation begins with massive peristalic waves passing through the

FIG. 13.4
Diagrammatic lay-out of a median section of a male pelvis.

colon which advance more faeces into the rectum. The rectum then contracts and expels faeces through a relaxed anal canal. Simultaneous contraction of the diaphragm and anterior abdominal wall helps this expulsion. The anal canal is emptied by the contraction of levator ani pulling forwards the anorectal angle and closing the lumen of the canal. Finally, contraction of the voluntary external anal sphincter occurs. Reflexes producing the desire to defaecate can be voluntarily inhibited as long as the anal sphincter is contracted. The anal canal is opened only during the passage of faeces or flatus, continence being maintained by the sphincter muscles.

On **digital examination** of the rectum, the tip of the coccyx and the sacrum can be felt posteriorly. Anteriorly, in the male, the firm prostate and above it the seminal vesicles and the ducti deferentia are palpable. In the female the cervix can be felt through the rectal and vaginal walls.

THE BLADDER (Figs. 13.4, 13.5, 13.6, 14.1)

This reservoir receives urine from the kidneys and subsequently expels it via the urethra. It is a hollow muscular organ lying in the anterior part of the pelvis, outside the peritoneum, and surrounded by extraperitoneal fibrous tissue. It is dilatable and its size and shape vary with the amount of urine it contains. When empty it is pyramidal and presents an apex

FIG. 13.5

Pelvic pneumogram. Air was injected into the peritoneal cavity and outlines the pelvic organs.

1. Urinary bladder
2. Uterus
3. Uterine tube
4. Ovary and tube
5. Rectum

behind the pubic symphysis, a base posteriorly and a superior and two inferolateral surfaces. When full it is ovoid and bulges up behind the anterior abdominal wall, especially in the child.

From the apex the median umbilical ligament, a remnant of the urachus, ascends to the umbilicus. The ureters enter the posterolateral angles of the base, and the urethra leaves inferiorly at the narrow neck, surrounded by the vesical sphincter.

Peritoneum covers its superior surface and, in the female, passes on to the body of the uterus thus forming the uterovesical pouch. In the male it descends over the upper part of the posterior surface before passing on to the rectum to form the rectovesical pouch.

Pelvic fascia surrounds the bladder and is thickened around its neck to form ligaments which attach it to the back of the pubis (pubovesical and puboprostatic), the lateral walls of the pelvis (lateral ligaments of the bladder) and the rectum (posterior ligament). In the male the bladder, is also supported by its continuity with the prostate. In the female the bladder, though fixed by pelvic fascia to the cervix and the anterior vaginal fornix, is more mobile.

The interior of the bladder is covered by mucous membrane which is thrown into many folds except over a smooth triangular area, the **trigone,** lying between the two ureteral orifices above and the internal urethral orifice below.

RELATIONS: the inferolateral surfaces are separated by a fat-filled retropubic space from the pubic bones, levator ani and obturator internus muscles. The superior surface is in contact with coils of intestine and, in the female, the uterus. The base lies in front of the rectum separated by the vagina in the female and the seminal vesicles and ducti deferentia in the male. Inferiorly the neck overlies the prostate in the male and the perineum in the female.

BLOOD SUPPLY: superior and inferior vesical branches of the internal iliac arteries; the veins drain via the vesical plexus into the internal iliac veins.

LYMPH DRAINAGE: to the internal and external iliac nodes.

NERVE SUPPLY: sympathetic fibres, from the 1st and 2nd lumbar segments via the pelvic plexuses—they may be motor to the vesical sphincter and inhibitory to the muscular wall. Parasympathetic fibres, from the pelvic splanchnic nerves (S2, 3, 4)—they are motor to the muscular wall and inhibitory to the vesical sphincter muscle. Sensory fibres are found in both the sympathetic and parasympathetic supplies.

HISTOLOGY: the bladder has mucous, submucous, muscular, subserous and serous (peritoneal) coats. The mucous coat is lined with transitional epithelium; the submucosa contains some elastic tissue; the muscular coat is composed of whorls of interlacing smooth muscle fibres (**detrusor** muscle) which are thickest around the internal urethral orifice and form the **vesical sphincter.** Thickenings around the ureteric orifices maintain the obliquity of the ureter in the bladder wall and prevent reflux of urine during micturition. The subserous coat contains much fibrous tissue and the serous coat covers only the superior surface and the upper part of the base of the organ.

EMBRYOLOGY: the bladder develops mainly from the ventral part of the cloaca (the urogenital sinus), though the trigone develops from the incorporated caudal ends of the mesonephric (Wolffian) ducts. The median umbilical ligament is a remnant of the urachus. Rarely its cavity persists in the umbilical cord and urine may then drain out at the umbilicus after birth. (See also page 26.)

MICTURITION

A urinary volume of more than about 300 ml in the adult bladder usually provokes the desire to micturate. Micturation begins with the slight relaxation of the vesical sphincter allowing some urine to enter the prostatic urethra. This initiates a reflex contraction of the bladder wall (detrusor muscles) and further relaxation of the vesical and urethral sphincter muscles. Reflexes producing the desire to micturate can be voluntarily inhibited; the urethral sphincter is contracted and this is accompanied by relaxation of the detrusor muscle and an increase in tone of the vesical sphincter. However, once urine enters the urethra, micturation becomes inevitable.

FEMALE INTERNAL GENITAL ORGANS (Fig. 13.7)

These comprise the uterus and uterine tubes, the ovaries and the vagina. They are all related to the broad ligament of peritoneum.

The **broad ligament** is a bilateral double fold of peritoneum extending from the lateral pelvic wall to the lateral margin of the uterus where it is continuous with the serous coat. The layers are separated by a variable amount of fat and fibrous tissue. The uterine tubes lie in the medial two-thirds of its free upper border; the remaining one-third, the **suspensory ligament** of the ovary, contains the ovarian vessels. The ovary is attached to the posterior surface by a peritoneal fold, the **mesovarium,** and the **ovarian ligament** passes between the two layers from the ovary to the body of the uterus where it is continuous with the **round ligament of the uterus.** Within the base of the broad ligament lies fibrous tissue, the **parametrium,** and its thickenings. The uterine artery crosses the ureter just lateral to the cervix of the uterus in the parametrium.

THE UTERUS (Figs. 13.5, 13.6, 13.7)

The adult uterus is a pear-shaped, thick-walled, hollow muscular organ lying between the bladder and rectum. It is about 8 cm long, 5 cm wide and 3 cm thick. The uterus opens into the vagina inferiorly and its long axis is usually directed forwards at right angles to the vagina. In this position it is said to be anteverted. It consists of two parts. The **body,** which forms the upper two-thirds, meets the cervix at an angle which faces forwards. This position of the uterus is known as anteflexion. The body is flattened anteroposteriorly and overhangs the bladder. It is pierced at its upper lateral angles by the uterine tubes. The part above the tubes is the **fundus.**

The cylindrical **cervix** projects through the upper part of the anterior vaginal wall. The larger supravaginal part of the cervix is surrounded by fibrous tissue, the parametrium, which is thickened to form three pairs of ligaments (see below). The conical vaginal part is surrounded by a sulcus, the **vaginal fornix,** which is deepest posteriorly. The cervix bears on its apex the smooth round external opening of the fusiform cervical canal. After childbirth, the opening becomes oval and more irregular in shape.

Peritoneum covers the larger part of the uterus. Posteriorly it covers the fundus, body and supravaginal parts of the cervix and passes on to the posterior wall of the vagina. Anteriorly it covers the fundus and the body only before passing forwards on to the superior surface of the bladder (Fig. 13.6). From the anterior and posterior surfaces the peritoneum passes laterally to the lateral pelvic wall to form the broad ligaments of the uterus.

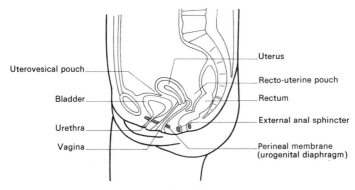

Uterus

Uterovesical pouch

Recto-uterine pouch

Bladder

Rectum

External anal sphincter

Urethra

Vagina

Perineal membrane
(urogenital diaphragm)

FIG. 13.6
Diagrammatic lay-out of a median section of a
female pelvis.

LIGAMENTS

The **round ligament** is a fibromuscular band which passes from the upper lateral angle of the uterus through the broad ligament to the deep inguinal ring and then through the inguinal canal to end in the labium majus. It is continuous with the ovarian ligament. Both are derived from the gubernaculum.

The **parametrium** surrounds the supravaginal cervix and is thickened to form three paired ligaments on the upper surface of levator ani:

(i) uterosacral ligaments—pass posteriorly around the rectum to the sacrum.

(ii) lateral cervical (cardinal) ligaments—lie in the base of the broad ligament and pass to the lateral pelvic wall.

(iii) pubocervical ligaments—pass forwards to the body of the pubis.

The uterus is supported and stabilised by the parametrial ligaments. The round ligaments pull the fundus forwards and help to maintain the anteverted position. Further support is afforded by the adjacent viscera and levator ani.

RELATIONS: posterosuperiorly, coils of small intestine and sigmoid colon separate it from the rectum. Anteroinferiorly is the bladder and on each side are the broad ligaments and their contents. The vaginal part of the cervix is surrounded by the fornix and vaginal walls which separate it from the rectum posteriorly and the ureter and uterine artery laterally.

145

BLOOD SUPPLY: the uterine artery, a branch of the internal iliac artery. The artery anastomoses superiorly with the ovarian artery, and inferiorly it supplies the vagina. The veins drain via the uterine venous plexus in the base of the broad ligament to the uterine and internal iliac veins.

LYMPH DRAINAGE: mainly to the external and common iliac nodes. Some vessels pass along the round ligament to the superficial inguinal nodes, and others with the ovarian vessels in para-aortic nodes.

NERVE SUPPLY: sympathetic and parasympathetic fibres from the pelvic plexus.

HISTOLOGY: the uterus has serous (peritoneal), muscular and mucous coats. The muscular coat (myometrium) is composed of bundles of smooth muscle fibres which interlace and are intermingled with collagen fibres and blood vessels. It is about 2 cm thick. The mucous coat (endometrium) consists of a vascular fibrous stroma, containing many leucocytes, covered by a single layer of columnar ciliated epithelium which is invaginated to form many simple glands which may extend into the myometrium. During menstruation the superficial endometrium disintegrates and is shed following haemorrhage from its blood vessels. After the menopause, the endometrium becomes thinner and less vascular. In the cervix the mucous membrane is less vascular, its branched glands are shorter. The earliest sign of cancer of the uterus or cervix may be intermenstrual or post-menopausal bleeding. These symptoms must therefore be fully investigated.

EMBRYOLOGY: the paramesonephric (Müllerian) ducts fuse caudally to form the uterus and upper vagina. Their cranial ends become the uterine tubes. (See also page 26).

AGE CHANGES: until puberty, the cervix and body are of equal size. After puberty the body enlarges. In pregnancy there is a 30-fold increase in size produced by hypertrophy of the muscle fibres. Atrophy of muscle and endometrium occurs after the menopause.

The uterus provides protection and nourishment for the fetus. Contraction of the muscle propels the fetus through the birth canal.

THE UTERINE TUBES (Figs. 13.5, 13.7)
These lie in the upper borders of the broad ligament. Each is about 10 cm long and opens medially into the superolateral angle of the uterus. It passes laterally to curl around and overlap the lateral surface of the ovary and open into the peritoneal cavity. It is usually divided, from medial to lateral, into:
  (i)   the uterine part, within the wall of the uterus,
 (ii)   the narrow isthmus,
(iii)   the dilated and convoluted ampulla,
 (iv)   the funnel-shaped infundibulum,
  (v)   the finger-like fimbriae, one of which is attached to the ovary.
  Throughout its course the tube is related to coils of small intestine.

BLOOD SUPPLY: uterine and ovarian vessels.

NERVE SUPPLY: sympathetic fibres from the pelvic plexus.

Fig. 13.7

Hysterosalpingogram. Radiopaque material has been injected through the cervix and fills the uterus and uterine tubes. Some has spilled into the peritoneal cavity.

1. Uterus
2. Uterine tube
3. Ampulla of tube
4. Radiopaque material in peritoneal cavity

LYMPH DRAINAGE: along the ovarian artery to the para-aortic nodes.

HISTOLOGY AND EMBRYOLOGY: the tube possesses three coats, a serous coat, a muscular coat of smooth muscle fibres and a thick mucous coat possessing numerous longitudinal folds of mucous membrane. It is covered by ciliated columnar epithelium with many mucous cells. The tube develops from the cranial part of the paramesonephric duct. Its function is to convey ova to the uterus.

The patency of the tubes can be demonstrated radiologically by using a contrast medium (see Fig. 13.7).

THE OVARY

This is an almond-shaped organ about 3 cm long, having medial and lateral surfaces, and tubal and uterine ends. It lies on the back of the broad ligament attached by a double fold of peritoneum, the mesovarium, which is continuous with the germinal epithelium that surrounds the ovary.

RELATIONS: the lateral surface is adjacent to the pelvic wall. Laterally the ovary is clasped by the infundibulum and fimbriae of the uterine tube. Its tubal end is attached to the tube by one of the fimbriae and its uterine end to the uterus by the fibrous ovarian ligament.

147

BLOOD SUPPLY: ovarian artery and branches of the uterine artery. Its veins drain via a pampiniform plexus to the ovarian vein and then to the inferior vena cava on the right side and the renal vein on the left.

LYMPH DRAINAGE: along the ovarian artery to para-aortic nodes.

NERVE SUPPLY: sympathetic fibres derived from the 10th thoracic segment via the aortic plexuses.

HISTOLOGY: the ovary is composed of a fibrous stroma surrounded by a layer of cubical cells, the **germinal epithelium.** The stroma contains a large number of developing **follicles** and small groups of interstitial cells. Its outer layer is condensed to form the **tunica albuginea.**

The immature follicle consists of an **ovum** surrounded by a single layer of cubical cells. After puberty, maturation of some follicles occurs; the follicular wall proliferates and a fluid-filled cavity incompletely divides it into a layer of cells surrounding the ovum, the cumulus oophorus, and an outer layer, the stratum granulosum.

At ovulation, the follicle ruptures and the ovum is expelled into the uterine tube. Its follicular remnant undergoes changes to form a lipoid-filled cyst, the **corpus luteum.** Fibrous remnants of old corpora lutea are seen in adult ovaries. The interstitial cells and the cells of the corpus luteum (under the influence of the pituitary gland) produce oestrogenic and progestational hormones.

EMBRYOLOGY: the ovary develops from the coelomic mesothelium adjacent to the paramesonephric ridge on the posterior abdominal wall. Like the testis, it descends, preceded by the gubernaculum which persists as the fibrous ligament of the ovary and the round ligament of the uterus. Occasionally remnants of the mesonephric ducts are found in the broad ligament near the ovary.

THE VAGINA (Fig. 13.6)

This is a canal about 8 cm long, extending from the uterus to the pudendal cleft. It lies behind the bladder and urethra and in front of the rectum, its axis forming an angle of 90° or so with the uterus. Its anterior and posterior walls are normally in contact except at its upper end into which projects the cervix surrounded by a deep sulcus, the fornix. This is deepest posteriorly. The lower end is partially occluded by a perforated membrane, the hymen.

RELATIONS: *anterior*—from above downwards, the uterus, the bladder and the urethra; *posterior*—from above downwards, the peritoneum of the uterorectal pouch (pouch of Douglas), separating the vagina from the rectum, then the anal canal and perineal body; *lateral*—the base of the broad ligament containing the ureter and the uterine vessels. Below this is levator ani, here forming the vaginal sphincter. The lowest part of the vagina lies in the perineum (p. 154).

BLOOD SUPPLY: the vaginal branches of the internal iliac and the uterine arteries. The veins drain via plexuses on its lateral walls to the internal iliac veins.

Lymph drainage: the upper two-thirds, to the internal and external iliac nodes, the lower one-third, to the upper superficial inguinal nodes.

Histology and embryology: the vagina has muscular and mucous coats. The muscular coat consists of outer longitudinal and inner circular layers of smooth muscle. It is lined by a corrugated mucous membrane covered by stratified squamous epithelium. There are no glands. The vagina is supported by the surrounding fascia continuous above with the pelvic fascia and below with the perineal body. Its upper part is derived from the lower ends of the fused paramesonephric ducts; the lower part by canalisation of an ectodermal thickening.

MALE INTERNAL GENITAL ORGANS (Fig. 13.4)

These comprise the prostate, ducti deferentia, seminal vesicles and ejaculatory ducts. See also page 26.

THE PROSTATE

This is a fibromuscular organ containing glandular tissue lying between the neck of the bladder and the perineal membrane. It resembles a truncated cone about 3 cm in diameter and possesses a base superiorly, an apex inferiorly, and anterior, posterior and two inferolateral surfaces. It is traversed by the urethra and more posteriorly, in its upper half, by the two ejaculatory ducts. These three structures and fibrous septa divide it into a median and two lateral lobes. The **median lobe** lies posteriorly between the urethra and ejaculatory ducts. The **lateral lobes** are below and lateral to the median lobe; they are continuous anteriorly but separated posteriorly by a midline sulcus. See also page 155.

Pelvic fascia invests the organ and its surrounding venous plexus to form the prostatic sheath. The sheath is continuous above, with the fascia around the bladder neck; in front, with the puboprostatic ligaments, and behind, with the rectovesical fascia covering the seminal vesicles and the front of the rectum.

Relations
Superior—the bladder neck and seminal vesicles,
Inferior—urethral sphincter,
Anterolateral—the levator ani muscles,
Posterior—the rectum.

Blood supply: the inferior vesical and middle rectal branches of the internal iliac artery. The veins drain via the prostatic and the vesical venous plexuses to the internal iliac veins and to the internal vertebral venous plexus.

Lymph drainage: to internal iliac nodes.

Nerve supply: sympathetic fibres are derived from the pelvic plexus, parasympathetic from the pelvic splanchnics (S2, 3 and 4).

Histology and embryology: the glandular alveoli are lined by columnar epithelium and surrounded by a fibromuscular stroma. Their ducts open into the prostatic urethra. The gland is surrounded by a

149

fibrous capsule and the prostatic venous plexus. The gland develops as outgrowths of the urogenital sinus. Its thin alkaline secretion is added to the seminal fluid. The prostatic urethra is described on page 155.

In middle age there is often hypertrophy of the glandular tissue particularly in the median lobe which enlarges and projects into the bladder interfering with micturition. Cancer of the prostate may produce the same symptoms but can be distinguished by the hard irregular surface palpable on rectal examination.

THE DUCTI DEFERENTIA, SEMINAL VESICLES AND EJACULATORY DUCTS

Ducti (vasa) deferentia—each is a narrow muscular tube. It is a continuation of the canal of the epididymis and extends from the tail of the epididymis through the scrotum, inguinal canal and pelvis to the ejaculatory duct. It is about 45 cm long. The ducts are ligated and cut in the operation of vasectomy.

RELATIONS: in the scrotum and the inguinal canal, where it is palpable, it forms part of the spermatic cord. It enters the pelvis at the deep inguinal ring, lateral to the inferior epigastric vessels, and then runs along the lateral wall of the pelvis, covered only by peritoneum, crossing in turn the external iliac vessels, the obliterated umbilical artery, obturator vessels and nerve, vesical vessels and the ureter. At the ischial spine it turns medially above the ureter and descends posterior to the bladder and medial to the seminal vesicles. Here it is dilated and known as the ampulla. Its terminal portion joins the duct of the seminal vesicle and forms an ejaculatory duct.

Seminal vesicles—each is a coiled, blind, sacculated diverticulum from the ductus deferens, about 5 cm long. It lies obliquely, above the prostate, behind the base of the bladder and lateral to the ampulla of the ductus. Posteriorly it is separated from the rectum by the rectovesical fascia below and the rectovesical pouch of peritoneum above. The narrow lower end joins the ductus just above the prostate and is here palpable on rectal examination.

Ejaculatory ducts—each is formed behind the neck of the bladder by the union of the duct of the seminal vesicle and the terminal part of the ductus. It traverses the upper half of the prostate to open into the prostatic urethra alongside the prostatic utricle (p. 155). It is 2 cm long.

BLOOD SUPPLY: all these structures are supplied by the inferior vesical and middle rectal arteries. Their veins drain through the vesical venous plexus to the internal iliac veins.

LYMPH VESSELS: pass to the internal iliac nodes.

NERVE SUPPLY: sympathetic fibres are derived from the pelvic plexuses; they are motor to the walls of the ductus deferens and seminal vesicles, and their section may produce sterility because ejaculation is not then possible.

EMBRYOLOGY: each ductus and ejaculatory duct develops from the mesonephric duct; and the seminal vesicle is a diverticulum from it.

FUNCTION: on ejaculation the ductus carries sperm to the ampulla where they are mixed with ampullary and vesicular secretions, before continuing along the ejaculatory duct and following the prostatic secretion down the urethra.

CHAPTER 14

THE PERINEUM

The perineum is the part of the pelvic cavity below the pelvic diaphragm. It is a diamond-shaped space between the pubic symphysis and the coccyx. It is bounded anterolaterally by the ischiopubic rami, laterally by the ischial tuberosities and posterolaterally by the lower borders of the sacrotuberous ligaments. It is divided by a line joining the ischial tuberosities into an anal triangle posteriorly and a urogenital triangle anteriorly.

The **anal triangle** contains the anal canal in the midline and the ischiorectal fossae laterally.

The **ischiorectal fossa** (Fig. 13.3) is a wedge-shaped space, lying with its base inferiorly between the ischium and the anal canal. It is bounded superomedially by levator ani attached to the obturator fascia above, and blending with the external anal sphincter below. Laterally it is bounded by fascia on obturator internus, and inferiorly by perineal skin. Posteriorly it extends between the sacrotuberous and sacrospinous ligaments deep to gluteus maximus; anteriorly it extends between levator ani and the superior fascia of the urogenital diaphragm.

The two fossae communicate with each other round the anal canal and are separated by the anococcygeal body, the anal canal and the perineal body. Each fossa contains:

(i) a mass of loose fatty tissue,

(ii) inferior rectal nerve and vessels which pass medially across its roof,

(iii) scrotal nerves and vessels,

(iv) perineal branch of the 4th sacral nerve which crosses the fossa to supply the peri-anal skin and the external sphincter muscle,

(v) the internal pudendal vessels and the pudendal nerve which lie in the lateral wall within a sheath, the pudendal canal, formed by a split in the fascia covering obturator internus. The canal lies about 3 cm above the ischial tuberosity.

The **urogenital triangle** (Fig. 13.3) is divided by the inferior fascia of the urogenital diaphragm (perineal membrane) into superficial and deep compartments (pouches).

The **urogenital diaphragm** is a triangular double layer of fascia (stronger in the male than the female) stretching across the pubic arch between its attachments to the ischiopubic rami. It has a free posterior border, the centre of which is attached to a fibrous mass, the **perineal body**. It is pierced by the urethra, vessels and nerves passing to structures in the superficial perineal pouch and, in the female, by the vagina. Its inferior layer (perineal membrane) gives attachment to the bulb and crura of the penis or clitoris. The superficial and deep perineal pouches differ markedly in the two sexes and are considered separately.

THE MALE UROGENITAL TRIANGLE

The **superficial perineal pouch** (Fig. 13.3) lies between the membranous layer of the superficial fascia and the inferior layer of the urogenital diaphragm. The superficial fascia is attached posteriorly to the free border of the diaphragm, laterally to the ischiopubic rami and anteriorly it is continuous between the pubic tubercles with the membranous layer of superficial fascia of the anterior abdominal wall. It provides inferiorly a fascial sheath around the penis and scrotum. The pouch contains the root and body of the penis, the superficial perineal muscles, the scrotal vessels and nerves. The testis and spermatic cord lying within the scrotum are in a space continuous with the superficial pouch (Fig. 13.3).

Extravasation of urine into the superficial perineal pouch spreads firstly into the subfascial tissues of the scrotum and penis and then ascends the anterior abdominal wall deep to the superficial fascia. This may occur in cases of rupture of the bulbar urethra.

The **penis** comprises three longitudinal cylinders of erectile tissue, the central corpus spongiosum and the two lateral corpora cavernosa, all covered by fascia and skin. It has a root attaching it to the perineal membrane, and a pendulous cylindrical body. The **corpus spongiosum** lies inferiorly (ventral) and is expanded to form the bulb of the penis posteriorly and the glans penis anteriorly. The bulb is attached to the perineal membrane and is covered by the bulbospongiosus muscle. The corpus spongiosum is traversed by the urethra which opens at the external urethral orifice on the apex of the glans. The two **corpora cavernosa** are united dorsally and their anterior extremities are embedded in the glans. Posteriorly, beneath the symphysis pubis they diverge and form the **crura** of the penis. The crura are covered by the ischiocavernosus muscles. The membranous layer of superficial fascia surrounds the body of the penis and fuses with the corpora just behind the glans. It gives attachment to the short suspensory ligament of the penis which descends from the front of the symphysis pubis. The outer layer of superficial fascia is devoid of fat, consists of loose areolar tissue and contains superficial vessels and nerves.

The skin over the body of the penis is thin and hairless and is prolonged forwards as a fold over the glans, the **prepuce**. The glans is covered with thin skin. Ventrally there is a narrow skin fold, the frenulum, between the glans and the prepuce. This contains a small artery which has to be ligated in excision of the prepuce (circumcision).

BLOOD SUPPLY: by branches of the internal pudendal artery. The artery to the bulb supplies the bulb, corpus spongiosum and the glans; the deep artery of the penis, the corpora cavernosa; and the dorsal artery of the penis, the skin. The veins correspond to the arteries; the corpora drain to the internal pudendal vein and also through the deep dorsal vein of the penis to the prostatic plexus.

LYMPH DRAINAGE: to the upper superficial inguinal nodes.

NERVE SUPPLY: the skin is supplied by the dorsal nerve of the penis and the ilio-inguinal nerve. Parasympathetic vasodilator nerves from the pelvic splanchnics supply the erectile tissue.

HISTOLOGY: each of the three corpora is surrounded by a thick fibrous coat (the tunica albuginea) and the two corpora cavernosa are separated by an incomplete fibrous septum. From the tunica and the septum numerous fibro-elastic trabeculae arise, subdividing the cavities of the corpora into blood-filled cavernous spaces lined by flattened endothelium. The tortuous terminal branches of the penile arteries open directly into these spaces. Erection of the penis is caused by an increased blood flow in the penile arteries distending the cavernous tissue.

EMBRYOLOGY: the penis forms from a swelling, the genital tubercle, lying cranial to the urogenital opening. The penile urethra develops from a ventral groove on the penis.

The **scrotum** is a pouch of thin, rugose skin enclosing the two testes and spermatic cords, and separating them is a midline septum. Its walls contain a layer of smooth muscle (the dartos). It develops from the fusion of two lateral scrotal swellings.

Superficial muscles of the perineum lie in the superficial perineal pouch. They are supplied by the perineal branch of the pudendal nerve.

(i) **bulbospongiosus**—covers the bulb of the penis. The two halves of the muscle arise from the perineal body and from a common midline raphé on the under surface of the bulb. The fibres wind around the penis to be attached to the dorsal surface.

(ii) **ischiocavernosus**—these two muscles cover the crura of the penis. Posteriorly each is attached to the ischiopubic ramus, anterior to the corpus cavernosum. Bulbospongiosus and ischiocavernosus constrict the corpora, playing a subsidiary role in erection and micturition.

(iii) **superficial transverse perineal muscle** is a scarcely definable transverse bundle running along the posterior edge of the perineal membrane.

The **deep perineal pouch** lies between the superior and inferior layers of the urogenital diaphragm and below levator ani. It is a closed space, filled mainly by the sphincter urethrae muscle surrounding the membranous urethra. The bulbo-urethral glands and ducts, the internal pudendal vessels and pudendal nerves and their branches, lie in the pouch and leave it by piercing the perineal membrane.

The **sphincter urethrae muscle** is a broad sheet of striated muscle surrounding the membranous urethra, attached on each side to the ischiopubic ramus. Urinary continence is largely dependent on the action of this muscle. It is supplied by the perineal branch of the pudendal nerve.

THE FEMALE UROGENITAL TRIANGLE

As in the male, the perineal membrane divides the triangle into superficial and deep pouches but these are almost completely divided again by the passage of the vaginal canal (Fig. 13.6).

The superficial pouch contains the crura of the clitoris, the bulb of the vestibule, the greater vestibular glands, superficial perineal muscles and the terminal parts of the urethra and vagina. The sphincter urethrae which lies in the deep pouch also gains attachment to the vaginal wall.

Female external genitalia comprise the **mons pubis**, a fatty elevation over the symphysis, and two pairs of skin folds, an outer **labia majora** and an inner **labia minora** surrounding a median cleft, the **vestibule,** into which opens the urethra and vagina. Anterior to the urethral opening is the **clitoris,** a small sensitive mass of erectile tissue attached to the ischiopubic rami. It is homologous with the penis and has a very similar structure, possessing two corpora cavernosa capped by a diminutive glans. A fibrous mass, the **perineal body**, separates the vagina and anal canal and is commonly damaged during childbirth. In the superficial pouch and alongside the vagina are the vestibular bulb and the greater vestibular glands.

(i) the **vestibular bulb** comprises two elongated masses of erectile tissue lying on the perineal membrane, one on either side of the vaginal opening. They are united anteriorly by a median commissure and are covered by the bulbospongiosus muscle.

(ii) the two **greater vestibular glands** lie behind the bulb, one on each side of the vaginal opening.

THE URETHRA (Figs. 13.4, 13.6, 14.1)

The **male urethra** is an S-shaped tube about 20 cm long extending from the internal (vesical) urethral orifice through the prostate, deep perineal pouch and corpus spongiosum to the external urethral orifice. It is divided into prostatic, membranous and spongy parts.

(i) the **prostatic urethra** is the widest and most dilatable part. It is about 3 cm long and descends through the gland in a slightly forward direction. The upper part of its posterior wall is marked by a fusiform elevation, the **urethral crest** which makes the urethral cavity ∩-shaped on transverse section. On the summit of the crest is a small pit, the **prostatic utricle**, on either side of which open the ejaculatory ducts. Into the groove on the sides of the crest open the 20–30 prostatic ducts.

(ii) the **membranous urethra** is narrow and more rigid. About 1 cm in length, it descends through the deep perineal pouch, about 3 cm behind the symphysis pubis, surrounded by the **sphincter urethrae** muscle. Two bulbo-urethral glands lie posterolateral to it embedded in the sphincter muscle. They secrete a lubricant fluid along ducts which pierce the perineal membrane and enter the spongy urethra.

(iii) the **spongy urethra** is about 16 cm long. It traverses the whole length of the corpus spongiosum. Its slit-like lumen is narrowest at the external urethral orifice and is dilated posteriorly in the bulb to form the intrabulbar fossa and anteriorly in the glans to form the navicular fossa.

BLOOD AND NERVE SUPPLY: from the inferior vesical and branches of the internal pudendal artery. Its veins drain to the prostatic venous plexus and the internal pudendal vein. The spongy mucous membrane is supplied by the pudendal nerve.

LYMPH DRAINAGE: from the prostatic and membranous parts—to the internal iliac nodes, and from the spongy part—to the superficial inguinal nodes.

HISTOLOGY: it possesses muscular, submucous and mucous coats. The mucous membrane is very vascular. In the prostatic part it is lined with

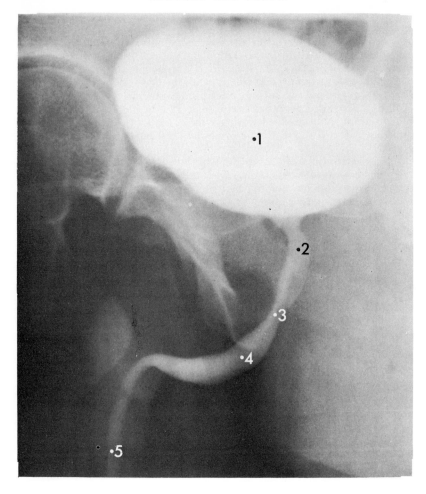

FIG. 14.1
Urethrogram. Radiopaque material, introduced into the bladder, outlines the bladder and urethra.

1. Urinary bladder
2. Prostatic urethra
3. Membranous urethra
4. Bulbous urethra
5. Spongy urethra

transitional epithelium, in the membranous and spongy parts with stratified squamous epithelium. It possesses numerous mucous glands.

EMBRYOLOGY: the prostatic and membranous parts of the urethra are developed from the urogenital sinus; the spongy part by the fusion of the lips of the urethral groove on the ventral surface of the penis. (See page 26).

The **female urethra** is about 3 cm long. It descends from the neck of the bladder through the deep perineal pouch where it is surrounded by the sphincter muscle, the superficial pouch and opens into the vestibule. The external urethral orifice lies between the clitoris and the vaginal opening. It is similar to the proximal parts of the male urethra in structure and develops from the urogenital sinus. (See page 26).

VESSELS AND NERVES OF THE PERINEUM

The **pudendal nerve** is a branch of the sacral plexus. It leaves the pelvis through the lower part of the greater sciatic foramen, crosses the ischial spine and enters the perineum through the lesser sciatic foramen. In the perineum it passes forwards within the pudendal canal where it ends by dividing into the perineal nerve and the dorsal nerve of the penis (clitoris).

BRANCHES

(i) inferior rectal nerve—arises in the posterior part of the pudendal canal. It passes medially across the roof of the ischiorectal fossa to reach and supply levator ani, the external anal sphincter and the peri-anal skin.

(ii) dorsal nerve of the penis—runs forwards on the medial side of the ischiopubic ramus into the deep perineal pouch and pierces the perineal membrane to gain the dorsum of the penis. It supplies the glans and skin of the penis and carries parasympathetic fibres to the corpora.

(iii) perineal nerve—runs forwards into the superficial pouch. It supplies the perineal muscles and, via its scrotal (labial) branch, the perineal and scrotal (labial) skin.

The **internal pudendal artery** is a branch of the internal iliac artery. It leaves the pelvis and enters the perineum alongside the pudendal nerve, and its branches correspond to those of the nerve to a large extent. It ends in the deep perineal pouch by dividing into deep and dorsal arteries of the penis (clitoris) and the artery to the bulb.

BRANCHES

(i) inferior rectal artery—accompanies the inferior rectal nerve and supplies the lower part of the anal canal.

(ii) scrotal (labial) branches.

(iii) artery to the bulb—arises in the deep perineal pouch. It pierces the perineal membrane to supply the corpus spongiosum.

(iv) deep artery of the penis—supplies the corpus cavernosum.

(v) dorsal artery of the penis—pierces the perineal membrane and passes along the dorsum of the penis to supply the prepuce and glans.

LYMPH DRAINAGE: from the perineal skin to the superficial and deep inguinal nodes.

CUTANEOUS NERVES: perineal skin is supplied by the perineal branch of the posterior femoral cutaneous nerve and the scrotal (labial) branches of the perineal nerve.

CHAPTER 15

THE BLOOD VESSELS, LYMPH DRAINAGE AND NERVES

ARTERIES

The Common Iliac Arteries

These arise at the aortic bifurcation on the front of the 4th lumbar vertebra slightly to the left of the midline. Each descends laterally to the front of the sacro-iliac joint where it ends by dividing into internal and external iliac arteries (Fig. 15.1).

RELATIONS: the common iliac veins lie behind and to the right of the arteries. Each artery is crossed anteriorly by sympathetic nerve fibres and, at its bifurcation, by the ureters. It is covered by peritoneum which separates it from coils of intestine. On the left it is also crossed by the superior rectal artery and the root of the sigmoid mesocolon. Posteriorly it crosses the bodies of the 4th and 5th lumbar vertebrae, sympathetic trunk, obturator nerve and the lumbosacral trunk. The origin of the inferior vena cava lies behind the right artery.

BRANCHES: none, other than its terminal branches.

The Internal Iliac Artery

This is a terminal branch of the common iliac artery. It arises in front of the sacro-iliac joint and descends on the posterior pelvic wall to the greater sciatic notch where it ends by dividing in a variable manner into parietal and visceral groups of branches.

RELATIONS

Anterior—the ureter which separates it from the rectum.

Posterior—the lumbosacral trunk and the sacro-iliac joint.

Lateral—the external iliac vein and obturator nerve separate it from psoas and obturator internus.

Medial—coils of intestines covered by peritoneum.

BRANCHES

Visceral group

(i) **superior vesical artery**—is a branch of the umbilical artery (see below) and supplies the upper part of the bladder.

(ii) **uterine artery**—passes medially on levator ani and crosses over the ureter just above the lateral fornix of the vagina, to gain the broad ligament in which it ascends tortuously to anastomose with the ovarian artery. It supplies the vagina, uterus and uterine tubes.

(iii) **middle rectal artery**—when present supplies the seminal vesicles, prostate and the muscular wall to the lower rectum.

(iv) **vaginal artery**—passes anteriorly to reach and supply the vagina, and bladder and ureter. (This corresponds to the inferior vesical artery

158

Fig. 15.1

Arteriogram of the aortic bifurcation and the main branches of the iliac arteries. (1) is the fine plastic catheter which is inserted into the femoral artery and along which the radiopaque material is injected. (See also Figs. 21.3 and 22.6.)

1. Catheter
2. Aorta
3. Lumbar arteries
4. Common iliac artery

5. Internal iliac artery
6. External iliac artery
7. Femoral artery

in the male which supplies the lower end of the ureter, the bladder, the ductus deferens, the seminal vesicles and the prostate.)

Parietal group

(i) **umbilical artery**—is obliterated soon after birth but can be seen passing forwards between the lateral pelvic walls and the bladder beyond its superior vesical branch.

(ii) **obturator artery**—runs forwards on the obturator internus below its nerve, leaves the pelvis by passing above the obturator membrane on whose outer surface it ramifies to supply adjacent muscles. It also gives a branch to the hip joint.

(iii) **internal pudendal artery**—passes backwards between piriformis and coccygeus, and leaves the pelvis through the greater sciatic foramen. Its subsequent course is described on page 157.

(iv) **inferior gluteal artery**—accompanies the pudendal artery and leaves the pelvis by the greater sciatic foramen. In the gluteal region it supplies the gluteal muscles, takes part in an anastomosis around the hip joint and gives a branch to the sciatic nerve.

(v) **superior gluteal artery**—runs backwards between the lumbosacral trunk and the sacral plexus and passes through the greater sciatic foramen above piriformis. In the gluteal region it is distributed to the gluteal muscles and takes part in an anastomosis around the hip joint.

(vi) **lateral sacral artery**—this descends anterior to the sacral plexus and anastomoses over the coccyx with the median sacral artery and its fellow of the opposite side. It supplies the contents of the sacral canal.

(vii) **iliolumbar artery**—ascends on the pelvic surface of the sacrum to the medial border of psoas. It supplies iliacus and the muscles of the posterior abdominal wall.

The External Iliac Artery

This is a terminal branch of the common iliac artery. It arises over the sacro-iliac joint and passes forwards around the pelvic brim to a point below the inguinal ligament, midway between the anterior superior iliac spine and the pubic symphysis (the midinguinal point) where it leaves the abdominal cavity to become the femoral artery.

RELATIONS

Posterior—psoas.

Medial—the external iliac vein.

In the male it is crossed by the testicular vessels and the ductus deferens; in the female by ovarian vessels and the round ligament. It is covered anteriorly by peritoneum.

BRANCHES

(i) **inferior epigastric artery**—ascends medial to the deep inguinal ring, behind the anterior abdominal wall to enter the rectus sheath whose contents it supplies and within which it anastomoses with the superior epigastric artery.

(ii) **deep circumflex iliac artery**—passes laterally towards the iliac crest and supplies the muscles in that region.

Both of these arteries arise just above the inguinal ligament.

VEINS

These drain mainly to the internal iliac vein, whose tributaries correspond to the branches of its artery. The veins from the viscera drain via venous plexuses surrounding the viscera. These plexuses, namely, the prostatic, vesical, uterine, vaginal and rectal, communicate with one another and with the external and internal vertebral venous plexuses.

(These communications may account for the frequent spread of cancer from pelvic organs to the vertebra and bones of the skull.)

The **internal** and **external iliac veins** unite at the pelvic brim to

Fig. 15.2

Lymphangiogram. A radiopaque substance is introduced into a lymph vessel in each foot and is then carried up to the external iliac nodes and thence to the para-aortic nodes (see also Fig. 24.2). Some radiopaque material has been excreted by the kidneys.

1. External iliac nodes
2. Common iliac nodes
3. Para-aortic nodes
4. Pelvis of ureter

form the common iliac vein. They lie posteromedial to the accompanying arteries and have a similar course and relations.

The **common iliac vein** is formed anterior to the sacro-iliac joint by the union of the internal and external iliac veins and ascends obliquely to meet its fellow on the right side of the 5th lumbar vertebra and to form the inferior vena cava. Both veins lie behind and on the right of their arteries and their relations correspond. The left vein is longer than the right and is crossed by the right common iliac artery. They also receive the iliolumbar veins.

The **gonadal veins**—pampiniform plexuses form veins which drain to the inferior vena cava on the right and the renal vein on the left side.

LYMPH DRAINAGE OF THE ABDOMEN AND PELVIS (Fig. 15.2)

ABDOMEN

The lymph vessels of the anterior abdominal wall pass to axillary, anterior mediastinal and superficial inguinal nodes. The abdominal viscera and posterior abdominal wall drain to aortic nodes which are subdivided into pre-aortic and para-aortic groups.

Pre-aortic nodes are arranged around the origins of the three arteries supplying the alimentary tract and its derivatives, and drain the corresponding structures. Their efferents unite to form the intestinal lymph trunk which enters the cisterna chyli.

Para-aortic nodes lie alongside the aorta around the origins of the paired lateral arteries. They drain the posterior abdominal wall, the kidneys, the suprarenals and the gonads and, through the common iliac nodes, the pelvic viscera and lower limbs. Their efferents unite to form the right and left lumbar lymph trunks.

The **cisterna chyli**—is a thin walled slender sac 5–7 cm long lying between the aorta and the right crus of the diaphragm in front of the upper two lumbar vertebra. It leads directly into the thoracic duct (p. 82) and receives the right and left lumbar lymph trunks, the intestinal lymph trunk and efferents from nodes in the lower posterior intercostal spaces.

PELVIS

The lymph nodes of the pelvis are arranged around the external and internal iliac vessels and are named accordingly. The former mainly receive vessels from the lower limb and lower abdominal wall but also drain the bladder, prostate, lower uterus and cervix. The latter group drain all the pelvic viscera except the ovary and, in addition, the gluteal region and perineum. Lymph vessels from the testis and ovary drain to the para-aortic nodes. A small group of sacral nodes drains the back of the rectum. From internal and external iliac nodes efferents pass to nodes around the common iliac arteries.

SPINAL NERVES

These comprise the sacral part of the lumbosacral and coccygeal plexuses, also the obturator nerve (p. 221), the femoral nerve (p. 226) and the sciatic nerve (p. 220).

The sacral part of the **lumbosacral plexus** is formed by the ventral rami of the 4th and 5th lumbar nerves and the upper four sacral nerves. It lies in front of the sacrum on the surface of piriformis deep to the pelvic fascia. Its branches can be conveniently divided into pelvic branches and those leaving the pelvis. (See also page 127).

BRANCHES
Pelvic
(i) muscular—to piriformis, levator ani, coccygeus and the external anal sphincter.
(ii) **pelvic splanchnics**—these form the pelvic parasympathetic outflow (p. 164) and are derived from the 2nd, 3rd and 4th sacral nerves.
Leaving the pelvis (most of these pass backwards through the greater sciatic foramen):
(i) **superior gluteal nerve**—leaves the pelvis above piriformis to enter the gluteal region where it lies between gluteus medius and gluteus minimus. (It supplies both these muscles and tensor fasciae latae.)
(ii) **inferior gluteal nerve**—supplying gluteus maximus; the nerve to quadratus femoris; the nerve to obturator internus; and the posterior femoral cutaneous nerve—supplying the skin over the back of the thigh. All leave the pelvis below piriformis, accompanied by the **sciatic nerve** (p. 220) and **pudendal nerve** (p. 157). The perforating cutaneous nerve pierces coccygeus and supplies the skin of the gluteal region.

The **coccygeal plexus** is formed of the ventral rami of the 4th and 5th sacral and the coccygeal nerves. It lies on coccygeus and its branches supply the skin over the coccyx.

AUTONOMIC NERVOUS SYSTEM IN ABDOMEN AND PELVIS

As elsewhere it is formed of sympathetic and parasympathetic parts.

Sympathetic

This is derived from the thoracic, lumbar and sacral sympathetic trunks, the fibres passing mainly through the coeliac, aortic, hypogastric and pelvic plexuses.

(*a*) **Lumbar sympathetic trunk**—enters the abdomen by passing under the medial arcuate ligament and descends on the medial margin of psoas to the pelvic brim. It usually has four ganglia.
BRANCHES
(i) somatic branches—pass to the lumbar nerves (grey rami communicantes).
(ii) visceral branches—pass to the aortic plexus and also descend anterior to the common iliac vessels to the hypogastric plexus.
(iii) vascular branches—pass to the common iliac artery.

(*b*) **Sacral sympathetic trunk**—descends on the pelvic surface of the sacrum medial to the pelvic sacral foramina to join its fellow in front of the coccyx at the ganglion impar. It is continuous under the iliac vessels with the abdominal sympathetic trunk above. It has four or five small ganglia.
BRANCHES
(i) somatic branches—pass to the sacral nerves (grey rami communicantes).
(ii) visceral branches—pass to the pelvic plexuses.

(*c*) **Coeliac plexus**—is formed of the two intercommunicating coeliac

163

ganglia which lie on each side of the origin of the coeliac artery. Each ganglion receives greater, lesser and least (renal) splanchnic nerves from the thoracic sympathetic trunk (p. 81) and branches pass down on the front of the aorta to form aortic plexuses. From the coeliac and aortic plexuses, postsynaptic fibres pass with branches of the aorta to supply the upper part of the alimentary tract and its derivatives, also the kidneys, and the gonads. Presynaptic fibres pass through the plexus and end in the suprarenal glands (medullary part).

(*d*) **Aortic plexus**—lies on the front of the lower abdominal aorta and receives branches from the coeliac plexus and the lumbar sympathetic trunk. Postsynaptic fibres pass along the inferior mesenteric artery to the lower abdominal viscera. It gives branches to the hypogastric plexus.

(*e*) **Hypogastric plexus**—lies in the midline below the aortic bifurcation. It is formed of branches from each lumbar sympathetic trunk and the aortic plexus. It divides into right and left branches which descend to the—

(*f*) **Pelvic plexuses**—each of which lies on the side wall of the rectum and is formed by branches from the hypogastric plexus, and the sacral sympathetic trunk. Postsynaptic fibres supply the pelvic viscera.

Parasympathetic

This is derived from the vagi (anterior and posterior vagal trunks) and the pelvic splanchnics (S2, 3, 4).

(*a*) **Anterior and posterior vagal trunks**—are a mixture of both vagi. They are distributed through the coeliac plexus and along the branches of the aorta to the alimentary tract and its derivatives as far as the splenic flexure. Duodenal ulcers usually heal if the gastric acid output is reduced by surgically dividing branches of the anterior and posterior vagal trunks. Such a vagotomy, however, reduces the motility of the stomach and in order to prevent gastric stasis and distension, the 'drainage' of the stomach has to be improved by anastomosing the stomach to the jejunum or by widening the pyloric aperture (pyloroplasty). See also page 81.

(*b*) **Pelvic splanchnic nerves**—pass to the hypogastric and pelvic plexuses. From the hypogastric plexus some fibres ascend to the inferior mesenteric artery and are distributed along it to supply the gut distal to the splenic flexure. From the pelvic plexuses fibres are distributed to the pelvic viscera.

UPPER LIMB

CHAPTER 16

THE SHOULDER REGION

The human upper limbs are specialised organs for sensation and pre-hension (grasping) and show little of the primitive functions of locomotion and support. Without great loss of power there has developed the ability to perform finely controlled movements. The power of the limb is dependent on the strength of its muscles, tendons and bones and on its capacity to fix the joints in positions which allow the muscles to work at their maximum

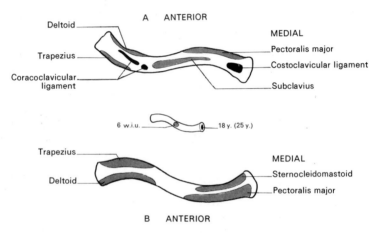

FIG. 16.1
The clavicle; A, lower and B, upper surfaces. Inset:
ossification (w.i.u., weeks in utero; y., years).

advantage. The ability of the limb to perform finely controlled movements is due to its well-developed sensory nerve supply, its large cerebral representation and its great mobility. This last factor includes the development of the movements of pronation of the forearm and opposition of the thumb. Much information about the state of the skeleton (age, etc.) and of the soft tissues can be obtained in the living person by radiological examination.

THE SHOULDER GIRDLE

Clavicle (Fig. 16.1)
    This is a long bone but atypical in that it lacks a medullary cavity. The expanded medial end articulates with the manubrium sterni and

166

first costal cartilage. The body has two curvatures, being convex anteriorly in its medial two-thirds and concave anteriorly in its lateral third.
The flattened lateral end articulates with the medial side of the acromion.
The inferior surface has a roughening at the medial end for the costoclavicular ligament and at the lateral end for the coracoclavicular ligament.
Pectoralis major medially and deltoid laterally are attached to the anterior
surface, sternocleidomastoid is attached to the superior surface medially
and trapezius to the posterior surface laterally.

The bone transmits part of the weight of the limb to the trunk and
also allows the limb to swing clear of the trunk. The clavicle is the first
bone in the body to ossify and does so mainly in membrane. It is one of
the last bones to stop growing. The bone is subcutaneous throughout its
length.

Scapula (Fig. 16.2)

This flat triangular bone is situated on the posterolateral aspect of
the chest wall over the 2nd to 7th ribs. It possesses costal and dorsal
surfaces; superior, medial and lateral borders; lateral, superior and inferior
angles.

The ridged **costal surface** is slightly concave and gives attachment
to subscapularis. The **dorsal surface** is divided by a shelf-like projecting
spine into a smaller supraspinous and larger infraspinous fossa giving
attachment to supraspinatus and infraspinatus muscles respectively. The
two areas communicate laterally around the base of the spine. The spine
is expanded laterally into a flattened **acromion** which projects laterally
and then anteriorly to articulate with the clavicle on its medial side. The
acromion and spine give attachment to trapezius and deltoid.

The superior border passes downwards and laterally. Near the lateral
end the beak-like **coracoid process** projects upwards and then forwards.
It gives attachment to coracobrachialis, short head of biceps and pectoralis
minor muscles and the coracoclavicular ligament. The border is notched
near the base of the coracoid process and a ligament turns the notch into
a foramen for the passage of the suprascapular nerve. The medial border
gives attachment to the levator scapulae and the two rhomboid muscles
dorsally, and the serratus anterior ventrally. The two teres muscles are
attached to the thickened lateral border.

The lateral angle is expanded to form the **glenoid cavity** for articulation with the humerus. Tubercles above and below the glenoid cavity
give attachment to the long heads of biceps and triceps respectively.
The latissimus dorsi, teres major and serratus anterior are attached to
the stout inferior angle.

The spine and acromion, the coracoid process and inferior angle are
palpable.

Humerus (Fig. 16.3)

This is a long bone possessing an upper end, body and lower end. The
upper end includes the head and greater and lesser tuberosities. The **head**
is hemispherical and articulates with the glenoid cavity of the scapula; it
is bounded by the **anatomical neck** of the bone. The **greater tuberosity**

Pectoralis minor

Biceps (short head)
and coracobrachialis

Biceps (long head)

Triceps (long head)

Subscapularis

Serratus anterior

A

Deltoid

Triceps (long head)

Teres minor

Infraspinatus

Teres major

Latissimus dorsi

Trapezius

Supraspinatus

Levator scapulae

Rhomboid minor

Rhomboid major

B

Puberty (25 y.)

10 y. (25 y.)

Puberty (25 y.)

1 y. (14 y.)

2 m.i.u.

Puberty (25 y.)

Puberty (25 y.)

Fig. 16.2

The scapula; A, costal and B, dorsal surfaces. Inset: ossification (m.i.u.,
months in utero; y., years).

168

lies laterally behind the **lesser tuberosity** and is separated from it by the **intertubercular groove**. It possesses three facets—a superior giving attachment to the supraspinatus, a middle to the infraspinatus and a lower to teres minor. Subscapularis is attached to the lesser tuberosity and the tendon of the long head of biceps lies in the intertubercular groove. The

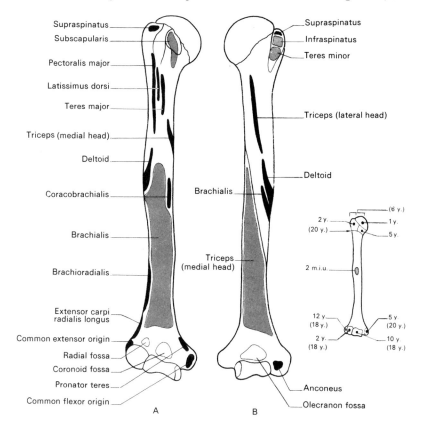

FIG. 16.3
The humerus; A, anterior and B, posterior surfaces. Inset: ossification (m.i.u., months in utero; y., years).

junction between the upper end and body is called the **surgical neck** because fractures occur in this region.

The **body** is stout, cylindrical superiorly and flattened anteroposteriorly below. Half way down its lateral surface is the V-shaped deltoid tuberosity. On the posterior aspect of the bone the **radial groove** runs downwards and laterally. Above it, is attached the lateral head of triceps, and below is the medial head of triceps. Coracobrachialis is attached to the medial side. Pectoralis major is attached to the lateral lip of the lower part of the intertubercular groove, latissimus dorsi to its floor and teres major to its medial lip. At the lower end of the shaft there are well-marked lateral and medial **supracondylar ridges**. To the former are attached brachioradialis and extensor carpi radialis longus. The lower anterior surface of the bone gives attachment to brachialis.

The **lower end** is expanded to form lateral and medial **epicondyles**. A rounded **capitulum** laterally and a pulley-shaped **trochlea** medially articulate with the radius and ulna respectively. The common extensor and flexor muscle origins are attached to the lateral and medial epicondyles respectively.

The epicondyles are palpable subcutaneously and the greater tuberosity is palpable through the lateral fibres of deltoid. Much of the body is also palpable.

Fractures of the humerus can be complicated by injury to closely related nerves and vessels. In particular, the axillary nerve may be injured in fractures of the surgical neck, the radial nerve in fractures of the body, the brachial artery in fractures of the supracondylar region, and the ulnar nerve in injuries to the medial epicondyle.

THE STERNOCLAVICULAR JOINT

This is a synovial joint with features of the ball and socket variety. The shallow concavity formed by the manubrium sterni and first costal cartilage articulates with the medial end of the clavicle. The joint surfaces are lined by fibrocartilage.

LIGAMENTS
(*a*) Capsule: attached to the articular margins of the joint.
(*b*) Capsular thickenings: anterior and posterior sternoclavicular ligaments.
(*c*) Accessory ligaments:
(i) **costoclavicular ligament**—a strong band between the inferior aspect of the medial end of the clavicle and the upper surface of the first costal cartilage.
(ii) **interclavicular ligament**—passes across the jugular notch to unite the medial ends of the two clavicles.

INTRACAPSULAR STRUCTURE: A fibrocartilaginous disc completely divides the joint into medial and lateral compartments each having its own synovial membrane.

FUNCTIONAL ASPECTS
Movement: the clavicular movements possible at this joint are elevation and depression, forward and backward movement in a horizontal plane, circumduction and axial rotation. These increase the range of movement of the upper limb and they are more fully discussed under scapular movements. The costoclavicular ligament acts as a fulcrum around which clavicular movements occur. Thus movement of the lateral end of the clavicle is accompanied by proportionately decreased movement of the medial end in the opposite direction.

170

Stability: this is maintained by the intra-articular disc and the joint ligaments, particularly the costoclavicular. The disc prevents the clavicle from overriding the sternum.

RELATIONS: the brachiocephalic veins are formed posterior to the joints.

THE ACROMIOCLAVICULAR JOINT

This is a synovial joint of the plane variety, it lies subcutaneously. The small oval facet on the lateral aspect of the clavicle articulates with the medial side of the acromion. In dislocation of the joint, the clavicle will ride over the acromion.

LIGAMENTS

(*a*) Capsule: weak, attached to articular margins.

(*b*) Capsular thickenings: none.

(*c*) Accessory ligaments:

(i) **coracoclavicular ligament**—between the upper surface of the coracoid process and the inferior surface of the lateral end of the clavicle. This ligament is strong and transmits much of the weight of the upper limb to the clavicle. It provides a fulcrum for scapular movements.

(ii) **acromioclavicular ligament**—a quadrangular band covering the upper aspect of the joint and uniting adjacent bony margins.

INTRACAPSULAR STRUCTURES: an articular disc is sometimes found but is rarely complete.

FUNCTIONAL ASPECTS

Movement: slight gliding and rotation are possible and these are always associated with scapular movements about the clavicle.

Stability: this is maintained mainly by the coracoclavicular ligament.

THE SHOULDER JOINT

This is a synovial joint of the ball and socket variety, between the shallow glenoid cavity of the scapula and the hemispherical head of the humerus. The glenoid cavity is deepened by the **glenoidal labrum**, a ring of fibrocartilage attached to its boundaries; even so its articular area remains less than a third of that of the humeral head.

LIGAMENTS

(*a*) Capsule: strong but lax, especially inferiorly. Attached proximally to the glenoidal labrum and distally to the articular margin of the head of the humerus, except inferiorly where it encroaches for 1–2 cm on to the neck of the bone.

(*b*) Capsular thickenings: anteriorly, the **glenohumeral ligaments**.

(*c*) Accessory ligaments:

(i) **coracohumeral ligament**—a broad band passing from the base of the coracoid process to the greater tuberosity.

(ii) **transverse humeral ligament**—unites the greater and lesser tuberosities, bridging the intertubercular groove and tying down the long tendon of biceps.

(iii) **glenoidal labrum.**

INTRACAPSULAR STRUCTURES: the synovial membrane lines the non-articular surfaces of the joint and communicates between the glenohumeral ligaments with the subscapular bursa. It encloses the tendon of the long head of biceps in a tubular sheath as this structure passes across the joint cavity.

FUNCTIONAL ASPECTS

Movement: the shoulder joint has a wider range of movement than any other joint; it is capable of flexion, extension, abduction, adduction, circumduction and medial and lateral rotation.

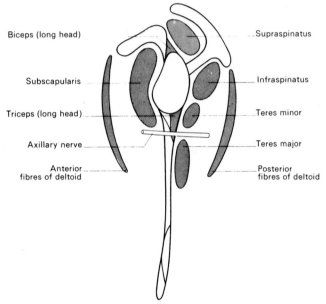

FIG. 16.4
Diagram indicating the main relations of the
shoulder joint.

However: (*a*) Associated movement of the shoulder girdle increases the range of these movements. (*b*) The plane of the joint is not sagittal, it passes forwards and medially. Thus anatomical flexion of the limb is accompanied by some abduction at the joint. (*c*) Abduction of the humerus beyond 90° is associated with lateral rotation, thus preventing the greater tuberosity from impinging on the acromion.

Flexion—clavicular head of pectoralis major, anterior fibres of deltoid and coracobrachialis.

Extension—posterior fibres of deltoid. Extension from a flexed position is reinforced by latissimus dorsi, the sternocostal head of pectoralis major, and teres major.

Abduction—initiated by supraspinatus and continued by deltoid.

Adduction—pectoralis major, latissimus dorsi, subscapularis and teres major.

172

Medial rotation—pectoralis major, anterior fibres of deltoid, latissimus dorsi, teres major and subscapularis.

Lateral rotation—posterior fibres of deltoid, teres minor and infraspinatus.

Stability: this joint is more frequently dislocated than any other. The short articular muscles, subscapularis, supraspinatus, infraspinatus, and teres minor, by their close proximity, are the most important factors in maintaining its stability. The absence of muscles inferiorly accounts for the frequency of downward dislocation. The lax capsule here is of little support and the shallow glenoid cavity affords little bony stability. The axillary nerve may be injured. Superiorly the coraco-acromial arch acts as a socket for the head of the humerus and prevents upward dislocation.

BLOOD SUPPLY: circumflex humeral and suprascapular arteries.

NERVE SUPPLY: axillary and suprascapular nerves.

RELATIONS (Fig. 16.4): *Anterior*—subscapularis muscle and bursa. *Posterior*—infraspinatus and teres minor. *Superior*—supraspinatus, subacromial bursa and coraco-acromial arch; inside the joint is the tendon of the long head of biceps. *Inferior*—long head of triceps and axillary nerve. The nerve may be damaged in downward dislocation of the humerus. Deltoid muscle embraces the joint.

BURSAE

(i) subscapular—lies deep to subscapularis, separating it from the neck of the scapula and shoulder joint. It communicates with the joint cavity.

(ii) subacromial—lies above supraspinatus and separates it from the coraco-acromial arch and the deep surface of deltoid.

MOVEMENTS OF THE SCAPULA AND SHOULDER GIRDLE

Scapular movements are always associated with movement at the sternoclavicular and acromioclavicular joints and usually with movement at the shoulder joint. The bone may be elevated, depressed, moved forwards or retracted on the chest wall and rotated laterally or medially.

(*a*) Elevation—upper fibres of trapezius and levator scapulae.

(*b*) Depression—serratus anterior and pectoralis minor aided by gravity.

During these movements the medial end of the clavicle moves in the opposite direction to the lateral end.

(*c*) Forward movement on the chest wall, as in pushing or punching —serratus anterior and pectoralis minor while latissimus dorsi holds the inferior angle of the bone on the chest wall.

(*d*) Retraction, as in bracing the shoulders—trapezius and the rhomboid muscles.

In forward movement and retraction of the scapula, the medial end of the clavicle swings in the opposite direction and there is slight gliding at the acromioclavicular joint.

(*e*) Lateral rotation involves lateral movement of the inferior angle and upward rotation of the glenoid fossa. It is produced by serratus anterior and trapezius.

(*f*) Medial rotation—levator scapulae, the rhomboid and pectoralis minor muscles.

MUSCLES CONNECTING THE UPPER LIMB TO THE TRUNK

Anterior Group

1. Pectoralis major—a powerful muscle arising from the anterior chest wall by two heads. It lies in the anterior axillary wall. Its upper border is separated from deltoid by the deltopectoral groove in which lies the cephalic vein.

ATTACHMENTS

Trunk

(i) clavicular head—medial half of the anterior surface of the clavicle.

(ii) sternocostal head—anterior surface of the sternum, the upper six costal cartilages and the upper part of the external oblique aponeurosis.

Humeral—lateral lip of the intertubercular groove.

ACTIONS

(i) adduction and medial rotation of the humerus.

(ii) the clavicular fibres flex the humerus.

(iii) the sternocostal fibres extend the humerus from a flexed position, e.g. the follow-through of a tennis player's service. With the arm raised and fixed, this action pulls the trunk upwards.

(iv) an accessory muscle of respiration.

NERVE SUPPLY: lateral and medial pectoral nerves (branches of the lateral and medial cords of the brachial plexus respectively).

2. Pectoralis minor—lies deep to pectoralis major in the anterior chest wall and overlaps the middle part of the axillary artery and the brachial plexus.

ATTACHMENTS

Costal—the 3rd, 4th and 5th ribs near their costochondral junctions.

Scapular—the medial border of the coracoid process.

ACTIONS

(i) draws the scapula forwards and medially around the chest wall.

(ii) directs the glenoid cavity downwards.

(iii) accessory muscle of respiration.

NERVE SUPPLY: medial pectoral branch of the medial cord of the brachial plexus.

3. Serratus anterior—covers the medial axillary wall.

ATTACHMENTS

Costal—near the angles of the upper eight ribs; the lower slips interdigitate with external oblique muscle.

Scapular—costal surface of the medial border of the scapula; the lower four slips pass to the inferior angle.

ACTIONS

(i) pulls the scapula forwards around the chest.

(ii) laterally rotates the scapula, directing the glenoid cavity upwards.

(iii) an accessory muscle of respiration.

NERVE SUPPLY: long thoracic nerve (from the 5th, 6th and 7th cervical nerves).

Posterior Group

1. Trapezius—a broad flat triangular muscle lying superficially on the back of the neck and upper trunk.

ATTACHMENTS

Trunk—the superior nuchal line of the occipital bone, the ligamentum nuchae, all the thoracic spines and the supraspinous ligaments.

Scapular

(i) the upper fibres run downwards and laterally to the posterior aspect of the lateral third of the clavicle.

(ii) the middle fibres run horizontally to the medial border of the acromion and the superior lip of the scapular spine.

(iii) the lower fibres ascend to the tubercle on the scapular spine.

ACTIONS

(i) rotation of the scapula in elevation and controlled descent of the arm.

(ii) retraction of the scapula (as in bracing the shoulders).

(iii) raising of the scapula.

(iv) the lower fibres may assist in depression of the scapula.

(v) one trapezius alone pulls the head backwards and laterally, both together extend the neck and head.

NERVE SUPPLY: spinal accessory nerve.

2. Latissimus dorsi—is a powerful muscle with an extensive origin.

ATTACHMENTS

Trunk

(i) spines and supraspinous ligaments of the lower six thoracic vertebrae.

(ii) by the lumbar fascia to the lumbar and sacral vertebral spines.

(iii) posterior part of the iliac crest.

(iv) lower four ribs (interdigitating with external oblique).

Its fibres pass upwards and laterally, gain a small slip from the inferior angle of the scapula, and converge on a narrow tendon which winds around the lower border of teres major to reach its humeral attachment.

Humeral—floor of the intertubercular groove.

ACTIONS

(i) a powerful extensor of the humerus particularly from the flexed position, e.g. the follow-through of a tennis player's service. With the arm fixed and raised above the head, this same movement will pull the trunk upwards.

(ii) adduction of the humerus.

(iii) medial rotation of the humerus.

NERVE SUPPLY: thoracodorsal branch of the posterior cord of the brachial plexus.

3. Levator scapulae and the **rhomboids** (major and minor) lie on the posterior thoracic wall deep to trapezius. They run downwards and laterally from the vertebral column to the medial border of the scapula. Levator scapulae is attached opposite the supraspinous fossa, rhomboid minor opposite the spine and rhomboid major opposite the infraspinous fossa.

175

ACTIONS: these three muscles act together to elevate and medially rotate the scapula.

NERVE SUPPLY: branches from 3rd to the 5th cervical nerves.

SCAPULOHUMERAL MUSCLES

1. Deltoid—is a powerful multipennate muscle. Deep to it lies the subacromial bursa, the short articular muscles around the shoulder joint, the upper end of the humerus and the shoulder joint.

ATTACHMENTS

Proximal—from the anterior border of the lateral third of the clavicle, the lateral border of the acromion and the lower lip of the scapular spine.

Distal—the V-shaped deltoid tuberosity on the lateral aspect of the body of the humerus.

ACTIONS

(i) lateral fibres—abduction of the humerus.

(ii) anterior fibres—medial rotation and flexion of the humerus.

(iii) posterior fibres—lateral rotation and extension of the humerus.

NERVE SUPPLY: axillary nerve (from the posterior cord of the brachial plexus).

2. Teres major—is a thick muscle forming part of the posterior axillary wall.

ATTACHMENTS

Scapular—lower part of the lateral border and the inferior angle.

Humeral—medial lip of the intertubercular groove.

ACTIONS: adduction and medial rotation of the humerus.

NERVE SUPPLY: branches from the posterior cord of the brachial plexus.

3. Short articular muscles (cuff-muscles)

(i) **Subscapularis**

ATTACHMENTS

Scapular—medial two thirds of the ridged costal surface (separated from the neck of the scapula by the subscapular bursa). It passes laterally to form part of the posterior axillary wall.

Humeral—lesser tuberosity.

It is supplied by branches from the posterior cord of the brachial plexus.

(ii) **Supraspinatus**—extends from the medial two-thirds of the supraspinous fossa of the scapula to the upper facet on the greater tuberosity of the humerus. It is supplied by the suprascapular nerve (from the upper trunk of the brachial plexus).

(iii) **Infraspinatus**—extends from the medial two-thirds of the infraspinous fossa of the scapula to the middle facet on the greater tuberosity of the humerus. It is supplied by the suprascapular nerve.

(iv) **Teres minor**—passes between the upper two-thirds of the lateral border of the scapula and the lower facet on the greater tuberosity of the humerus. It is supplied by the axillary nerve.

The tendons of these four muscles blend closely with the shoulder joint capsule and are important factors in maintaining the joint's stability.

ACTIONS

Subscapularis—medial rotation of the humerus.

Supraspinatus—abduction of the humerus.

Infraspinatus and teres minor—lateral rotation of the humerus.

CHAPTER 17

THE AXILLA AND UPPER ARM

THE AXILLA

This is a fat-filled space between the lateral thoracic wall and the upper limb. Its shape is that of a truncated pyramid with apex, base and four walls.

Apex—is bounded by the superior border of the scapula, the outer border of the 1st rib and the middle third of the clavicle. Through it the axilla communicates with the posterior triangle of the neck.

Base—formed by axillary fascia, subcutaneous tissue and skin.

Anterior wall—contains superficially pectoralis major and deep to this pectoralis minor enclosed in the clavipectoral fascia.

Posterior wall—extends lower than the anterior and is composed of subscapularis, latissimus dorsi and teres major, from above downwards.

Medial wall—comprises the upper ribs and intercostal spaces, these structures being covered by slips of serratus anterior.

Lateral wall—the narrow intertubercular groove on the humerus into which muscles of the anterior and posterior walls are inserted.

CONTENTS
(*a*) axillary artery and vein.
(*b*) cords and terminal branches of the brachial plexus.
(*c*) coracobrachialis and biceps.
(*d*) axillary lymph nodes and lymph vessels.
(*e*) fat.

THE AXILLARY ARTERY

This is the continuation of the subclavian artery beyond the outer border of the 1st rib. It arches downwards and laterally through the axilla to become the brachial artery at the lower border of teres major.

RELATIONS
As the artery passes through the axilla it is surrounded by the cords and branches of the brachial plexus. The axillary vein lies medial to this neurovascular bundle, coracobrachialis muscle and the short head of biceps are lateral. The vessels and nerves are crossed superficially by pectoralis minor and lie on the muscles of the posterior wall of the axilla.

BRANCHES
(i) **superior thoracic artery**—to the anterior thoracic wall.
(ii) **acromiothoracic artery**—pierces the clavipectoral fascia and supplies branches to the anterior axillary wall.
(iii) **lateral thoracic artery**—supplies lateral thoracic wall. (In the female it contributes to the blood supply of the breast.)

(iv) **subscapular artery**—the largest branch of the axillary artery. Its circumflex scapular branch passes backwards round the lateral border of the scapula into the infraspinous fossa. The arteries take part in the anastomosis around the scapula.

(v) **anterior** and **posterior circumflex humeral arteries**—anastomose around the surgical neck of the humerus and supply the shoulder joint.

Scapular anastomosis: this provides a collateral circulation to the upper limb from the beginning of the subclavian artery to the last part of the axillary artery by means of anastomotic connections between branches of the thyrocervical trunk (namely the suprascapular and the deep branch of the transverse cervical) proximally, and the subscapular artery and its circumflex branch distally.

THE AXILLARY VEIN

This is the continuation of the brachial vein above the lower border of teres major. It passes upwards and medially, medial to the axillary artery to reach the outer border of the 1st rib where it becomes the subclavian vein. Most of its tributaries correspond to the branches of the axillary artery. The **cephalic vein,** which it receives, drains the area supplied by the acromiothoracic artery and the superficial structures on the lateral aspect of the limb.

THE BRACHIAL PLEXUS (Fig. 17.1)

This plexus of nerves supplies the upper limb. It is usually formed from the ventral rami of the lower four cervical and the greater part of the first thoracic nerves. These ventral rami are the *five roots* of the plexus and emerge between the anterior and middle scalene muscles in the neck. They unite to form *three trunks* in the posterior triangle of the neck. The upper two roots (C5 & 6) form the upper trunk, the middle root (C7) continues as the middle trunk and the lower two roots (C8 & T1) form the lower trunk. Behind the middle of the clavicle, where the neck and the axilla are in continuity, each trunk divides into *anterior* and *posterior divisions*. The three posterior divisions form the *posterior cord*. The anterior divisions of the upper and middle trunks form the *lateral cord*, and the anterior division of the lower trunk is continued as the *medial cord*. The posterior cord and its branches supply structures on the dorsal (extensor) surface of the limb. The medial and lateral cords and their branches supply structures on the ventral (flexor) surface. The three cords pass into the axilla; they are named according to their arrangement around the middle part of the axillary artery. The posterior cord ends on the posterior wall of the axilla by dividing into axillary and radial nerves. The lateral cord divides into the musculocutaneous nerve and the lateral head of the median nerve. The medial cord ends as the ulnar nerve and the medial head of the median nerve (which passes anterior to the lower part of the axillary artery to join the lateral head).

BRANCHES

1. ROOTS: A number of branches pass to the vertebral and back muscles. The C5 root contributes to the phrenic nerve (see page 338).

179

The **long thoracic nerve** (C5, 6 & 7) passes downwards behind the trunks and vessels to reach the medial wall of the axilla and supply serratus anterior.

2. TRUNKS: The **suprascapular nerve** arises from the upper trunk, runs laterally across the root of the neck, passes through the suprascapular foramen to supply supraspinatus and infraspinatus.

3. DIVISIONS: None.

4. CORDS

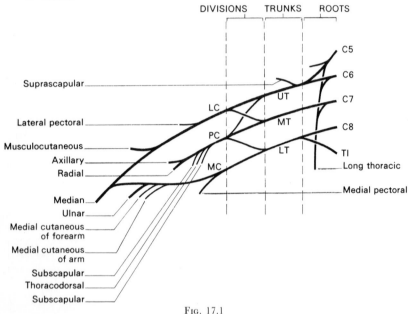

FIG. 17.1

Diagrammatic lay-out of the brachial plexus. U.T., M.T., L.T.,: upper, middle and lower trunks; L.C., P.C., M.C.: lateral, posterior and medial cords.

Lateral

(i) **lateral pectoral nerve** supplies pectoralis major.

(ii) **musculocutaneous nerve** (see page 182).

(iii) lateral head of the **median nerve** (see pages 183 and 196).

Medial

(i) **medial pectoral nerve**—pierces pectoralis minor to reach pectoralis major; it supplies both these muscles.

(ii) **ulnar nerve**—the largest branch of the medial cord (see pages 183 and 194.

(iii) medial head of the **median nerve** (see pages 183 and 196).

(iv) and (v) **medial cutaneous nerves of the arm** and **of the forearm** —pass distally on the medial side of the limb, supplying the skin of this area. The former pierces the deep fascia halfway down the arm, the latter nearer the elbow.

Posterior
(i) **subscapular nerves**—pass downwards on the posterior axillary wall to supply subscapularis and teres major.
(ii) **thoracodorsal nerve** (to latissimus dorsi)—enters the upper border of the muscle.
(iii) **axillary nerve**—passes downwards on subscapularis and then turns posteriorly round the surgical neck of the humerus, accompanied by the posterior circumflex humeral artery. It supplies deltoid and teres minor, the shoulder joint, and ends as the upper lateral cutaneous nerve of the arm.
(iv) **radial nerve** (see pages 183 and 195).

THE UPPER ARM

MUSCLES

Anterior Group
1. Coracobrachialis—passes between the tip of the coracoid process of the scapula (medial to short head of biceps) and half-way down the medial side of the humerus. It adducts and flexes the humerus.

2. Biceps
ATTACHMENTS
Scapular
(i) short head—the tip of the coracoid process.
(ii) long head—the supraglenoid tubercle.
The tendon of the long head lies in the shoulder joint, in the intertubercular groove and in the arm. The synovial sheath which surrounds it inside the joint capsule is prolonged under the transverse humeral ligament into the intertubercular groove. This head unites with the short head in the distal third of the arm.
Radial—the posterior part of the radial tuberosity and also by the bicipital aponeurosis into the deep fascia over the medial side of the forearm and the posterior subcutaneous border of the ulna.
ACTIONS: it is a powerful supinator and flexor of the forearm.

Brachialis
ATTACHMENTS
Humeral—distal half of the anterior surface of the humerus and the medial intermuscular septum.
Ulnar—anterior surface of the coronoid process.
ACTION: flexion of the forearm.
NERVE SUPPLY: the musculocutaneous nerve supplies the three muscles.

Posterior Group
Triceps—a powerful muscle occupying the entire posterior compartment of the arm.

181

ATTACHMENTS

Proximal—by three heads

(i) long head—the infraglenoid tubercle of the scapula.

(ii) lateral head—a linear attachment from the upper border of the radial groove of the humerus.

(iii) medial head—the whole posterior surface of the humerus below the radial groove and the adjacent medial and lateral intermuscular septa.

The medial head lies deep to the lateral and long heads. A bursa separates the tendon from the posterior aspect of the elbow joint.

Distal—by a strong tendon into the olecranon of the ulna.

ACTION: extension of the forearm.

NERVE SUPPLY: branches from the radial nerve.

THE BRACHIAL ARTERY

The brachial artery lies on the medial side of the upper arm and begins at the lower border of teres major as the continuation of the axillary artery. It descends in the anterior compartment of the upper arm and ends in the cubital fossa by dividing into radial and ulnar arteries.

RELATIONS: throughout its course it is covered only by skin and fascia and lies medial to biceps. It is accompanied by veins and the median nerve, the latter crossing over it from lateral to medial halfway down the upper arm. In the cubital fossa the artery lies medial to biceps tendon and is crossed by the median cubital vein, separated from it only by the bicipital aponeurosis. As this vein is commonly used for venepuncture, this close relation should be specially noted.

BRANCHES

(i) profunda brachii artery—accompanies the radial nerve in the radial groove and supplies the posterior muscles of the upper arm and the elbow joint.

(ii) muscular and articular branches.

(iii) nutrient artery—to the humerus.

THE MUSCULOCUTANEOUS NERVE

This is a terminal branch of the lateral cord of the brachial plexus and descends, deeply placed in the upper arm, to end anterior to the elbow joint as the lateral cutaneous nerve of the forearm.

RELATIONS: in the axilla, it lies lateral to the axillary artery and pierces coracobrachialis to lie between biceps and brachialis. Emerging lateral to these muscles, it pierces the deep fascia in front of the elbow.

BRANCHES

(i) muscular—to coracobrachialis, biceps and brachialis.

(ii) articular—to the elbow joint.

(iii) the nerve continues as the lateral cutaneous nerve of the forearm and supplies both surfaces of the radial side of the forearm as far as the thenar eminence.

THE RADIAL NERVE (in the axilla and upper arm). See also page 195.

The radial nerve arises as a terminal branch of the posterior cord of the brachial plexus behind the axillary artery. It leaves the axilla and takes an oblique course through the posterior compartment of the arm. It pierces the lateral intermuscular septum, passes anterior to the elbow joint and enters the forearm.

RELATIONS

In the axilla—at its origin it is behind the axillary artery, and lies on the posterior wall of the axilla. It then passes between the long head of triceps and the shaft of the humerus into—

The posterior compartment of the arm. It runs with the profunda brachii artery in the radial groove of the humerus between medial and lateral heads of triceps. It pierces the lateral intermuscular septum and comes to lie anterior to the elbow joint between brachialis and brachioradialis.

BRANCHES

In the axilla

(i) muscular—to triceps.

(ii) posterior cutaneous nerve of arm—to skin of posterior and medial aspects of upper arm.

In the posterior compartment of arm

(i) muscular—to triceps, brachioradialis and extensor carpi radialis longus.

(ii) lower lateral cutaneous nerve of arm—to skin of the lower lateral aspect of arm.

(iii) posterior cutaneous nerve of forearm—to skin of the posterior aspect of forearm.

THE MEDIAN NERVE (in the axilla and upper arm). See also page 196.

The median nerve arises in the lower axilla by the union of its medial and lateral heads, these being terminal branches of the corresponding cords of the brachial plexus. It descends through the anterior compartment of the upper arm to reach the cubital fossa.

RELATIONS: the nerve first lies lateral to the axillary and brachial arteries but halfway down the upper arm it passes in front of the latter to reach its medial side. The nerve is anterior to triceps and brachialis. The median nerve has no branches above the elbow joint.

THE ULNAR NERVE (in the axilla and upper arm). See also page 194.

This is a terminal branch of the medial cord of the brachial plexus and descends on the medial side of upper arm, initially in the anterior compartment but pierces the medial intermuscular septum to continue in the posterior compartment. It passes behind the medial epicondyle and enters the forearm.

RELATIONS: the nerve lies medial to the axillary and brachial arteries. It leaves the latter by passing backwards and pierces the medial intermuscular septum halfway down the upper arm. It then descends between the medial head of triceps and the septum. It has no branches in the upper arm.

CHAPTER 18

THE ELBOW AND THE FOREARM

ELBOW REGION

Radius (Fig. 18.1)

This is the lateral bone of the forearm; it has an upper end, body and lower end.

The **upper end** has a head, neck and tuberosity. The **head** is a cupped circular disc which articulates with the capitulum of the humerus and

Flexor digitorum superficialis

Brachialis

Pronator teres

Biceps

Supinator

Flexor digitorum profundus

Flexor digitorum superficialis

Pronator teres

Flexor pollicis longus

Pronator quadratus

Brachioradialis

Triceps

Anconeus

Supinator

Biceps

Abductor pollicis longus

Pronator teres

Extensor pollicis longus

Extensor pollicis brevis

Extensor indicis

10 y. (18 y.)

5 y. (18 y.)

2 m.i.u.

2 m.i.u.

5 y. (20 y.)

2 y. (20 y.)

A   B

Fig. 18.1
The radius and ulna; A, anterior and B, posterior aspects. Inset:
ossification (m.i.u., months in utero; y., years).

radial notch of the ulna. On the medial side of the bone is the **radial tuberosity** for the attachment of biceps tendon.

184

The **body** has a slight lateral convexity and expands from above downwards. The upper part is cylindrical and is crossed by the anterior oblique line which runs from the radial tuberosity downwards and laterally to the point of maximum convexity. The lower part has anterior, posterior and lateral surfaces; and interosseous, anterior and posterior borders. The areas of muscle attachments are indicated in Fig. 18.1.

The **lower end** is large and is extended distally into the **styloid process.** The posterior surface has a prominent **dorsal tubercle** around which hooks the tendon of extensor pollicis longus and less prominent ridges, to which septa from the extensor retinaculum are attached. The medial surface has an ulnar notch for articulation with the head of the ulna. The inferior surface has facets for the scaphoid and lunate bones and medially it gives attachment to the base of an articular disc.

The radial head posteriorly, the lower end anteriorly and posteriorly, and the styloid process are all palpable. A fall on the outstretched hand may produce a fracture of the lower end of the radius in an older person, or a separation of the epiphysis in a young person.

Ulna (Fig. 18.1)

This is the medial bone of the forearm; it has an upper end, body and lower end.

The **upper end** has a deep **trochlear notch** anteriorly between two projections; above is the **olecranon** giving attachment to the triceps and below is the **coronoid process** to which brachialis is attached. On its medial side, the flexor digitorum superficialis and pronator teres are attached. The notch articulates with the trochlea of the humerus. On the lateral side of the coronoid process there is a shallow **radial notch** for articulation with the head of the radius; its anterior and posterior borders give attachment to the annular ligament. Below the radial notch the bone is hollowed out to give clearance to the radial tuberosity in pronation and supination. This area is limited posteriorly by the **supinator crest** for the attachment of supinator muscle. The medial aspect of the upper end gives attachment to flexor digitorum profundus.

The **body** narrows from above downwards. It has anterior, medial and posterior surfaces but towards the lower end it becomes cylindrical. Its numerous muscle attachments are shown in Figure 18.1. The interosseous border gives attachment to the interosseous membrane.

The **lower end** has a rounded **head** and a medial distal extension— the conical **styloid process.** The extensor carpi ulnaris tendon rests in the posterior groove between the two. The head articulates with the lower end of the radius and with the articular disc which takes origin from the base of the styloid process.

The posterior part of the olecranon, the posterior border of the shaft and lower medial surface are subcutaneous. The ulnar styloid is palpable on the postero-medial aspect of the wrist in the anatomical position and is 1 cm proximal to the radial styloid. In full pronation the anterior surface of the head of the ulna is palpable.

CUBITAL FOSSA

This triangular fossa is situated in front of the elbow joint.
Base—a line between humeral epicondyles; lateral border—brachioradialis; medial border—pronator teres; floor—supinator and brachialis overlie the capsule of the elbow joint; roof—deep fascia of forearm strengthened by the bicipital aponeurosis. Lying on the roof are the anterior branches of medial and lateral cutaneous nerves of the forearm, and the median cubital vein joining cephalic and basilic veins.
Contents: from medial to lateral side, embedded in fat—
(i) median nerve.
(ii) brachial artery and its terminal branches the radial and ulnar arteries (the common interosseous branch of the ulnar artery is also present).
(iii) biceps tendon.
(iv) radial and posterior interosseous nerves (usually overlapped by the brachioradialis).

THE ELBOW JOINT

This is a synovial joint of the hinge variety, between the lower end of the humerus and upper ends of the radius and ulna. The humerus presents a rounded capitulum and a saddle-shaped trochlea for articulation with the cupped head of the radius and the trochlear notch of the ulna respectively.

LIGAMENTS

(*a*) Capsule: attached around the upper boundaries of the olecranon, coronoid and radial fossae on the humerus and to its articular margins medially and laterally. Inferiorly it is attached to the olecranon and coronoid process, the medial edge of the trochlear notch and laterally blends with the upper border of the annular ligament of the proximal radio-ulnar joint.

(*b*) Capsular thickenings
(i) **radial collateral ligament,** strong, triangular-shaped with its apex attached to the lateral epicondyle and its base to the annular ligament.
(ii) **ulnar collateral ligament** is in three parts: the anterior and posterior bands radiate from the medial epicondyle to the bases of coronoid process and olecranon respectively, the oblique band joins the latter two attachments.

INTRACAPSULAR STRUCTURES: the synovial membrane lines the inside of the capsule and is continuous with the synovial membrane of the proximal radio-ulnar joint. Fat pads are found between synovial membrane and capsular ligament in the olecranon and coronoid fossae.

FUNCTIONAL ASPECTS

Movement: Flexion and extension occur. (The humeroradial articulation is also involved in the movements of pronation and supination of the forearm.) Flexion—brachialis and biceps assisted by brachioradialis, pronator teres and the common flexor muscles. Extension—triceps muscle.

Stability: this is good and is contributed to by the shapes of the bones, the strong capsule and close proximity of brachialis and triceps.

BLOOD SUPPLY: branches of brachial, radial and ulnar arteries which form a rich anastomosis.

NERVE SUPPLY: median, radial, ulnar, musculocutaneous and posterior interosseous nerves.

RELATIONS

Anterior—the cubital fossa and its contents.

Posterior—triceps.

Medial—the common flexor origin and ulnar nerve.

Lateral—the common extensor origin.

THE RADIO-ULNAR JOINTS

Proximal Radio-ulnar Joint

This is a synovial joint of the pivot variety. The sides of the disc-shaped head of the radius articulate within the osseofascial ring formed by the radial notch of the ulna and the annular ligament.

LIGAMENTS: a strong **annular ligament,** which is lined by articular hyaline cartilage, encircles the head of the radius and is attached to the anterior and posterior borders of the radial notch on the ulna (the capsule of the elbow joint is attached to the upper border of the ligament).

INTRACAPSULAR STRUCTURES: the synovial membrane lines the non-articular surface of the joint and is continuous with that of the elbow joint.

STABILITY: the annular ligament is narrower below than above and holds firmly the reciprocally shaped head of the adult radius. Dislocation is more common in the child.

Distal Radio-ulnar Joint

This is a synovial joint of the pivot variety, the head of the ulna articulates with the ulnar notch on the radius. (A triangular **fibro-cartilaginous disc** lies distal to the ulna and contributes to the articular surface of the wrist joint. Its apex is attached to the base of the ulnar styloid and its base to the medial edge of the distal articular surface of the radius.

LIGAMENTS: the capsular ligament is weak and is attached to the articular margin, except inferiorly where it gains attachment to the margins of the articular disc.

INTRACAPSULAR STRUCTURES: the synovial membrane lines the non-articular surface of the joint and is not usually continuous with the synovial membrane of the wrist joint.

STABILITY: this is dependent on the strength of the articular disc.

Interosseous Membrane

This is a fibrous membrane connecting the adjacent interosseous borders of the two bones of the forearm, and giving attachment to the deep flexor and extensor muscles. Its fibres are directed downwards and medially. Thus a force passing upwards from the hand through the radius is transmitted to the elbow joint via the ulna as well as through the head of the radius, e.g. leaning on the hand, or punching.

MOVEMENTS AT RADIO-ULNAR JOINTS

The movements possible at these joints are supination and pronation. These movements occur about an axis joining the centre of the radial head above and the styloid process of the ulna below.

In the anatomical position, the forearm is in the fully **supinated** attitude. While the head of the radius rotates within the annular ligament, its lower end, bearing the hand and tethered by the articular disc, moves ventrally around the head of the ulna. This movement is called **pronation.** After full pronation from the anatomical position the palm faces dorsally. The range of these movements, usually about 180°, is greatly increased by simultaneous rotation of the humerus, provided the elbow joint is fully extended. Both movements are more effective when the elbow is flexed.

Supination—is produced by biceps and supinator.

Pronation—is produced by pronator teres and pronator quadratus.

FOREARM

ANTERIOR MUSCLES OF THE FOREARM

Superficial Group

All these muscles arise from the common flexor origin on the anterior aspect of the medial epicondyle of the humerus and are therefore weak flexors of the elbow joint as well as having other actions on the forearm and hand. Pronator teres has an additional attachment to the medial side of the coronoid process of the ulna and flexor digitorum superficialis is also attached to the ulnar coronoid and to the anterior oblique line on the radius. Flexor carpi ulnaris has a second attachment to the upper part of the posterior subcutaneous border of the ulna. Flexor carpi ulnaris is supplied by the ulnar nerve, all the other superficial muscles are supplied by branches of the median nerve.

1. Pronator teres

ATTACHMENTS

Proximal—by two heads:

(i) common flexor origin.

(ii) medial side of the coronoid process of the ulna.

Distal—the middle of the lateral surface of the body of the radius.

ACTION: pronation of the forearm.

The muscle forms the medial border of the cubital fossa, and the median nerve leaves the fossa between the two heads.

2. Flexor carpi radialis

ATTACHMENTS

Proximal—common flexor origin.

Distal—the palmar surface of the base of the 2nd and 3rd metacarpal bones.

ACTION: flexion and abduction at the wrist joint.

3. Palmaris longus—extends from the common flexor origin on the humerus to the apex of the palmar aponeurosis and flexor retinaculum. It flexes the wrist joint and tightens the palmar aponeurosis. It is supplied by the median nerve. It is a vestigial muscle and is often absent.

4. Flexor digitorum superficialis—this large muscle lies deeper than the other muscles of the group. It arises from both bones of the forearm, and the tendinous arch formed between them covers the ulnar artery and median nerve. The median nerve is adherent to its deep surface.

ATTACHMENTS
Proximal
(i) the humero-ulnar head from the common flexor origin, the ulnar collateral ligament of the elbow joint and the medial aspect of the coronoid process.
(ii) the radial head from the anterior oblique line on the radius.

Distal—its four tendons pass deep to the flexor retinaculum. Those to the middle and ring fingers lie anterior to the tendons to the index and little finger and so are more liable to be involved in lacerations of the front of the wrist. The tendons diverge in the palm, one passing to each finger. Over the proximal phalanx each tendon splits and passes dorsally to encircle the corresponding tendon of flexor digitorum profundus. After partial decussation the tendon is attached to the sides of the middle phalanx.

ACTION: flexes the middle and then the proximal phalanx; it also flexes the wrist.

5. Flexor carpi ulnaris—lies on the medial border of the forearm. The ulnar nerve enters the forearm between its two proximal heads of attachment.

ATTACHMENTS
Proximal
(i) common flexor origin.
(ii) upper two-thirds of the posterior subcutaneous border of the ulna.

Distal—pisiform bone and thence into the hamate and the medial aspect of the base of the 5th metacarpal bone.

ACTIONS: flexion and adduction at the wrist joint.

Deep Muscles of the Forearm

1. Flexor pollicis longus

ATTACHMENTS
Proximal—anterior aspect of the radius between the anterior oblique line and the attachment of pronator quadratus, and the adjacent interosseous membrane.
Distal—the tendon passes deep to the flexor retinaculum and is attached to the palmar surface of the base of the distal phalanx of the thumb.

189

ACTION: flexes the thumb, expecially the distal phalanx.

NERVE SUPPLY: anterior interosseous branch of the median nerve.

2. Flexor digitorum profundus

ATTACHMENTS

Proximal—anterior and medial surfaces of the upper three-quarters of the ulna, and the adjacent interosseous membrane.

Distal—the four tendons pass under the flexor retinaculum, deep to flexor digitorum superficialis, the tendon for the index finger being separate from the others. Diverging in the palm, each tendon passes through the split tendon of superficialis to gain attachment to the palmar surface of the base of the terminal phalanx of the finger. (The tendons give attachment to the lumbrical muscles in the palm, see page 206.)

ACTION: flexion of the distal phalanges. It assists in flexion of the middle and proximal phalanges, and of the wrist.

NERVE SUPPLY: medial part—ulnar nerve; lateral part—anterior interosseous nerve.

3. Pronator quadratus—this small square muscle runs transversely between the lower quarters of the anterior surfaces of the radius and ulna. It is a pronator of the forearm and is supplied by the anterior interosseous nerve.

Flexor Synovial Sheaths

At their points of maximum friction, beneath the flexor retinaculum and within the digital fibrous flexor sheaths, the long flexor tendons are invested with synovial sheaths. Deep to the flexor retinaculum, the tendons of profundus and superficialis have a common sheath, the **ulnar bursa,** and the tendon of flexor pollicis longus also has its own sheath, the **radial bursa.** They begin 2–3 cm above the wrist joint and occasionally communicate with each other. The ulnar bursa ends at the middle of the palm but a medial prolongation around the tendons of the little finger extends as far as the distal phalanx. The radial bursa continues within the fibrous flexor sheath of the thumb as far as the distal phalanx. The tendons of the index, middle and ring fingers have their own digital synovial sheaths extending from the heads of the metacarpals to the bases of the distal phalanges.

POSTERIOR AND LATERAL MUSCLES OF THE FOREARM

Superficial Group

The superficial muscles that are not attached to common extensor origin are supplied by the radial nerve as it lies in the arm.

1. Brachioradialis

ATTACHMENTS

Proximal—upper two thirds of the lateral supracondylar ridge of the humerus.

190

Distal—lateral aspect of the lower end of the radius.

ACTIONS: flexion at the elbow joint (most strongly in the midprone position). It may be a supinator or a pronator of the forearm according to the position of the hand.

2. Extensor carpi radialis longus

ATTACHMENTS
Proximal—lower third of the lateral supracondylar ridge on the humerus.
Distal—dorsal surface of the base of the 2nd metacarpal bone (Fig. 19.2).
ACTION: extension and abduction at the wrist joint.

Posterior Group

The muscles are attached to the common extensor origin which is situated on the anterior aspect of the lateral epicondyle of the humerus. These muscles are therefore weak flexors at the elbow joint as well as having actions at more distal joints. All are supplied by the posterior interosseous nerve (a branch of the radial nerve).

1. Extensor carpi radialis brevis

ATTACHMENTS
Proximal—common extensor origin.
Distal—dorsal aspect of the base of the 3rd metacarpal bone (Fig. 19.2).
ACTION: extension and abduction at the wrist joint.

2. Extensor digitorum

ATTACHMENTS
Proximal—common extensor origin.
Distal—just above the wrist the muscle divides into four tendons which pass through a compartment of the extensor retinaculum within a common synovial sheath. The tendons diverge on the back of the hand one passing to each finger. The tendons to the middle, ring and little fingers are interconnected by a variable number of bands. As each tendon passes a metacarpophalangeal joint it forms a triangular **dorsal expansion** which covers the proximal phalanx. The base of this expansion gives attachment to the corresponding interosseous and lumbrical muscles. At the apex of the triangle the long tendon reforms and then divides into three slips over the proximal interphalangeal joint. The middle slip is attached to the base of the middle phalanx, the outer two pass distally and reunite before being attached to the base of the terminal phalanx (Fig. 19.2).

ACTIONS:
(i) extension of the proximal phalanges of the fingers.
(ii) extension at the wrist joint.
(iii) extension of the middle and distal phalanges of the fingers when assisted by the interossei and lumbrical muscles.

3. Extensor digiti minimi—passes from the common extensor origin on the humerus to the dorsal expansion of the little finger. It aids extensor digitorum in its actions on the little finger.

4. Extensor carpi ulnaris

ATTACHMENTS
Proximal
(i) common extensor origin.
(ii) by an aponeurotic attachment to the posterior subcutaneous border of the ulna.
Distal—the tendon passes, in its own compartment of the extensor retinaculum and its own synovial sheath, to the ulnar side of the base of the 5th metacarpal bone (Fig. 19.2).
ACTION: extension and adduction at the wrist joint.
(Figs. 18.1, 19.1, 19.2.)

Deep group
All these muscles are supplied by the posterior interosseous nerve.

1. Supinator—this muscle hooks round the upper end of the radius and forms part of the floor of the cubital fossa. The posterior interosseous nerve passes between its humeral and ulnar heads of attachment.

ATTACHMENTS
Humero-ulnar—common extensor origin and supinator crest on the ulna.
Radial—the ulnar fibres first pass laterally, then anteriorly around the lateral aspect of the upper third of the radius, to be attached to its anterior surface as far medially as the anterior oblique line. The humeral fibres pass downwards to the same area (Fig. 18.1).
ACTION: supination of the forearm.

2. Abductor pollicis longus

ATTACHMENTS
Proximal—the posterior surface of the ulna and of the radius and the intervening interosseous membrane (Figs. 18.1, 19.1).
Distal—the long tendon passes downwards and laterally with the tendon of extensor pollicis brevis. They cross the two radial extensors of the carpus, the lower attachment of brachioradialis and the radial artery before passing, in separate synovial sheaths, under the most lateral compartment of the extensor retinaculum. They here form the anterior boundary of the anatomical snuff box. The tendon is attached to the radial side of the base of the 1st metacarpal bone.
ACTIONS: abduction and extension at the carpometacarpal joint of the thumb.

3. Extensor pollicis brevis

Proximal—the posterior surface of the radius and adjacent interosseous membrane, distal to abductor pollicis longus.

Distal—the tendon accompanies abductor pollicis longus and is attached on the dorsal surface of the base of the proximal phalanx of the thumb (Fig. 19.2).

ACTIONS: extends the proximal phalanx and the metacarpal bone of the thumb.

4. Extensor pollicis longus

ATTACHMENTS
Proximal—the posterior surface of the ulna and adjacent interosseous membrane distal to abductor pollicis longus (Fig. 18.1).

Distal—the tendon passes downwards under the extensor retinaculum, grooving the medial side of the dorsal tubercle of the radius. It forms the posterior boundary of the anatomical snuff box as it crosses laterally over the wrist joint, the two radial extensors of the carpus and the radial artery. It has its own synovial sheath and is attached to the dorsal aspect of the base of the distal phalanx of the thumb (Fig. 19.2).

ACTIONS: extends the distal phalanx, the proximal phalanx and the metacarpal bone of the thumb.

5. Extensor indicis

ATTACHMENTS
Proximal—the posterior surface of the ulna and adjacent interosseous membrane distal to extensor pollicis longus (Fig. 18.1).

Distal—the tendon passes under the extensor retinaculum in a common synovial sheath with extensor digitorum; it lies medial to the index tendon of that muscle. It gains attachment to the dorsal expansion of the index finger (Fig. 19.2).

ACTION: aids extensor digitorum in extending the index finger.

Anatomical Snuff Box

This is a depression formed on the lateral side of the wrist when the thumb is extended. Bounded anteriorly by the tendons of abductor pollicis longus and extensor pollicis brevis, and posteriorly by extensor pollicis longus, it overlies the radial styloid process, the wrist joint, the scaphoid and trapezium and the base of the 1st metacarpal bone. Crossing the floor are the two tendons of the radial extensors of the wrist and the radial artery. It is crossed superficially by the cephalic vein and branches of the radial nerve.

Extensor Retinaculum and Extensor Synovial Sheaths

The extensor retinaculum is a thickened band of deep fascia 2–3 cm in width. It passes obliquely over the dorsum of the wrist from the anterior border of the distal end of the radius to the medial side of the carpus. It is attached by fibrous septa to the bones of the forearm forming osseofascial tunnels for the passage of the tendons. (See **Fig. 19.3**). The synovial sheaths round the tendons begin at the upper border of the retinaculum. Those of abductor pollicis longus and extensor carpi radialis longus and brevis reach the distal attachments of the muscles while the others end at about the middle of the dorsum of the hand.

THE RADIAL ARTERY

The radial artery is a terminal branch of the brachial artery and is formed near the apex of the cubital fossa. It descends through the anterior compartment of the forearm, over the lateral aspect of the wrist and on to the dorsum of the hand. It then passes between the heads of the first dorsal interosseous muscle and ends in the palm.

RELATIONS: it leaves the cubital fossa and passes deep to the brachio-radialis which covers its upper part. It descends near the regions of attachment of the forearm muscles to the radius (see Fig. 18.1A). In the lower forearm it is subcutaneously situated on the lower end of the radius. The radial nerve lies on its lateral side in the middle of the forearm.

The artery crosses the lateral aspect of the wrist joint, passes deep to the three tendons bordering the anatomical snuff box and on to the dorsum of the hand. It passes between the two heads of the first dorsal interosseous muscle and then the two heads of adductor pollicis to form the deep palmar arterial arch.

BRANCHES
(i) muscular—to muscles on the radial side of the forearm.
(ii) articular—to elbow and wrist joints.
(iii) superficial palmar—when present, completes the superficial palmar arch (p. 206).
(iv) to the thumb—arises deep to adductor pollicis and divides to give palmar digital branches to each side of the thumb.
(v) to the index finger—arises deep to adductor pollicis and supplies the radial side of the index finger.
(vi) deep palmar arch (see page 206).

THE ULNAR ARTERY

It is a terminal branch of the brachial artery. It arises near the apex of the cubital fossa (at the level of the neck of the radius), descends through the anterior compartment of the forearm, crosses anterior to the wrist and ends in the hand as superficial and deep palmar branches.

RELATIONS: in the forearm, after leaving the cubital fossa, it lies on flexor digitorum profundus and deep to the muscles attached to the common flexor origin. In the lower forearm, under flexor carpi ulnaris, the ulnar nerve lies on its medial side. At the wrist the artery lies between the tendons of flexor carpi ulnaris and flexor digitorum profundus, crosses anterior to the flexor retinaculum and ends on the lateral side of the pisiform bone.

BRANCHES
(i) muscular—to muscles on the ulnar side of the forearm.
(ii) articular—to the elbow and wrist joints.
(iii) **common interosseous artery**—arises in the cubital fossa, passes to the upper border of the interosseous membrane and divides into an anterior and a smaller posterior interosseous artery. The **anterior** branch

descends on the interosseus membrane but pierces it above the wrist to end on the back of the carpus. It gives nutrient arteries to the radius and ulna, muscular branches and articular branches to the wrist. The **posterior interosseous artery** passes back above the interosseous membrane and then descends to supply the deep extensor muscles of the forearm.

(iv) superficial palmar branch—passes laterally over the hook of the hamate, and deep to the palmar aponeurosis it forms the superficial palmar arch (p. 206).

(v) deep palmar branch—passes deeply between flexor and abductor digiti minimi on to the opponens digiti minimi, where it joins the deep palmar arch (p. 206).

THE RADIAL NERVE (in the forearm and hand)

This lies on the antero-lateral aspect of the forearm overlapped by brachioradialis. Proximal to the wrist it turns posteriorly under the tendon of brachioradialis and ends on the dorsum of the hand as digital branches.

RELATIONS

In the forearm

Superficial—brachioradialis and its tendon.

Deep—lies on the deep forearm muscles.

Medial—radial artery throughout most of its length.

In the hand—it reaches the dorsum of the hand by passing between the radius and brachioradialis tendon, crosses superficial to the tendons bounding the anatomical snuff-box and divides into terminal digital branches.

BRANCHES

In the forearm

(i) articular—to elbow joint.

(ii) posterior interosseous nerve (see below).

In the hand—digital branches supplying the lateral side of the dorsum of the hand and the posterior aspects of the lateral $2\frac{1}{2}$ digits as far as the distal phalanx.

Posterior Interosseous Nerve

This arises under cover of brachioradialis at the level of the elbow joint, pierces supinator and in its substance curves laterally around the neck of the radius to gain the extensor compartment of the forearm. It reaches the interosseous membrane and ends on the back of the carpus.

RELATIONS

Superficial—muscles arising from common extensor origin and more distally, extensor pollicis longus and extensor indicis.

Deep—the deepest muscles of the forearm, the interosseous membrane, wrist joint and posterior aspect of carpus.

BRANCHES

(i) muscular—to all extensors except extensor carpi radialis longus.

(ii) articular—to elbow, wrist and intercarpal joints.

195

THE MEDIAN NERVE (in the forearm and hand)

The nerve lies in the anterior compartment of the forearm, crosses anterior to the wrist joint and ends in the palm as medial and lateral branches.

RELATIONS: in the cubital fossa the nerve is medial to the brachial and ulnar arteries but as it passes between the heads of pronator teres it crosses in front of the ulnar artery, separated from it by the deep head of the muscle. The nerve then lies between flexor digitorum superficialis and flexor digitorum profundus, adherent to the former. It emerges lateral to superficialis to lie between the tendons of flexor carpi radialis and superficialis and under palmaris longus at the wrist. It enters the hand by passing deep to the flexor retinaculum, lying on the synovial sheath of the long flexor tendons and ends just distal to the retinaculum.

BRANCHES

In the forearm

(i) muscular—to all superficial flexor muscles except flexor carpi ulnaris.

(ii) **anterior interosseous nerve**—arises after the median nerve has pierced pronator teres. It passes distally on the interosseous membrane between flexor pollicis longus and flexor digitorum profundus and then deep to pronator quadratus to end on the front of the carpus. It supplies flexor pollicis longus, the radial half of flexor digitorum profundus, pronator quadratus and gives articular branches to the distal radio-ulnar joint and the joints at the wrist.

(iii) palmar cutaneous nerve—supplies the radial side of the palm.

In the hand

(i) recurrent muscular branch to the abductor pollicis brevis, flexor pollicis brevis and opponens pollicis (lateral branch).

(ii) palmar digital nerves which pass to the palmar surface of the lateral $3\frac{1}{2}$ digits, and also supply the lateral two lumbrical muscles. The palmar digital nerves lie deep to the superficial palmar arch but cross the digital arteries to lie anterior to them in the fingers and thumb. These nerves innervate the finger tips and nail beds and also give articular branches to the metacarpophalangeal and interphalangeal joints.

As it lies in the fibro-osseous tunnel formed by the flexor retinaculum and bones of the carpus the median nerve is occasionally subject to compression. This can produce numbness and pain in the thumb and lateral fingers and weakness of the hand muscles it supplies.

THE ULNAR NERVE (in the forearm and hand)

From behind the medial epicondyle the nerve descends deep to the flexor carpi ulnaris on the medial side of the forearm. It enters the hand lateral to the pisiform bone and ends by dividing into superficial and deep branches.

RELATIONS: it lies medial to the elbow joint, enters the forearm between the two heads of the flexor carpi ulnaris and continues deep to this muscle on flexor digitorum profundus. At the wrist it lies superficially, lateral to the tendon of flexor carpi ulnaris, and passes anterior to the flexor retinaculum. The ulnar artery lies on its lateral side in the lower forearm and hand.

BRANCHES

In the forearm

(i) articular—to the elbow joint.

(ii) muscular—to flexor carpi ulnaris and the ulnar half of flexor digitorum profundus.

(iii) dorsal cutaneous branch—arises 5 cm above the wrist and passes on to the back of the hand where it divides into digital branches which supply the ulnar half of the dorsum of the hand and the medial $2\frac{1}{2}$ fingers as far as the distal phalanx.

(iv) palmar cutaneous branch—supplies the ulnar side of the palm.

In the hand

(i) superficial terminal branch—divides into palmar digital nerves supplying the palmar surface of the medial $1\frac{1}{2}$ fingers. The digital nerves also supply the finger tips, nail beds and the joints of the fingers.

(ii) deep terminal branch—accompanies the deep branch of the ulnar artery between abductor and flexor digiti minimi and then deep to the flexor tendons. It supplies the hypothenar muscles, all the interossei, 3rd and 4th lumbricals and adductor pollicis.

CHAPTER 19

THE WRIST AND HAND

SKELETON

Carpus (Figs. 19.1, 19.2)

The carpal bones are arranged as a proximal row of three bones, a distal row of four and an anteromedially situated pisiform. The proximal row is made up, from lateral to medial, of scaphoid, lunate and triquetral; collectively they form the distal articular surface of the wrist joint. The **scaphoid** has an anterior **tubercle** to which the flexor retinaculum is attached. The **lunate** has no muscular attachments. The **triquetral** gives attachment to both flexor and extensor retinacula.

The distal row has the ridged **trapezium** laterally, neighboured by the small **trapezoid**. The **capitate** and then the medially situated **hamate** complete the row. The trapezium gives attachment to the flexor retinaculum; in its groove lies the tendon of flexor carpi radialis. The large capitate has a rounded head proximally which articulates with the proximal carpals; its distal surface articulates with the 2nd, 3rd and 4th metacarpal bones. The hamate has an anterior hook which gives attachment to the flexor retinaculum. The **pisiform** is pea-shaped and articulates with the triquetral. It gives attachment to the flexor and extensor retinacula, and flexor carpi ulnaris. (It may be described as a sesamoid bone.)

The lateral surface of the scaphoid, the medial surface of the triquetral and the four bony points of attachment of the flexor retinaculum are all palpable. The scaphoid may be fractured in a fall on the outstretched hand, particularly in the younger age group. There is a high incidence of non-union of this fracture because the blood supply to the bone is often impaired by such an injury.

Metacarpal Bones (Figs. 19.1, 19.2)

These are five long bones. Their expanded bases articulate with the distal row of carpals and, in the case of the medial four, with each other. The slender bodies give attachment to the interossei, opponens and adductor pollicis muscles. The rounded heads articulate with the proximal phalanges. The first metacarpal is the shortest, strongest and most mobile. Its orientation differs from the others, being rotated almost through a right angle. Its base has a saddle-shaped surface for articulation with the trapezium.

Phalanges (Figs. 19.1 19.2)

These are long bones, two in the thumb, three in the medial four fingers. The bases of the proximal phalanges have cupped articular

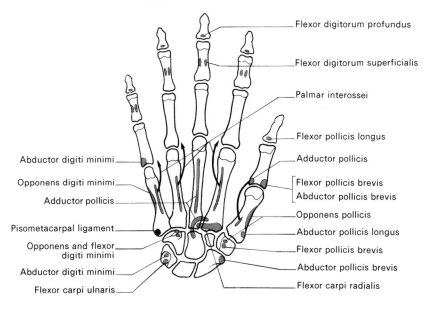

Flexor digitorum profundus

Flexor digitorum superficialis

Palmar interossei

Flexor pollicis longus

Adductor pollicis

Flexor pollicis brevis
Abductor pollicis brevis

Opponens pollicis

Abductor pollicis longus

Flexor pollicis brevis

Abductor pollicis brevis

Flexor carpi radialis

Abductor digiti minimi

Opponens digiti minimi

Adductor pollicis

Pisometacarpal ligament

Opponens and flexor digiti minimi

Abductor digiti minimi

Flexor carpi ulnaris

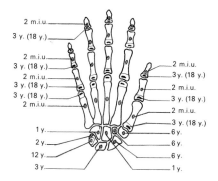

FIG. 19.1
The bones of the wrist and hand, palmar surface. The attachments
of the palmar interossei are indicated by the bold arrows. Inset:
ossification (m.i.u., months in utero; y., years).

surfaces while those of the middle and distal have grooved trochlear
surfaces. The bodies of the proximal and middle phalanges are flattened
on their palmar surfaces and rounded dorsally; their heads have paired
condyles. The distal phalanges taper distally, where they have anterior
tuberosities.

The phalanges give attachments to all the small muscles of the hand
except the opponens muscles, and to the long flexor and extensor tendons
of the thumb and fingers.

199

WRIST REGION (radiocarpal, intercarpal and carpometacarpal joints)

The Radiocarpal (Wrist) Joint

This is a synovial joint of the condyloid variety. The faceted lower end of the radius and fibrocartilaginous disc overlying the head of the

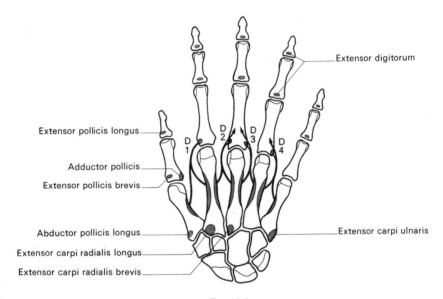

FIG. 19.2

The bones of the wrist and hand, dorsal surface. The attachments of the dorsal interossei are indicated by the bold arrows.

ulna articulate with the rounded surfaces of the proximal row of carpal bones, the scaphoid, lunate and triquetral.

LIGAMENTS

(*a*) Capsule: attached to the articular margins of the joint.

(*b*) Capsular thickenings: anterior and posterior ligaments and medial and lateral collateral ligaments.

INTRACAPSULAR STRUCTURES: the synovial membrane lines the non-articular surfaces of the joint. The triangular articular disc overlies the head of the ulna, its apex is attached to the base of the ulnar styloid and its base to the lower end of the radius. Only on the rare occasions when this disc is perforated does the wrist joint communicate with the distal radio-ulnar joint.

The Intercarpal Joints

These are synovial joints. The extensive composite joint between the proximal and distal rows of carpal bones is called the midcarpal joint; it is of the condyloid variety. Other intercarpal joints are of the plane variety. The bones are bound together by palmar, dorsal and interosseous

200

ligaments. The intercarpal joints greatly increase the mobility of the hand, the midcarpal having particular effect on the movements of flexion and abduction at the wrist.

The Carpometacarpal Joints of the Fingers
These are synovial joints of the plane variety. The 2nd and 3rd are less mobile than the 4th and 5th and they are all less mobile than the joint of the thumb.

FUNCTIONAL ASPECTS
Movement at the wrist—the movements possible are flexion, extension, abduction, adduction and circumduction. Flexion is greater than extension and adduction greater than abduction. Since these movements take place at the radiocarpal, midcarpal and carpometacarpal joints simultaneously they are considered here together. The full analysis of these movements is dependent on radiological examination and detailed measurements.

Flexion (mainly at the midcarpal joint)—flexor carpi radialis and flexor carpi ulnaris, assisted by the long digital flexors.

Extension (mainly at radiocarpal joint)—extensor carpi radialis longus and brevis and extensor carpi ulnaris, assisted by the long digital extensors.

Abduction (mainly at the midcarpal joint)—extensor carpi radialis longus and brevis and flexor carpi radialis.

Adduction (mainly at the radiocarpal joint)—extensor carpi ulnaris and flexor carpi ulnaris.

Stability of wrist—this is mainly dependent on its ligaments, assisted by the many tendons crossing it and very few dislocations occur.

The Carpometacarpal Joint of the Thumb
This is a synovial joint possessing considerable mobility by virtue of its saddle-shaped articulation and lax capsule. The thumb is medially rotated at the carpometacarpal joint and therefore the terms used to describe its movements do not have their usual meaning. Flexion and extension occur in a plane at right angles to the thumb nail and abduction and adduction in the same plane as the nail. Flexion, extension, abduction, adduction, circumduction and rotation are all possible. Because of the shapes of the bony surfaces flexion is always accompanied by medial rotation and extension by lateral rotation. The combined movement of flexion, medial rotation and adduction brings the thumb into contact with the other finger tips and is known as **opposition.**

Flexion and medial rotation—flexor pollicis longus and brevis and opponens pollicis.

Extension and lateral rotation—abductor pollicis longus and extensor pollicis longus and brevis.

Abduction—abductor pollicis longus and brevis.

Adduction—adductor pollicis.

Opposition—opponens pollicis.

BLOOD SUPPLY: branches from the radial and ulnar arteries.

NERVE SUPPLY: anterior and posterior interosseous nerves.

RELATIONS: a knowledge of the relations of the wrist joint assist greatly in understanding the anatomy of the forearm. The student should therefore study the diagram, Figure 19.3.

The Metacarpophalangeal Joints

These are synovial joints of the condyloid variety. The rounded heads of the metacarpals articulate with the cupped bases of the

FIG. 19.3
Diagram showing principal structures seen in a transverse section of the forearm just proximal to the wrist joint.

proximal phalanges. The palmar thickenings of the joint capsules are strong and those of the medial four digits are joined together to form the deep transverse ligaments of the palm.

The movements possible are flexion, extension, abduction, adduction and circumduction. Active thumb movements are limited to flexion and extension.

Flexion—long digital flexor muscles and flexor pollicis longus, assisted by the interossei, lumbricals, flexor pollicis brevis and flexor digiti minimi.

Extension—in the fingers, extensor digitorum, extensor indicis and extensor digiti minimi; in the thumb, extensor pollicis longus and brevis.

Abduction—abductor pollicis longus and brevis in the thumb and the dorsal interossei and abductor minimi in the fingers.

Adduction—palmar interossei and adductor pollicis.

The Interphalangeal Joints

These are synovial hinge joints. Their joint capsules are thickened by palmar and collateral ligaments and completed posteriorly by the extensor tendons.

Flexion at the joints is brought about by the long digital flexor muscles and extension mainly by the lumbrical and interosseous muscles.

The metacarpophalangeal and interphalangeal joints are supplied by adjacent nerves and vessels.

202

THE PALM

To facilitate grasping, the skin of the palmar surface of the hand is thick, ridged and has no hair or sebaceous glands. There are, however, many sweat glands. It has constant creases where it is bound to underlying fibrous tissue.

Palmar aponeurosis—the deep fascia of the palm consists of a central strong, triangular part, the palmar aponeurosis, and weaker portions covering the hypothenar and thenar muscles. The palmar aponeurosis is firmly connected to the palmar skin and overlies the superficial palmar arch and the long flexor tendons. Its apex is continuous with the flexor retinaculum and receives the attachment of palmaris longus. Distally its base divides into four digital slips which bifurcate around the long flexor tendons and gain attachment to the fibrous flexor digital sheaths and the deep transverse ligaments of the palm.

The **flexor retinaculum** is a thickening of deep fascia, 2–3 cm square. Medially it is attached to the pisiform and the hook of the hamate, and laterally to the tubercle of the scaphoid and the ridge of the trapezium, crossing the concavity of the carpus to form an osseofascial **carpal tunnel** for the long flexor tendons. Superficially it gives origin to the muscles of the thenar and hypothenar eminences and is crossed by the ulnar nerve and artery, palmar branches of the ulnar and median nerves and the tendon of palmaris longus. It covers the median nerve, the long flexor tendons, and the radial and ulnar bursae.

Fibrous flexor sheaths—the deep fascia of the fingers is modified to form fibrous flexor sheaths which are in continuity with the digital slips of the palmar aponeurosis. They form osseofascial tunnels by arching over the tendons and gaining attachment to the sides of the phalanges. Each extends to the base of the distal phalanx and is weaker and more flexible in front of the joints. A similar sheath is present in the thumb. The continuity of the flexor retinaculum, the palmar aponeurosis and the fibrous flexor sheaths prevents the long flexor tendons 'bowstringing' across the palm during contraction. This would interfere with the power and efficiency of the grip.

The Palmar Spaces

Two septa pass dorsally from the lateral and medial margins of the palmar aponeurosis to the shafts of the 1st and 5th metacarpal bones and divide the palm into three spaces:

(i) lateral, containing the thenar muscles.
(ii) medial, containing the hypothenar muscles.
(iii) central, containing the superficial palmar arch, median nerve, long flexor tendons and lumbricals, and the deep palmar arch.

Deep to the flexor tendons the central palmar space may be further divided by an immediate palmar septum which extends from the deep surface of the flexor tendon sheaths to the palmar surface of the 3rd metacarpal. Through these palmar spaces the web-spaces of the fingers communicate with a fascial plane deep to the long flexor tendons in the forearm. Because of this communication infection in the fingers may spread to the forearm.

MUSCLES OF THE THENAR AND HYPOTHENAR EMINENCES

They are attached proximally to the radial and ulnar sides respectively of the flexor retinaculum and its supports.

Thenar Muscles

These are all supplied by a recurrent branch of the median nerve.

1. Abductor pollicis brevis—is superficial to the other two muscles and therefore attached proximal to them.

ATTACHMENTS
Proximal—the tubercle of the scaphoid and the adjacent flexor retinaculum.
Distal—the radial side of the base of the proximal phalanx of the thumb.

ACTION: abduction of the thumb.

2. Opponens pollicis

ATTACHMENTS
Proximal—the ridge of the trapezium and adjacent flexor retinaculum.
Distal—the whole length of the radial margin of the 1st metacarpal bone.

ACTION: flexion, adduction and medial rotation of the 1st metacarpal bone. This combined movement brings the thumb into opposition with the tips of the flexed fingers.

3. Flexor pollicis brevis—is separated with difficulty from opponens pollicis.

ATTACHMENTS
Proximal—ridge of the trapezium and adjacent flexor retinaculum.
Distal—radial side of the base of the proximal phalanx of the thumb.

ACTION: flexion of the proximal phalanx and metacarpal bone of the thumb.

Hypothenar Muscles

These are, in most respects, weaker mirror-images of the thenar muscles. They are all supplied by the deep branch of the ulnar nerve.

1. Abductor digiti minimi

ATTACHMENTS
Proximal—the pisiform bone.
Distal—the ulnar side of the base of the proximal phalanx of the little finger.

ACTION: abduction of the little finger.

2. Opponens digiti minimi

ATTACHMENTS
Proximal—the hook of the hamate and adjacent flexor retinaculum.
Distal—the whole length of the ulnar margin of the 5th metacarpal bone.
ACTION: flexion and a little rotation of the 5th metacarpal. It thus deepens the hollow of the palm.

3. Flexor digiti minimi

ATTACHMENTS
Proximal—the hook of the hamate and the adjacent flexor retinaculum.
Distal—the ulnar side of the base of the proximal phalanx of the little finger.
ACTION: flexion of the proximal phalanx and metacarpal bone of the little finger.

DEEP MUSCLES OF THE HAND

1. Adductor pollicis

ATTACHMENTS
Lateral—into the ulnar side of the base of the proximal phalanx of the thumb and by a small tendon into the radial side of the base of the proximal phalanx. Both tendons contain sesamoid bones (Fig. 1.1).
Medial—by two heads:
(i) oblique head—the palmar surface of the bases of the 2nd and 3rd metacarpals and adjacent carpal bones.
(ii) transverse head—the palmar surface of the body of the 3rd metacarpal.
ACTIONS: adducts and assists in opposition of the thumb.

2. Interossei

The interossei lie deeply between the metacarpals; there are four dorsal and four palmar muscles. Each group is numbered one to four from the radial side.

ATTACHMENTS
Proximal—these muscles are attached to the shafts of the metacarpal bones, the palmar muscles by a single head to the palmar surfaces of the 1st, 2nd, 4th and 5th bones. The dorsal muscles are larger and more powerful and arise by two heads from adjacent sides of the metacarpal bones.
Distal—the muscles of both groups gain attachment to the base of the corresponding proximal phalanx and the extensor expansion.
ACTION: the attachments are such that the Palmar ADduct (PAD) and the Dorsal ABduct (DAB) the fingers about an axial line passing along the middle finger (see Figs. 19.1, 19.2). Both groups, acting with the

205

lumbricals, flex the proximal phalanx, and through their attachments to the expansion of the extensor tendons help to extend the middle and distal phalanges.

3. Lumbricals

These are four slender muscles which arise in the palm from the radial side of each of the four tendons of flexor digitorum profundus. Distally each is attached to the radial side of the dorsal expansion of the same finger.

ACTIONS: acting with the interossei they flex the proximal phalanx and help to extend the middle and distal phalanges.

NERVE SUPPLY: the adductor pollicis and the interossei are supplied by the deep branch of the ulnar nerve. The lateral two lumbricals are supplied by the median nerve and the medial two by the ulnar nerve.

ARTERIES

Superficial Palmar Arch

This is a continuation of the ulnar artery in the hand. It is completed laterally by a branch of the radial artery. The summit of its convexity is at the level of the web of the thumb. The arch is deep to the palmar aponeurosis and lies on the long flexor tendons and the digital nerves.

BRANCHES

Four palmar digital branches—three supply the clefts between, and then by bifurcating the adjacent sides of the fingers. The medial digital branch supplies the ulnar side of the little finger. All the branches communicate with the deep palmar arch.

Deep Palmar Arch

This is a continuation of the radial artery in the hand. It is completed medially by the deep branch of the ulnar artery. It lies 1 cm proximal to the superficial arch on the metacarpal bones and interossei muscles, and deep to the long flexor tendons. The deep branch of the ulnar nerve lies within its convexity.

BRANCHES

Three palmar metacarpal arteries (which anastomose with the palmar digital arteries), and perforating arteries to the dorsum of the hand.

The hand is an important sensory organ as well as a manipulator. Course grips (lifting a weight) and fine grips (writing) are enhanced by the very large areas of the brain which are concerned with the motor control of the hand in man.

CHAPTER 20

THE FASCIA, VEINS, LYMPH DRAINAGE AND NERVES

DEEP FASCIA

In the shoulder girdle region the deep fascia invests all the muscles and is drawn out as a tubular prolongation over the arm. The axillary floor is formed from this fascia. The fascia invests pectoralis minor and extends above to the clavicle (forming the clavipectoral fascia). In the arm the deep fascia invests the muscles and is condensed medially and laterally to form the medial and lateral intermuscular septa. Inferiorly these are attached to the respective supracondylar ridges of the humerus.

In the elbow region the deep fascia firmly ensheathes the muscles and provides an attachment for many of their fibres. It is reinforced by the bicipital aponeurosis. The deep fascia of the forearm is attached to the ulna posteriorly along its subcutaneous border. At the wrist it forms the flexor and extensor retinacula, and in the hand the palmar aponeurosis and fibrous flexor sheaths. The fascial spaces of the hand are described on page 203.

VENOUS DRAINAGE

The veins of the upper limb can be divided into superficial and deep groups. Numerous valves are found in most veins.

Superficial group—the digital veins drain into a **dorsal venous arch** on the back of the hand. From this arise the cephalic vein laterally and the basilic vein medially. The **cephalic vein** ascends on the radial side of the forearm, crosses anterior to the cubital fossa and lies lateral to biceps in the upper arm. It turns medially in the deltopectoral groove, pierces and clavipectoral fascia and joins the axillary vein. The **basilic vein** ascends on the ulnar side of the forearm, crosses anterior to the cubital fossa and lies medial to biceps. In the middle of the upper arm it pierces the deep fascia to join the brachial veins. The **median cubital vein,** usually chosen for venepuncture, joins the cephalic and basilic veins and runs across the cubital fossa, superficial to the bicipital aponeurosis. For intravenous infusions the veins of the forearm and dorsum of the hand are most frequently chosen. Stability of the needle and infusion tubing is more easily obtained when the needle puncture site is not too close to the wrist or elbow joint.

Deep group—accompanying the arteries, the radial and ulnar veins join to form the brachial veins which continue as the axillary vein at the lower border of teres major (see page 179).

207

Fig. 20.1

Diagrammatic lay-out of the cutaneous innervation of the upper limb.

Lateral supraclavicular nerve

Upper lateral cutaneous nerve of arm

Posterior cutaneous nerve of arm

Medial cutaneous nerve of arm

Posterior cutaneous nerve of forearm

Lateral cutaneous nerve of forearm (posterior branch)

Radial nerve

Medial cutaneous nerve of forearm (posterior branch)

Ulnar nerve (dorsal branch)

Lateral and intermediate supraclavicular nerves

Intercostobrachial nerve

Medial cutaneous nerve of arm

Medial cutaneous nerve of forearm (anterior branch)

Palmar branch of ulnar nerve

Digital branches of ulnar nerve

Upper lateral cutaneous nerve of arm

Lower lateral cutaneous nerve of arm

Lateral cutaneous nerve of forearm (anterior branch)

Palmar branch of median nerve

Digital branches of median nerve

C3
C4
C5
T2
T1
C6
C8
C7

LYMPH DRAINAGE

In the upper limb there are two groups of lymph vessels—superficial and deep.

The **superficial group** drains the skin. Medially, the vessels accompany the basilic vein and drain (some via the supratrochlear node at the elbow), into the axillary nodes. The lateral group accompany the cephalic vein and drain into infraclavicular nodes and thence to the axillary nodes.

The **deep group,** draining bones and muscles, run with the deep veins and drain into the lateral group of axillary nodes.

The Axillary Nodes

These are arranged in five groups

(i) **pectoral**—deep to pectoralis major; drains the lateral and anterior chest wall and mammary gland.

(ii) **lateral**—on the lateral axillary wall; receives the efferents of the upper limb.

(iii) **subscapular**—on the posterior axillary wall; drains the back of the trunk.

(iv) **central**—a scattered group around the axillary vessels.

(v) **apical**—at the apex of the axilla; they are continuous with the inferior deep cervical nodes and drain the preceding groups. Blockage of the central or apical groups may lead to swelling of the limb—lymphoedema.

The **infraclavicular group,** around the termination of the cephalic vein, drains to the apical nodes. The efferent vessels from the apical nodes form the subclavian lymph trunk which, on the left side, joins the thoracic duct and on the right, opens into the internal jugular or subclavian vein.

NERVE SUPPLY

The **cutaneous nerve supply** is summarized in Figure 20.1

NERVE INJURIES

Injury to the nerves of the upper limb at different sites produces characteristic disabilities.

Brachial Plexus Injuries

These produce signs of a segmental nature.

(*a*) Upper trunk damage may result from a birth injury. Deltoid and teres minor (axillary nerve), supraspinatus and infraspinatus (suprascapular nerve), biceps and brachialis (musculocutaneous nerve), are paralysed. The limb therefore hangs limply, medially rotated and fully pronated in the 'tip'-position. There is sensory diminution on the radial side of the arm and the forearm.

(*b*) Lower trunk injury may be caused by pressure from a cervical rib and produces paralysis of the small muscles of the hand and the long digital flexors. This results in the characteristic 'clawed hand'. There is sensory diminution on the ulnar side of the arm and forearm.

Peripheral Nerve Injuries

(a) Radial nerve

(i) in the forearm—produces a small area of diminished sensitivity over the radial side of the dorsum of the hand. There is no paralysis.

(ii) in the radial groove—produces paralysis of the long digital and carpal extensors (posterior interosseous nerve) causing wrist-drop. Extension of the middle and distal phalanges by the interossei and lumbricals, the extension of the forearm by the triceps are retained. (Brachioradialis may escape injury.) There is diminished sensitivity over the radial side of the dorsum of the hand.

(iii) in the axilla—paralysis of triceps and brachioradialis are added to the effects produced by a radial groove injury.

(b) Median nerve

(i) at the wrist—produces paralysis of the thenar and 1st and 2nd lumbrical muscles and loss of sensation over the front of the thumb and index fingers. No opposition of the thumb is possible and the index and middle fingers are flexed and partly 'clawed'.

(ii) at the elbow—paralysis of the forearm flexors is added to the effects produced by injury at the wrist. No pronation of the forearm is possible.

(c) Ulnar nerve

(i) at the wrist—produces paralysis of the interossei, adductor pollicis, the hypothenar muscles and the 3rd and 4th lumbricals. This results in a partly 'clawed hand' in which the long digital flexors, unopposed by the lumbricals and the interossei, flex the middle and distal phalanges especially of the little and ring fingers. The consequent pull exerted on the long digital extensor tendons produces hyperextension of the metacarpophalangeal joints. Adduction of the thumb is lost. Sensation is diminished over the ulnar side of the palm.

(ii) at the elbow—paralysis of flexor carpi ulnaris and weakening of flexor digitorum profundus and loss of sensation on the ulnar side of the dorsum of the hand are added to the effects of the previous injury.

(d) Axillary nerve—may be injured in downward dislocation at the shoulder joint and fractures of the surgical neck of the humerus, which produces deltoid paralysis and sensory loss over the humeral attachment of this muscle. Abduction of the humerus is greatly impaired.

LOWER LIMB

CHAPTER 21

THE HIP AND THIGH

The lower limb is similar in its basic structure to the upper limb but is modified in accordance with its functions of supporting and propelling the body. During development the lower limb rotates medially on its long axis so that its ventral (flexor) surface comes to lie posteriorly and the sole of the foot to face downwards.

The pelvic girdle, unlike the pectoral girdle, is firmly attached to the vertebral column and the body weight is transmitted through it to the lower limb whose bones, muscles and ligaments are correspondingly stronger than those of the upper limb. The centre of gravity of the body in the anatomical position is in the pelvis just in front of the second piece of the sacrum. When standing up straight the line of weight (passing through the centre of gravity) passes down behind the hip joint and in front of the knee and ankle joints. The weight is distributed between the heel and the balls of the toes. When standing upright, most of the body weight is carried by bones and ligaments, little muscle activity in the lower limbs being necessary to maintain stability. This is very different situation from that in the upper limb where weight has to be carried by muscles.

The pelvic girdle is described on page 135.

The blood supply of the limb comes in the adult from the external iliac artery, though in the early embryo the axial vessel is a branch of the inferior gluteal artery which arises from the internal iliac artery.

The nerves are derived from the lumbosacral plexus. Due to rotation of the limb the plan may not be so clear as in the upper limb. The plexus is formed by the anterior (ventral) rami of L1 to S5 spinal nerves. The three largest branches are the obturator nerve from the anterior divisions of L2, 3 and 4 supplying muscles on the inside of the thigh, the femoral nerve from the posterior divisions of L2, 3 and 4 supplying muscles in front of the thigh, and the sciatic nerve from L4, 5, S1, 2 and 3 supplying all other muscles. The anterior divisions of L4–S3 enter the tibial part of the sciatic nerve and the posterior divisions of L4–S2 enter the common peroneal part.

Hip Bone (Fig. 13.1 and page 131)

The gluteal surface of the **ala of the ilium** is smooth and faces laterally. It is bounded above by the iliac crest, in front by the anterior border of the ilium, behind by the posterior border and below by the greater sciatic notch and the acetabulum. It is crossed by three curved **gluteal lines** which ascend from the greater sciatic notch, the inferior to the anterior border, and the middle and posterior to the iliac crest. They divide the alar surface into four areas; two large central areas for the gluteus medius (posteriorly) and minimus, a small posterior area for gluteus maximus and the sacrotuberous ligament, and a small antero-inferior area for rectus femoris and the iliofemoral ligament. The greater sciatic notch is separated from the lesser notch by the **ischial spine.** Below the lesser sciatic notch is the **ischial tuberosity.** The sciatic notches are turned into foramina by the sacrotuberous and sacrospinous ligaments. The anterior border of the ilium has prominent **superior** and **inferior iliac spines** and is then continued into the **superior ramus of the pubis.** The acetabular fossa and the obturator foramen are readily identified. The **inferior ramus of the pubis** and the **ramus of the ischium** (together forming the **ischiopubic ramus**) join the body of the pubis (with the symphyseal surface) and the ischial tuberosity. Ilium, ischium and pubis contribute to the **acetabular fossa.** The **obturator foramen** is bounded by pubis and ischium. The obturator membrane is attached to the edges of the foramen except anteriorly where the obturator vessels and nerve pass in the obturator groove.

Femur (Fig. 21.1)
This is a long bone having an upper end, a body and a lower end.

The **upper end** consists of a head, a neck and greater and lesser trochanters. The **head** articulates with the acetabular fossa of the hip bone, it forms two-thirds of a sphere and near its centre there is a small pit (fovea) for the ligament of the head of the femur. The narrow elongated **neck** passes upwards, forwards and medially forming an angle of about 125° with the body. Its anterior surface and the larger part of its posterior surface lie within the capsule of the joint. The **greater trochanter** is a projection from the upper lateral part of the bone. To it are attached gluteus medius and minimus laterally, and the obturator internus and externus medially, the latter into a small pit. Piriformis is attached to the upper border. The gluteus minimus is attached along the anterior border of the trochanter and the medius to much of the lateral surface. The **lessor trochanter** lies at the junction of the body and the neck. It is joined to the greater trochanter anteriorly by a thin roughened ridge, the **intertrochanteric line,** and posteriorly by a thick rounded ridge, the **intertrochanteric crest.** A slight elevation on the middle of the crest is known as the quadrate tubercle and gives attachment to the quadratus femoris. The psoas is attached to the lesser trochanter and the iliacus and pectineus to the **body** below it.

The **body** inclines medially at an angle of about 20° to the vertical. Posteriorly there is a longitudinal ridge, the **linea aspera,** passing along the middle third of the bone. To the linea aspera are attached the adductor muscles, the short head of biceps and the vastus medialis and lateralis. A roughened area for the attachment of gluteus maximus (the **gluteal tuberosity**) lies between the quadrate tubercle and the ridge. In the lower third of the shaft, the edges of the ridge are continued as the medial and lateral supracondylar lines and limit the smooth popliteal surface of the bone. The medial supracondylar line ends at the **adductor tubercle** just above the medial condyle; the line and tubercle give attachment to the adductor magnus. The smooth medial, lateral and anterior surfaces of the body are covered by the vasti muscles.

The **lower end** is expanded to form two large masses, the medial and lateral **condyles** for articulation with the tibial condyles and the patella. The femoral condyles are separated posteriorly by the inter-condylar notch and united anterosuperiorly by the concave articular

Fig. 21.1

The femur; A, anterior and B, posterior surfaces. Inset: ossification (m.i.u., months in utero; y., years).

facet for the patella. The tibial articular surface of each condyle covers its inferior and posterior aspects and is continuous anteriorly with the articular area for the patella. The tibial surface is markedly convex anteroposteriorly and slightly convex from side to side. The medial tibial surface is longer than the lateral. On the outer nonarticular surface of each condyle there is a small elevation, the **epicondyle;** these give attachments to the medial and lateral ligaments of the knee joint. A shallow groove below the lateral epicondyle gives attachment to the popliteus tendon.

Parts of the condyles, epicondyles and greater trochanter are sub-

214

cutaneous and palpable. Fractures of the neck of the femur are common in the elderly and frequently complicated by nonunion due to a critical decrease in the blood supply of the femoral head. Fractures of the body of the femur are accompanied by a considerable amount of bleeding into the thigh due to associated injuries to the surrounding muscles and blood vessels.

THE HIP JOINT

This is a synovial joint of the ball and socket variety between the acetabulum of the hip bone and the head of the femur. The articular

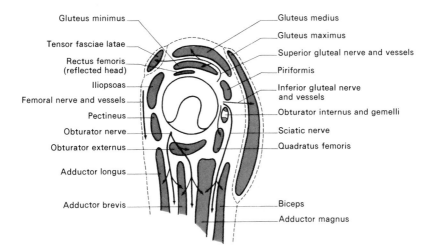

Gluteus minimus

Tensor fasciae latae

Rectus femoris
(reflected head)

Iliopsoas

Femoral nerve and vessels

Pectineus

Obturator nerve

Obturator externus

Adductor longus

Adductor brevis

Gluteus medius

Gluteus maximus

Superior gluteal nerve and vessels

Piriformis

Inferior gluteal nerve
and vessels

Obturator internus and gemelli

Sciatic nerve

Quadratus femoris

Biceps

Adductor magnus

Fig. 21.2
Diagram showing the main relations of the hip joint.

surface of the acetabulum is ∩-shaped, being deficient inferiorly at the acetabular notch. The acetabulum is cupped and deepened by the **acetabular labrum,** a rim of fibrocartilage attached to its borders, and bridging the acetabular notch is the transverse acetabular ligament.

Ligaments

(a) Capsule: strong and dense, attached proximally to the acetabular labrum and the edge of the notch. Distally it is attached to the femur along the intertrochanteric line and to the neck 1 cm above the inter-trochanteric crest. Superiorly it crosses the neck medial to the tendinous insertions of the obturator muscles. Some of the capsular fibres turn back along the neck and are known as **retinacula;** they carry blood vessels towards the head.

(b) Capsular thickenings:

(i) **iliofemoral ligament**—is a powerful λ-shaped band attached above to the anterior inferior iliac spine and bifurcating inferiorly to gain attachment to each end of the intertrochanteric line.

(ii) **pubofemoral ligament**—passes from the iliopubic eminence to the lower part of the capsule and undersurface of the neck.

(iii) **ischiofemoral ligament**—passes upwards from the acetabular margin to the upper end of the intertrochanteric line. Note that all three ligaments spiral in such a way as to limit extension at the joint.

(*c*) Accessory ligaments:

(i) ligament of the head of the femur—passes from the pit to the articular notch; it is lax and may contain some small vessels of special importance in the child.

(ii) acetabular labrum and transverse acetabular ligament.

INTRACAPSULAR STRUCTURES: the **synovial membrane** lines the non-articular surfaces of the joint and ensheaths the ligament of the head of the femur. The cavity of the joint communicates with the psoas bursa between the iliofemoral and pubofemoral ligaments. A pad of fat is found in the acetabular notch.

FUNCTIONAL ASPECTS

Movement: the hip joint is capable of flexion, extension, abduction, adduction, circumduction, and medial and lateral rotation. In the anatomical position, the line of weight passes behind the axis of the joint and so encourages extension at the joint.

Flexion—iliopsoas, assisted by rectus femoris, sartorius and pectineus. Movement is limited when the knee is flexed by the thigh coming into contact with the anterior abdominal wall, and when the knee is extended, by tension in the hamstrings. If the line of weight passes in front of the hip joint (as when leaning forwards slightly), then gravity is a major factor in flexion.

Extension—gluteus maximus, assisted by gravity, the hamstrings and the tensor fasciae latae. The movement is limited by the three capsular thickenings.

Abduction—gluteus medius and minimus. This movement occurs in every step of walking when the pelvis is tilted on the femur of the grounded leg, thus allowing the foot of the swinging leg to clear the ground as it swings forwards.

Adduction—adductor muscles of the thigh, gracilis and gravity.

Rotation occurs around an axis joining the centre of the head of the femur to the intercondylar notch of the femur.

Medial rotation—iliopsoas, assisted by the anterior fibres of gluteus medius and minimus.

Lateral rotation—gluteus maximus, assisted by the short muscles applied to the back of the joint, piriformis and quadratus femoris.

When the femur is fixed, as when the foot is on the ground, the same groups of muscles act on the pelvis assisting in flexion and extension of the trunk and in walking (p. 259).

Stability: in spite of its great mobility, it is a very stable joint. This is because of the deep cup of the acetabulum clasping the femoral head, the strong capsule and its thickenings, particularly the iliofemoral ligament and the large number of closely applied short articular muscles. Dislocation does occur as a congenital abnormality; however, it is rare in the adult. When it occurs there is usually an associated fracture of the acetabular rim, and the closely related sciatic nerve may also be damaged. The joint may be affected in older people by degenerative joint disease (osteo-arthritis).

BLOOD SUPPLY: rich anastomoses formed from the two gluteal and two circumflex femoral arteries. The ligament of the head of the femur carries a small branch of the obturator artery. The retinacula on the neck carry vessels to the head.

NERVE SUPPLY: branches of the femoral, obturator and sciatic nerves.

RELATIONS (Fig. 21.2)

Anterior—iliopsoas and pectineus separate the joint from the femoral vessels and nerve.

Posterior—piriformis, obturator internus and quadratus femoris separate the joint from the sciatic nerve and gluteus maximus.

Superior—gluteus minimus and the oblique head of the rectus femoris.

Inferior—obturator externus.

BURSAE: the psoas bursa separates the iliopsoas tendon from the iliac fossa and superior pubic ramus. It may communicate with the cavity of the hip joint between the iliofemoral and pubofemoral ligaments.

THE GLUTEAL REGION

This fleshy region behind the pelvis is composed mainly of the three gluteal muscles which overlie the muscles, nerves and vessels leaving the inside of the pelvis and passing to the lower limb. The gluteal muscles are important extensors and abductors at the hip joint.

1. Gluteus maximus—is the most superficial of the group. It is a large flat quadrilateral mass forming the prominence of the buttock.

ATTACHMENTS

Pelvic—from an extensive area including the gluteal surface of the ilium behind the posterior gluteal line, and the posterior surfaces of the sacrum, coccyx and sacrotuberous ligament.

Lower—the fibres pass downward and laterally into the iliotibial tract (see below and page 254) and the gluteal tuberosity of the femur.

ACTIONS: it is a powerful lateral rotator and extensor at the hip joint and, acting through the iliotibial tract, it extends and stabilises the knee joint.

NERVE SUPPLY: inferior gluteal nerve (Fig. 21.2).

RELATIONS: the deep relations of this muscle should be noted. It lies behind the hip joint and overlies gluteus medius, piriformis obturator internus, quadratus femoris, the ischial attachments of the hamstrings, and the structures passing through the greater and lesser sciatic foramina.

2. Tensor fasciae latae—is attached above to the anterior quarter of the outer lip of the iliac crest and below to the iliotibial tract. Through its action on the iliotibial tract it extends and stabilises the knee joint. It is supplied by the superior gluteal nerve.

217

The **iliotibial tract** is a broad thickening of the fascia lata passing from the outer lip of the iliac crest to the anterolateral aspect of the upper end of the tibia. The tract receives the attachments of the tensor fasciae latae and gluteus maximus and these muscles, acting through it, extend and stabilise the knee joint.

3. Gluteus medius

ATTACHMENTS
Pelvic—gluteal surface of the ilium between the middle and posterior gluteal lines.
Femoral—an oblique ridge on the lateral surface of the greater trochanter.

4. Gluteus minimus—is the deepest of the gluteal muscles and is covered completely by gluteus medius.

ATTACHMENTS
Pelvic—gluteal surface of the ilium between the middle and inferior gluteal lines.
Femoral—anterior border of the greater trochanter.

ACTIONS AND NERVE SUPPLY: gluteus medius and minimus are powerful abductors and weak medial rotators at the hip joint. They are supplied by the superior gluteal nerve.

5. Piriformis—arises inside the pelvis from the anterior surface of the sacrum (p. 138) and passes laterally out of the greater sciatic foramen to be attached to the upper border of the greater trochanter of the femur. It is supplied by branches of the sacral plexus.

6. Quadratus femoris—this small muscle is attached medially to the outer edge of the ischial tuberosity and laterally to a small tubercle on the intertrochanteric crest. It helps to stabilise the hip joint and is a weak lateral rotator of the femur. It is supplied by a branch of the sacral plexus.

7. Obturator externus—this short articular muscle lies close to the hip joint, above adductor brevis. It passes from the outer surface of the obturator membrane and the adjacent bone, and its tendon winds below and behind the hip joint to reach a pit on the medial surface of the greater trochanter.

ACTION: it supports and stabilises the hip joint and is a weak lateral rotator of the femur.

NERVE SUPPLY: obturator nerve.

VESSELS AND NERVES OF THE GLUTEAL REGION
These are branches of the internal iliac artery and the lumbosacral plexus respectively. They pass from the pelvis to the gluteal region above or below the piriformis in the greater sciatic foramen.
Above piriformis: the superior gluteal artery (p. 160) and nerve (p. 163)

218

pass upwards and laterally between gluteus medius and minimus to supply these muscles and tensor fasciae latae. The artery takes part in an anastomosis around the hip joint.

Below piriformis

(i) sciatic nerve—emerges lateral to the ischial spine (p. 220).

(ii) inferior gluteal nerve (p. 163)—after a short course, enters the substance of gluteus maximus. The inferior gluteal artery (p. 160) ramifies in the lower part of the buttock and takes part in an anastomosis around the hip joint.

(iii) internal pudendal vessels and the pudendal nerve—descend over the ischial spine and sacrospinous ligament and pass through the lesser sciatic foramen into the perineum (p. 157).

(iv) nerve to obturator internus (p. 163)—descends across the ischial spine.

(v) nerve to quadratus femoris—emerges deep to the sciatic nerve and lies on the ischium and the hip joint.

(vi) posterior femoral cutaneous nerve emerges superficial to the sciatic nerve and descends in the midline of the thigh, beneath the deep fascia. It supplies the skin of the buttock, the perineum, the posterior aspect of the thigh and the popliteal region.

THE BACK OF THE THIGH

This is often known as the hamstring compartment of the thigh. It contains the three hamstring muscles semimembranosus, semitendinosus and biceps femoris) and the sciatic nerve which supplies them. They are extensors at the hip joint and flexors at the knee joint.

1. Semimembranosus—derives its name from its thin superior membranous tendon. It is the most medial muscle of the group.

ATTACHMENTS

Upper—a facet on the ischial tuberosity.

Lower—a groove on the posteromedial aspect of the tibial condyle and by tendinous expansions upwards on to the lateral femoral condyle (oblique popliteal ligament) and downwards on to the soleal line of the tibia (forming the popliteal fascia over the popliteus muscle).

2. Semitendinosus—derives its name from its very long inferior tendon. It lies lateral to semimembranosus.

ATTACHMENTS

Upper—a facet on the ischial tuberosity.

Lower—upper part of the medial surface of the tibia behind the attachment of the gracilis tendon.

3. Biceps—has ischial and femoral heads.

ATTACHMENTS

Upper

(i) long head from a facet on the ischial tuberosity.

(ii) short head—the lateral lip of the linea aspera and the upper part of the lateral supracondylar line of the femur. The upper fibres are often continuous with those of gluteus maximus.

Lower—the two heads join to form a single tendon attached to the front of the apex of the fibula.

ACTIONS: these three muscles act across both the hip and the knee joints. They are powerful flexors at the knee and extensors at the hip. When the knee is flexed, the muscles can produce a small amount of medial and lateral rotation at the knee joint.

NERVE SUPPLY: they are supplied by the sciatic nerve.

THE SCIATIC NERVE (Fig. 21.2)

This is the largest nerve in the body. It is derived from the lumbosacral plexus (L4, 5; S1, 2, 3) and is formed in the pelvis on the anterior surface of piriformis (p. 163). It descends through the greater sciatic foramen, enters the gluteal region and continues its descent through the posterior compartment of the thigh to end by dividing into tibial and common peroneal nerves, usually just above the popliteal fossa.

RELATIONS: the nerve enters the gluteal region below piriformis. Anteriorly the nerve lies on the ischium, obturator internus, quadratus femoris and adductor magnus from above downwards, and is covered posteriorly by gluteus maximus and the hamstring muscles.

BRANCHES
(i) articular—to the hip and knee joints.
(ii) muscular—to the hamstrings and the ischial part of adductor magnus.
(iii) tibial and common peroneal nerves (pages 241 and 242).

There are no large vessels in the back of the thigh so that its structures are supplied by a deeply placed longitudinal anastomotic chain which receives blood from the inferior gluteal and the medial femoral circumflex arteries above, the four perforating branches of the profunda femoris artery, and the popliteal artery below.

THE FRONT AND MEDIAL SIDE OF THE THIGH

The oblique line of the sartorius passing downwards and medially separates the adductor muscles of the hip superomedially from the extensor muscles of the knee inferolaterally.

The Adductor Group of Muscles

These are arranged in three vertical layers; anteriorly pectineus and adductor longus lie in the same plane in front of adductor brevis which separates them from the posteriorly placed adductor magnus (Fig. 21.2). Gracilis lies superficial to these on the medial side of the thigh.

1. Pectineus

ATTACHMENTS
Pelvic—pectineal line and upper surface of the pubic bone.
Femoral—along a line joining the lesser trochanter to the linea aspera.

2. Adductor longus

ATTACHMENTS
Pelvic—anterior surface of the body of the pubis.
Femoral—linea aspera.

3. Adductor brevis

ATTACHMENTS
Pelvic—outer surface of the body and the inferior ramus of the pubis.
Femoral—upper half of the linea aspera.

4. Adductor magnus—is a large triangular muscle of composite origin, part derived from the adductor muscles and part from the hamstrings.

ATTACHMENTS
Pelvic—in a continuous line on the outer surface of the ischiopubic ramus and the ischial tuberosity.

Femoral—linea aspera, the medial supracondylar line and by a tendon into the adductor tubercle on the upper aspect of the medial femoral condyle.

5. Gracilis—this thin strap-like muscle passes from the inferior border of the ischiopubic ramus to the upper part of the medial surface of the tibia between the attachments of sartorius and semitendinosus.

ACTIONS: these muscles adduct the femur. In addition pectineus and adductor longus medially rotate the femur, adductor magnus extends it and pectineus also helps flex the femur.

NERVE SUPPLY: pectineus is supplied by the femoral nerve, the hamstring (ischial) part of adductor magnus by the sciatic nerve. The other muscles in this group are supplied by the obturator nerve.

The Obturator Nerve

This is a branch of the upper part of the lumbosacral plexus (L2, 3, 4). Its course in the pelvis is described on page 127. It enters the thigh through the obturator groove where it divides into anterior and posterior divisions.

Anterior division: this descends between pectineus and adductor longus anteriorly and adductor brevis posteriorly to end in the subsartorial plexus on the medial side of the thigh.

BRANCHES
(i) muscular—to gracilis, adductor brevis and adductor longus.
(ii) articular—to the knee joint.
(iii) cutaneous—to the medial side of the thigh.

Posterior division: this pierces obturator externus and descends between adductor brevis anteriorly and adductor magnus posteriorly. It later descends with the femoral and then popliteal arteries to the knee joint.

Branches
(i) muscular—to obturator externus and adductor magnus.
(ii) articular—to the knee joint.

The obturator artery, a branch of the internal iliac, accompanies the nerve through the obturator groove and, on emerging, divides into two branches which encircle the obturator membrane. It gives branches to the hip joint and the adductor muscles.

The Anterior Group of Thigh Muscles

1. Sartorius—is a long strap-like muscle which, in its upper part, forms the lateral boundary of the femoral triangle (p. 223).

Attachments
Pelvic—anterior superior iliac spine.
Tibial—upper part of the medial surface of the tibia in front of the attachments of gracilis.

Actions: it is a weak flexor at both the hip and knee joints and a lateral rotator of the femur at the hip joint.

Nerve supply: femoral nerve.

2. Quadriceps—this extensive muscle mass forms the bulk of the anterior region of thigh. It is divided into four separate muscles.

(*a*) **Rectus femoris**—this muscle lies superficially along the middle of the thigh.

Attachments
Superior—by two heads.
(i) straight head—from the anterior inferior iliac spine.
(ii) reflected head—from the ilium just above the acetabulum.
Inferior—by a tendon into the upper border of the patella.

(*b*) **Vastus lateralis**—lies deep to rectus femoris and also covers the lateral side of the femoral body.

Attachments
Superior—by an aponeurosis from the lateral side of the great trochanter and the gluteal tuberosity, and the lateral lip of the linea aspera.
Inferior—its tendon passes to the lateral side of the patella and blends with fibres of rectus femoris.

(*c*) **Vastus medialis**—lies deep to rectus femoris and also covers the medial side of the femoral body.

Attachments
Superior—by an aponeurosis from the spiral line joining the lesser trochanter to the linea aspera, the medial lip of the linea aspera and the medial supracondylar line of the femur.
Inferior—the muscle passes to the medial side of the patella and blends with fibres of rectus femoris. The lower fibres are almost horizontal.

(*d*) **Vastus intermedius**—this muscle covers the front of the femur deep to rectus femoris.

222

ATTACHMENTS

Superior—the anterior and lateral surfaces of the upper part of the femoral body.

Inferior—to the upper border of the patella deep to the previous three muscles.

The four portions of the quadriceps are thus attached to the upper border and sides of the patella, forming a single musculotendinous expansion. From the apex of the patella a strong tendon, the **patellar ligament,** descends to gain attachment to the tibial tubercle. On each side of the patellar ligament the capsule of the joint is formed largely by downward fibrous expansions of the quadriceps (the **retinacula**) through which the muscles gain attachment to the tibial condyles.

ACTIONS: the whole muscle is a powerful extensor at the knee joint. Rectus femoris also flexes the hip joint. The lower fibres of vastus medialis prevent the patella moving too far laterally when the lower leg is being extended.

NERVE SUPPLY: each part is supplied by branches of the femoral nerve.

THE FEMORAL TRIANGLE

This area on the front of the upper part of the thigh is bounded by the inguinal ligament superiorly, sartorius laterally and the medial border of adductor longus medially. Its floor is formed by the adductor longus, pectineus and iliopsoas from medial to lateral and its roof is the fascia lata of the thigh. There is an oval deficiency, the **saphenous opening,** in the fascia lata about 3 cm below and lateral to the pubic tubercle. This opening has a well-defined lateral margin and is filled by the cribriform fascia, a condensation of the superficial fascia. The opening is traversed by the great saphenous vein and some small cutaneous vessels. In the triangle are the femoral vessels contained within the femoral sheath, the femoral nerve and their branches.

The **femoral sheath** is a tube-like downwards continuation of the extraperitoneal fascia into the thigh. It is formed anteriorly from the transversalis fascia and posteriorly from the iliac fascia. The femoral vessels evaginate the fascial envelope of the abdomen as they leave the cavity. Inferiorly the sheath fuses with the adventitiae of the vessels about 3 cm below the inguinal ligament. Septa divide it into three compartments containing the femoral artery laterally, the femoral vein centrally, and fatty connective tissue and lymph nodes medially. The latter compartment is known as the **femoral canal** and is limited inferiorly by the blending of its medial wall with the adventitia over the laterally placed femoral vein. Superiorly the canal communicates with the extraperitoneal abdominal fascial space by an opening, the **femoral ring.** The ring is bounded anteriorly by the inguinal ligament, posteriorly by pectineus on the pubis, medially by the pectineal part of the inguinal ligament, and laterally by the femoral vein. These relations should be noted as herniation of abdominal contents into the femoral canal may occur and the femoral ring then provides a constriction around the hernial sac. During exercise, the femoral vein enlarges and is accommodated by the canal medially.

THE FEMORAL ARTERY (Fig. 21.3)

This is a continuation of the external iliac artery. It enters the thigh below the inguinal ligament, descends vertically and slightly backwards through the femoral triangle and the subsartorial canal. It ends

FIG. 21.3
Femoral arteries filled with radiopaque material which has been injected into the abdominal aorta (see also Figs. 15.1 and 22.6).

1. Femoral artery
2. Profunda femoris artery

by piercing adductor magnus about 10 cm above the knee joint. It then becomes the popliteal artery.

RELATIONS: the artery begins deep to the inguinal ligament, halfway between the anterior superior iliac spine and the symphysis pubis (the midinguinal point). In the femoral triangle it is covered only by fascia and descends on the psoas tendon (which separates it from the hip joint), pectineus and adductor longus from above downwards. The artery leaves the triangle at its apex to enter the **subsartorial canal** in company with its vein, the saphenous nerve and the nerve to vastus medialis. The canal is a narrow intermuscular passage deep to the middle third of sartorius. It is bounded posteriorly by adductor longus above and adductor magnus below and anterolaterally by vastus medialis. The femoral artery leaves the lower end of the canal by passing through an opening in adductor magnus just above the adductor tubercle.

Above, the femoral vein is medial to the artery, in most of the subsartorial canal it is posterior, and in the popliteal fossa, the vein retains this relationship to the artery.

BRANCHES

(i) small cutaneous branches—pierce the cribriform fascia and are distributed to the skin of the inguinal region and lower abdomen.

(ii) **profunda femoris artery**—arises in common with the medial and lateral femoral circumflex arteries in the femoral triangle and passes backwards and downwards between the adductor muscles. Just above the knee, it pierces the magnus muscle to supply the lower part of the back of the thigh. Its three main branches also pierce adductor magnus to supply the posterior part of the thigh. They are called perforating arteries.

(iii) **medial femoral circumflex artery**—passes posteriorly between pectineus and psoas to reach the upper border of adductor magnus where it divides into muscular and articular branches.

(iv) **lateral femoral circumflex artery**—passes laterally between the branches of the femoral nerve, then deep to sartorius and rectus femoris and gives off muscular and articular branches.

(v) articular branches—to the knee joint.

The femoral artery is one of the commonest sites of peripheral arterial disease, particularly at the point where the artery passes under the tendon of the adductor magnus. The blood supply to the calf may be markedly reduced and exercise pain (intermittent claudication) and ischaemic changes of the lower leg may occur.

THE FEMORAL VEIN

This begins at the opening in the lower end of adductor magnus as the continuation of the popliteal vein. It accompanies the femoral artery and ends at the level of the inguinal ligament by becoming the external iliac vein. As it ascends it lies behind the artery and ends on its medial side.

TRIBUTARIES

(i) profunda femoris vein.

(ii) great saphenous vein (p. 254)—pierces the cribriform fascia to enter the femoral vein about 3 cm below the inguinal ligament.

(iii) and (iv) medial and lateral femoral circumflex veins.

(v) small subcutaneous veins—draining the lower abdominal wall, enter the femoral vein at the termination of the saphenous vein.

THE FEMORAL NERVE (Fig. 21.2)

This is a branch of the upper part of the lumbosacral plexus (L2, 3, 4) (p. 127). It descends in the pelvis in the groove between psoas and iliacus, and enters the thigh deep to the inguinal ligament. Here it lies on iliacus lateral to the femoral artery. After a short course, it divides into a number of terminal branches which are separated into superficial and deep groups.

BRANCHES
(i) anterior femoral cutaneous nerve.
(ii) medial femoral cutaneous nerve.
(iii) muscular branches—to pectineus, sartorius, rectus femoris, vastus lateralis, vastus intermedius and vastus medialis. This last branch lies on the lateral side of the femoral artery through the femoral triangle and the subsartorial canal, supplying the muscle and the knee joint.
(iv) **saphenous nerve**—is the largest branch of the femoral nerve. It accompanies the femoral artery through the femoral triangle and subsartorial canal and just above the knee emerges from under sartorius to descend subcutaneously over the medial side of the knee joint. In the leg it accompanies the great saphenous vein and passes in front of the medial malleolus into the foot. It supplies the skin over the medial border of the leg and foot as far as the ball of the big toe.

CHAPTER 22

THE KNEE, LEG AND DORSUM OF THE FOOT

Patella (Fig. 22.1)
This is a sesamoid bone, triangular in shape with its apex inferiorly and
having anterior and posterior surfaces. The roughened anterior surface
is subcutaneous. The posterior has a medial and a larger lateral facet for
articulation with the articular surface on the front of the femoral condyles.

Lateral articular facet

Patellar ligament

Quadriceps femoris

Retinaculum

5 y.

A   B

Fig. 22.1
The patella; A, posterior and B, anterior surfaces. Inset: ossification (y., years).

The quadriceps is attached to the upper border, and the patellar ligament
to the apex. Some muscle fibres from vastus medialis are attached to its
medial border and tendinous expansions from the vastus medialis and
lateralis, known as retinacula, pass to the medial and lateral borders of
the patella and to the tibia.

Tibia (Fig. 22.2)
This is a long bone possessing an upper end, a body and a lower end.
The **upper end** is expanded to form two masses, the medial and
lateral **condyles.** It is flattened superiorly and this surface has oval
medial and lateral facets articulating with the femoral condyles. A central
anteroposterior ridge across the upper surface, the intercondylar area,
separates the articular surfaces and gives attachment to the ends of the
cartilaginous menisci and to the anterior and posterior cruciate ligaments.
A prominent **tibial tuberosity** is situated anteriorly below the superior
surface and receives the attachment of the patellar ligament. Semimembranosus is attached to a wide groove along the side of the medial
condyle. The postero-inferior surface of the lateral condyle bears an oval
facet for the head of the fibula.
The **body** is triangular in cross section having medial, lateral and
posterior surfaces. The medial surface gives attachment superiorly to the
tibial collateral ligament of the knee joint and to sartorius, gracilis and
semitendinosus. Below these muscles the medial surface and the sharp

227

anterior border lie subcutaneously. The lateral surface is hollowed for tibialis anterior. The posterior surface is bounded by the medial and interosseous (lateral) borders. It is crossed by an oblique ridge, the **soleal line,** passing downwards and medially, and below this is a prominent nutrient foramen. The ridge gives attachment to soleus and the surface above it to popliteus. The area below the ridge is divided by a vertical line; tibialis posterior is attached laterally and flexor digitorum longus medially. The interosseous membrane is attached to the lateral border.

The expanded **lower end** projects downwards on the medial side to form the **medial malleolus.** The inferior surface of the bone and the lateral surface of the malleolus articulate with the talus. The anterior surface is smooth and is crossed by the tendons of the muscles in the anterior compartment of the leg. The posterior surface is grooved medially by the tibialis posterior tendon. The lateral surface bears a roughened area for the interosseous ligament of the inferior tibiofibular joint.

The tibial condyles, the anterior border, the medial surface and the medial malleolus are palpable. Because of the subcutaneous position of the tibia, fractures are usually compound (p. 5) and prone to infection.

Fibula (Fig. 22.2)

This is a long bone possessing an upper end (head), a body and a lower end.

The expanded **head** bears an oblique anterosuperior oval articular facet for the tibia and, posterolateral to this, an upward projection, the **apex.** The fibular collateral ligament of the knee joint is attached to the top of the apex and the biceps tendon at its base. The head is attached to the body by a narrow **neck.**

The **body** is long and slender and has a slight spiral twist. The narrow anterior surface gives attachment to the extensor muscles; the posterior to the flexor muscles (its upper third above an oblique ridge gives attachment to soleus); and the lateral surface to the peroneal muscles.

The expanded **lower end** is flattened from side to side. It forms the **lateral malleolus** which extends to a lower level than the medial malleolus and articulates on its medial side by a triangular facet with the talus. There is a triangular roughening above the facet, for the interosseous ligament of the inferior tibiofibular joint. A marked **malleolar fossa,** situated on the posteromedial aspect behind the articular facet, gives attachment to the posterior talofibular ligament and forms a useful marker when orientating the bone.

The head and the lateral malleolus of the fibula are palpable. The common peroneal nerve may be crushed as it passes round the neck. The lower end may be fractured above the interosseous ligament in injuries to the ankle joint.

THE KNEE JOINT (Fig. 22.3, 22.4)

This is a synovial joint of a modified hinge variety between the lower end of the femur, the patella and the upper end of the tibia.

The femoral articular area is formed of three continuous surfaces, a

Fɪɢ. 22.2

The tibia and fibula; A, anterior and B, posterior surfaces. Inset: ossification
(m.i.u., months in utero; y., years).

middle anterosuperior concave surface for the patella, and medial and
lateral condylar surfaces for the tibia. These condylar surfaces are
markedly convex anteroposteriorly and mediolaterally. The posterior
surface of the patella has a medial and a larger lateral facet for articulation
with the sides of the femoral concavity. The facets are always in contact
with the femur, their upper parts in flexion and their lower in extension.
The upper surface of each tibial condyle is oval and slightly concave.

Lɪɢᴀᴍᴇɴᴛs

(*a*) Capsule: on the femur this is attached near the articular margins
anteriorly, medially and laterally. Posteriorly it is attached above the
intercondylar notch. It is attached to the patellar margins and to the
periphery of the upper end of the tibia except anteriorly where it descends
to include the tibial tuberosity and posterolaterally where it is pierced by
popliteus tendon. The capsule is variable in thickness.

(*b*) Capsular thickenings: **coronary ligaments**—are the two parts
of the capsule binding down the margins of the medial and lateral
menisci to the outer margins of the tibial condyles.

229

FIG. 22.3

Radiograph of right knee, anteroposterior view. Note that soft tissue shadows are seen and that overlapping of bones leads to very white (dense) area, indicating the position of the patella.

1. Femur
2. Patella
3. Medial femoral condyle

4. Lateral femoral condyle
5. Tibia
6. Fibula

(c) Accessory ligaments:

(i) **patellar ligament**—passes from the apex of the patella to the tibial tuberosity.

(ii) **patellar retinacula**—are tendinous expansions of the vasti muscles passing to the sides of the patella and beyond to the tibial condyles.

(iii) **tibial collateral ligament**—is a broad flat band about 10 cm long passing from the medial epicondyle of the femur to the upper medial surface of the tibial shaft. It is attached to the capsule.

(iv) **fibular collateral ligament**—is a rounded cord passing from the lateral epicondyle of the femur to the apex of the fibula and is separate from the capsule.

(v) **oblique popliteal ligament**—this extension of the semimembranosus tendon passes upwards from the medial tibial condyle across the posterior surface of the capsule.

(vi) **anterior** and **posterior cruciate ligaments**—are strong ligamentous bands found inside the capsule. The anterior ligament passes upwards, backwards and laterally from the front of the intercondylar area to the medial surface of the lateral femoral condyle. The posterior ligament passes forwards, upwards and medially from the back of the intercondylar area to the lateral surface of the medial femoral condyle.

INTRACAPSULAR STRUCTURES

(*a*) The **synovial membrane** develops from the linings of the three separate joint cavities that originally form the knee joint: the anterior between the patella and the femur, and the two posterior each between a femoral and a tibial condyle. The cavity of the patellofemoral joint later communicates on each side with the tibiofemoral joints but the inferior portion of synovial membrane, connecting the inferior border of the patella to the femoral intercondylar notch, persists as the **infrapatellar fold.** Remnants of the partitions originally separating the anterior and two posterior cavities persist as two fringes, the **alar folds,** which pass horizontally away from each side of the infrapatellar fold. The anterior and posterior cruciate ligaments develop in the fibrous septum between the tibiofemoral joints and a communication between these two joint cavities is formed across the septum in front of the ligaments.

The adult shape of the synovial membrane (Fig. 22.5) may be likened to a vertically running sleeve of synovia passing between the femur and tibia, horseshoe-shaped in transverse section with its concavity facing posteriorly. Superiorly the sleeve is attached to the periphery of the articular area of the femur. Inferiorly the attachment includes the two tibial articular facets and the front of the intercondylar area.

This arrangement is modified: (i) an anterior central portion of the sleeve is replaced by the articular surface of the patella. (ii) The membrane below the patella is invaginated to gain attachment to the front of the intercondylar notch of the femur. The fold so formed is named the infrapatellar fold. (iii) The membrane above the patella is extended upwards between the quadriceps and the femur as the suprapatellar bursa. (iv) The two menisci are attached by their outer margins to the capsule, thus breaking the continuity of the synovial membrane on each side. (v) The joint cavity communicates with the suprapatellar, popliteal and gastrocnemius bursae.

(*b*) The **menisci** are two crescentic pieces of fibrocartilage with thickened outer margins. Each lies on a tibial condyle with its ends, the anterior and posterior horns, attached to the intercondylar area and its outer margin attached to the capsule. The medial cartilage is larger

Fig. 22.4
Radiograph of knee—lateral view. Note the soft tissue shadows.

1. Femur
2. Patella
3. Medial and lateral femoral condyle

4. Tibia
5. Fibula

and semicircular; its central attachments embrace those of the lateral. The lateral cartilage is smaller and forms three-fifths of a circle. It is separated from the capsule posteriorly by the tendon of the popliteus which is partly attached to the cartilage, thus increasing its mobility.

(c) The anterior and posterior cruciate ligaments, the tendon of the popliteus, and a fat pad within the infrapatellar fold between the synovial membrane and the capsule are also present.

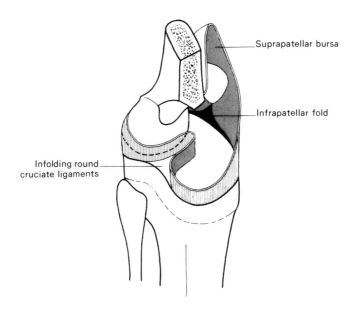

Suprapatellar bursa

Infrapatellar fold

Infolding round cruciate ligaments

Fig. 22.5
Diagram showing some of the relations of the synovial membrane of the left knee joint.

FUNCTIONAL ASPECTS

Movement: the knee joint is capable of flexion, extension and a small amount of rotation.

Flexion—hamstrings, aided by gastrocnemius. The movement is limited by the apposition of the surfaces of the calf and thigh.

Extension—quadriceps and iliotibial tract muscles. The femoral condyles roll on the tibial condyles and also glide backwards. The capsular and cruciate ligaments become taut when the leg is nearly straight and so prevent further backward gliding of the lateral femoral condyle. Further extension (hyperextension) is therefore accompanied by backward movement only of the medial femoral condyle (around the axis of the taut anterior cruciate ligament). This movement is medial rotation of the femur on the tibia. The direction of fibres of the collateral and oblique popliteal ligaments is such that it limits this rotation and when the limit is reached the knee is said to be in the 'locked' and stable position.

233

The joint is 'unlocked' by popliteus which rotates the femur laterally on the tibia. This muscle is also attached to the lateral meniscus and pulls this structure backwards, preventing it being crushed between the lateral femoral and tibial condyles.

A small amount of lateral and medial rotation may be produced by the hamstrings when the knee is flexed at a right angle.

Stability: the bony surfaces contribute little to the stability of the joint, this being dependent on strong ligaments and powerful muscles. As it is predominantly a hinge joint, the inextensible ligaments are placed medially and laterally. Anteriorly the joint is stabilised by the quadriceps and posteriorly by hamstrings and gastrocnemius muscles. The anterior and posterior cruciate ligaments limit anteroposterior gliding and distraction of the bones.

Quadriceps tends to pull the patella laterally as well as superiorly because of the obliquity of the femur. This lateral displacement is minimised by the anterior prominence of the lateral femoral condyle and those fibres of the vastus medialis which are attached to the medial side of the patella. When standing on the extended knee the line of weight passes in front of the axis of rolling of the joint. The posterior ligaments take the strain and when these are stretched, reflex contraction of the hamstrings limits hyperextension.

Tears of the menisci occur when the slightly flexed weight-bearing knee is subjected to severe lateral strain as in sporting injuries. Removal of the damaged meniscus may be required to restore normal function to the knee joint.

BLOOD SUPPLY: from the anastomosis around the knee joint which receives a number of branches from the popliteal, femoral and anterior tibial arteries.

NERVE SUPPLY: branches from the tibial, common peroneal, obturator and femoral nerves.

RELATIONS: the joint is mainly subcutaneous, being separated from the skin anteriorly by quadriceps, the patella and the patellar ligament, laterally by the biceps tendon, and medially by semimembranosus and semitendinosus. Posteriorly it is related to popliteus, the popliteal vessels, the tibial and common peroneal nerves, and the muscular boundaries of the popliteal fossa.

BURSAE: there are many bursae around the knee joint, the more important being:

Anterior
(i) suprapatellar, deep to quadriceps.
(ii) prepatellar.
(iii) superficial and deep infrapatellar, related to the patellar ligament.

Posterior
(i) popliteus, deep to the muscle.
(ii) gastrocnemius, deep to the medial head of this muscle.
(iii) semimembranosus, between this muscle and the medial head of gastrocnemius.

A bursa may be present between each collateral ligament and the capsule. The suprapatellar, popliteus and gastrocnemius bursae communicate with the joint cavity and the semimembranosus may communicate with the gastrocnemius bursa and thus with the joint cavity.

THE TIBIOFIBULAR JOINTS

(i) **superior tibiofibular joint**—this is a synovial joint of the plane variety between the inferior surface of the lateral tibial condyle and the oval facet on the head of the fibula. The capsule is thickened anteriorly and posteriorly, and the synovial membrane lining the nonarticular surface of the joint may be continuous with that of the knee joint.

(ii) **inferior tibiofibular joint**—is a fibrous joint between the adjacent inferior surfaces of the two bones. The surfaces are united by a short strong band, the interosseous tibiofibular ligament, and reinforced by anterior and posterior inferior tibiofibular ligaments.

(iii) **interosseous membrane**—is a fibrous membrane uniting the interosseous borders of the two bones. It separates and gives attachment to the deep flexor and extensor muscles of the leg.

Little movement occurs between the tibia and the fibula.

THE POPLITEAL FOSSA

This is a diamond-shaped fossa behind the knee joint. It is bounded superomedially by semitendinosus and semimembranosus, superolaterally by biceps, and inferiorly by the medial and lateral heads of gastrocnemius. It is roofed in by thickened fascia lata. Its floor is formed from above downwards by the popliteal surface of the femur, the posterior surface of the capsule of the knee joint and the fascia covering the popliteus muscle.

The fossa contains the popliteal vessels and branches (p. 241), the tibial and common peroneal nerves and branches (p. 241), much fat and a few lymph nodes.

THE LEG AND DORSUM OF THE FOOT

The muscles of the leg are divided into anterior, lateral and posterior groups by the tibia, interosseous membrane, and anterior and posterior intermuscular septa which pass inwards from the thick investing deep fascia to the fibula. The anterior intermuscular septum passes to the anterior border of the fibula and separates the anterior (dorsiflexor) compartment from the lateral (evertor) compartment. The posterior septum passes to the posterior border of the fibula and separates the lateral from the posterior (plantar flexor) compartment.

The Anterior (Dorsiflexor) Group of Muscles

1. Tibialis anterior

ATTACHMENTS
Upper—upper two-thirds of the lateral surface of the tibia and adjoining interosseous membrane.

235

Lower—the fibres converge on to a central tendon which descends in front of the ankle joint deep to the superior and inferior extensor retinacula to end on the medial surface of the medial cuneiform and of the base of the 1st metatarsal bone.

ACTIONS: dorsiflexion and inversion of the foot.

2. Extensor hallucis longus

ATTACHMENTS
Upper—middle two-quarters of the anterior surface of the fibula and adjoining interosseous membrane.

Lower—its long tendon passes under the extensor retinacula, in front of the ankle joint and crosses the dorsum of the foot to reach the base of the distal phalanx of the great toe.

ACTIONS: dorsiflexion of the great toe and it assists in dorsiflexion of the foot.

3. Extensor digitorum longus

ATTACHMENTS
Upper—upper two-thirds of the anterior surface of the fibula lateral to the attachment of extensor hallucis longus, and from the adjacent intermuscular septum.

Lower—above the ankle the muscle divides into four tendons which pass under the extensor retinacula. Diverging on the dorsum of the foot a tendon passes to each of the lateral four toes and is attached in a similar manner to extensor digitorum in the hand, i.e. there is a dorsal expansion which is attached to the dorsum of the middle and terminal phalanges.

ACTIONS: dorsiflexion of the toes and it assists in dorsiflexion of the foot.

4. Peroneus tertius—a thin sheet of muscle attached to the lower third of the anterior surface of the fibula. Its tendon descends under the extensor retinacula to the 5th metatarsal. It is a weak dorsiflexor and evertor of the foot.

5. Extensor digitorum brevis—this is the only short muscle on the dorsum of the foot.

ATTACHMENTS
Proximal—anterior part of the upper surface of the calcaneum.

Distal—the muscle divides into four small tendons which pass obliquely forwards to the medial four toes. The 1st tendon is attached to the base of the proximal phalanx of the great toe, the remainder join the lateral side of the extensor tendons passing to the 2nd, 3rd, and 4th toes.

ACTIONS: dorsiflexion of the medial four toes.

NERVE SUPPLY: the deep peroneal nerve supplies all the muscles of this group.

The **extensor retinacula**—lie across the extensor tendons in the lower part of the leg and in front of the ankle joint:

(i) superior extensor retinaculum—is a thickening of deep fascia stretching between the anterior borders of the tibia and fibula about 3 cm above the ankle joint. It covers, from medial to lateral, the tendons of tibialis anterior and extensor hallucis longus, the anterior tibial vessels and the deep peroneal nerve, and the tendons of extensor digitorum longus and peroneus tertius.

(ii) inferior extensor retinaculum—is a thicker bifurcate structure extending medially from the anterior part of the upper surface of the calcaneus over the front of the ankle joint and dividing into two limbs. The upper limb is attached to the medial malleolus and the lower curves around the medial border of the foot to blend with the plantar aponeurosis.

The **synovial sheaths** of the long extensor tendons lie deep to the inferior retinaculum, only that of tibialis anterior extends proximally under the superior retinaculum. Extensor hallucis longus has its own sheath and there is a common sheath for extensor digitorum longus and peroneus tertius.

The Lateral (Evertor) Group of Muscles

1. Peroneus longus

ATTACHMENTS
Upper—upper two-thirds of the lateral surface of the fibula.
Lower—its tendon descends behind the lateral malleolus, separated from it by the tendon of peroneus brevis and crosses the lateral surface of the calcaneus below the peroneal tubercle to reach the cuboid. It passes medially in the groove on the under surface of the cuboid and runs obliquely across the sole of the foot deep to the long plantar ligament (p. 249) to gain attachment to the lateral side of the base of 1st metatarsal and the adjacent area of the medial cuneiform bone.

2. Peroneus brevis

ATTACHMENTS
Upper—lower two-thirds of the lateral surface of the fibula.
Lower—in its descent, the tendon lies anterior to that of peroneus longus. It passes behind the lateral malleolus, across the lateral surface of the calcaneus above the peroneal tubercle, to the tuberosity on the base of the 5th metatarsal.

ACTIONS: both these muscles evert and possibly plantarflex the foot. Peroneus longus also helps to maintain the lateral longitudinal arch of the foot.

NERVE SUPPLY: superficial peroneal nerve supplies both muscles.

The tendons of both these muscles are bound down to the lateral malleolus and the side of the calcaneus by two condensations of deep fascia, the **superior and inferior peroneal retinacula.** The tendons are enclosed in a common synovial sheath which is prolonged over each tendon to its distal attachment.

The Posterior (Plantar Flexor) Group of Muscles

A. Superficial muscles—these comprise gastrocnemius, soleus and plantaris.

1. Gastrocnemius—is the most superficial muscle in the calf.

ATTACHMENTS

Upper—by medial and lateral heads to the back of the corresponding femoral condyles.

Lower—the two fleshy bellies form the inferior boundaries of the popliteal fossa and unite to form a tendon which joins that of soleus in the lower calf to form the conjoined **tendo calcaneus** which is attached to the middle of the posterior surface of the calcaneus. A bursa and a pad of fat separate the tendon from the upper part of the calcaneal surface.

2. Soleus—lies deep to gastrocnemius.

ATTACHMENTS

Upper—in a continuous line from the upper part of the posterior surface and head of the fibula, a tendinous arch over the posterior tibial vessels and tibial nerve, and the soleal line on the tibia.

Lower—the tendon unites with that of gastrocnemius to form the tendo calcaneus.

3. Plantaris—this vestigial muscle is attached above to the lower end of the lateral supracondylar line and by a long tendon below to the medial side of the tendo calcaneus.

ACTIONS: both gastrocnemius and soleus are powerful plantar flexors of the foot and as such are important in both posture and locomotion. In gastrocnemius and soleus, and between them is a plexus of veins. Contraction of the muscles pumps the blood upwards.

NERVE SUPPLY: branches from the tibial nerve supply all the calf muscles.

B. Deep muscles—these comprise popliteus above the soleal attachment and the flexor digitorum longus, tibialis posterior and flexor hallucis longus from medial to lateral below soleus.

1. Popliteus—this triangular muscle lies deep in the lower part of the popliteal fossa.

ATTACHMENTS

Tibial—posterior surface of the tibia above the soleal line.

Femoral—the muscle converges on to a tendon which pierces the capsule of the knee joint to gain attachment to the pit below the lateral epicondyle. It also sends a slip to the lateral meniscus. The popliteal bursa lies between the muscle and the upper part of the tibia.

ACTIONS

(i) lateral rotation of the femur on the tibia.

(ii) retraction of the lateral meniscus.

238

These two actions occur simultaneously in 'unlocking' the extended knee joint (p. 234). The backward movement of the lateral femoral condyle is preceded by the retraction of the cartilage which thus avoids injury.

NERVE SUPPLY: a branch from the tibial nerve.

2. Flexor digitorum longus

ATTACHMENTS
Upper—medial side of the posterior surface of the tibia below the soleal line.

Lower—the tendon crosses over tibialis posterior and may groove the lower end of the tibia lateral to the tendon of tibialis posterior, before passing deep to the flexor retinaculum to enter the sole of the foot where it divides into four slips. These slips pass to the terminal phalanges of the lateral four toes (their attachment being similar to that of the tendons of flexor digitorum profundus in the hand). In the foot, the main tendon gives attachment to flexor accessorius and the four slips to the four lumbricals.

ACTIONS: plantar flexion of the interphalangeal and metatarso-phalangeal joints. It is also a weak plantar flexor of the foot.

3. Tibialis posterior

ATTACHMENTS
Upper—posterior surface of the interosseous membrane and the adjoining surfaces of the tibia and fibula.

Lower—the tendon inclines medially deep to flexor digitorum longus, grooves the back of the medial malleolus, passes under the flexor retinaculum and then lies on the deltoid ligament. In the sole it is attached mainly to the tuberosity of the navicular but also to all other tarsal bones except the talus.

ACTIONS: inversion of the foot and helps to support the medial longitudinal arch.

4. Flexor hallucis longus

ATTACHMENTS
Upper—lower two-thirds of the posterior surface of the fibula.

Lower—the muscle becomes tendinous behind the lower end of the tibia where it lies lateral to the tendons of flexor digitorum longus and tibialis posterior. It grooves the back of the tibia and the talus and the under surface of the sustentaculum tali, and enters the sole. Here it is crossed over by the tendon of flexor digitorum longus and runs forwards between the two heads of the flexor hallucis brevis. It passes in the fibrous flexor sheath of the great toe to be attached to the plantar surface of the base of the distal phalanx.

ACTIONS: powerful plantar flexor of the great toe. It also helps in plantar flexion of the foot and is of importance in walking (p. 259) and in the maintenance of the medial longitudinal arch.

Fig. 22.6
Popliteal arteries filled with radiopaque material which has been injected into the abdominal aorta (see also Figs. 15.1 and 21.3).

1. Popliteal artery
2. Anterior tibial artery

3. Posterior tibial artery
4. Peroneal artery

NERVE SUPPLY: these three deep muscles are supplied by the tibial nerve.

The **flexor retinaculum**—is a thickened band of deep fascia passing from the medial malleolus to the medial tubercle of the calcaneus. It overlies from medial to lateral, the tendons of tibialis posterior and flexor digitorum longus, posterior tibial vessels, tibial nerve and the flexor hallucis longus tendon. Each tendon is enclosed in a separate synovial sheath, those of flexor hallucis longus and flexor digitorum longus passing into the sole of the foot.

240

VESSELS AND NERVES OF THE LEG

THE POPLITEAL ARTERY (Fig. 22.6)

This is a continuation of the femoral artery. It descends from the opening in the adductor magnus to the lower border of popliteus where it divides into anterior and posterior tibial arteries.

RELATIONS: it descends on the floor of the popliteal fossa (p. 235), deep to its vein which separates it throughout its course from the tibial nerve.

BRANCHES

(i) muscular branches.

(ii) articular branches—to the knee joint.

(iii) **anterior tibial artery**—passes forwards above the interosseous membrane and accompanies the deep peroneal nerve in its descent through the extensor compartment of the leg. Below the ankle joint it continues as the **dorsalis pedis artery** which passes forwards on the dorsum of the foot to reach the space between the 1st and 2nd metatarsal bones. It enters the sole of the foot between these bones and anastomoses with the lateral plantar artery (p. 252).

(iv) **posterior tibial artery**—is also a terminal branch of the popliteal artery. It begins at the lower border of popliteus and descends through the flexor compartment of the leg with the tibial nerve. It ends behind the medial malleolus by dividing into medial and lateral plantar arteries.

(v) **peroneal artery**—descends between the fibula and flexor hallucis longus. It gives off muscular branches and an articular branch to the ankle joint.

THE POPLITEAL VEIN

This is formed by the union of the anterior and posterior tibial veins. Throughout its course it lies between the popliteal artery and tibial nerve. Its tributaries correspond mainly to the branches of the artery but the **small saphenous vein** enters it after piercing the fascial roof of the popliteal fossa. It receives blood which has been pumped up by contraction of the calf muscles.

THE TIBIAL NERVE

This is a terminal branch of the sciatic nerve. It is formed just above the popliteal fossa and descends almost vertically through the fossa to pass deep to soleus. It descends through the flexor compartment of the leg to reach the back of the medial malleolus where it ends by dividing into medial and lateral plantar nerves.

RELATIONS

In the popliteal fossa: in most of its course it lies subcutaneously in the popliteal fat superficial to the popliteal vessels, the vein separating it from the artery.

In the calf: it descends deep to soleus lying between flexor digitorum longus medially and flexor hallucis longus laterally. It lies on tibialis posterior superiorly and the capsule of the ankle joint inferiorly and ends deep to the flexor retinaculum.

BRANCHES

(i) **sural nerve**—this cutaneous branch descends on the posterior surface of gastrocnemius to unite with a branch of the common peroneal nerve halfway down the leg. It continues in company with the small saphenous vein behind the lateral malleolus and along the lateral side of the foot. It supplies the skin over the back of the leg, the ankle joint and the lateral border of the foot and 5th toe.

(ii) articular branches—to the knee and superior tibiofibular joints.

(iii) muscular branches—to the medial and lateral heads of gastrocnemius, plantaris, popliteus, soleus and the more deeply placed tibialis posterior, flexor hallucis longus and flexor digitorum longus.

(iv) medial and lateral plantar nerves (p. 253).

THE COMMON PERONEAL NERVE

This also is a terminal branch of the sciatic nerve formed just above the popliteal fossa. It descends along the lateral margin of the fossa, and passes into peroneus longus where it divides into superficial and deep peroneal nerves.

RELATIONS: in its descent it lies on the lateral head of gastrocnemius and then the neck of the fibula. It is overlapped by biceps in its upper course but is subcutaneous on the neck of the fibula.

BRANCHES

(i) a branch which pierces the roof of the popliteal fossa and descends to join the sural nerve halfway down the leg.

(ii) lateral cutaneous nerve of the leg—descends over the lateral head of gastrocnemius to supply the lateral aspect of the leg.

(iii) articular branches—to the knee and superior tibiofibular joints.

(iv) **superficial peroneal nerve**—is a terminal branch of the main trunk. It begins in the substance of peroneus longus and descends deep to this muscle, between it and peroneus brevis. In the lower part of the leg it emerges between peroneus brevis and peroneus tertius and divides into medial and lateral cutaneous branches.

Branches

(a) muscular branches—to peroneus longus and brevis.

(b) cutaneous branches—to the skin over the lower lateral part of the leg.

(c) medial and lateral cutaneous branches—these descend over the extensor retinacula on to the dorsum of the foot and there divide into dorsal digital branches. The medial branch supplies the medial side of the great toe and the 2nd interdigital cleft; the lateral branch supplies the 3rd and 4th interdigital clefts.

(v) **deep peroneal nerve**—is also a terminal branch of the main trunk. It continues around the neck of the fibula, pierces the anterior intermuscular septum and then descends in the extensor compartment in company with the anterior tibial artery initially between extensor digitorum longus laterally and tibialis anterior medially and then between extensor hallucis longus laterally and tibialis anterior medially. At the ankle joint it passes under the extensor retinaculum lateral to the artery and divides into medial and lateral terminal branches.

Branches

(a) muscular—to the long dorsiflexor muscles.
(b) lateral terminal branch—passes deep to extensor digitorum brevis, supplying it and the ankle joint.
(c) medial terminal branch—continues on the dorsum of the foot lateral to the dorsalis pedis artery and supplies the skin of the 1st interdigital cleft.

CHAPTER 23

THE FOOT

The foot is an arched platform consisting of a number of separate bones bound together by ligaments and muscles. The arched nature of the foot supports the body's weight, acts as a lever which is sufficiently rigid to propel the body forwards, and yet is resilient enough to absorb sudden

Fig. 23.1

The bones of the foot, dorsal aspect. Inset: ossification (m.i.u., months in utero; y., years).

shocks. Less important functions of the foot concern the obtaining of proprioceptive information, and under special circumstances its use in grasping. As long as an artificial foot will carry the body's weight and permit reasonable walking, it is functionally adequate and can be aesthetically acceptable. In the hand, however, sensory and manipulative abilities are of prime importance and most artificial substitutes are functionally very inadequate.

244

SKELETON

Tarsus (Figs. 23.1, 23.2)

This comprises the talus, calcaneus, navicular, cuboid and the three cuneiform bones.

Talus—forms the connecting link between the bones of the leg and those of the foot. It has a body, a neck and a head, and has no muscular attachments.

The **body** lies posteriorly. Its articular superior surface is markedly convex anteroposteriorly, slightly concave from side to side, and articulates with the inferior surface of the tibia. This facet is widest in front and is continuous with a facet on each side of the bone for articulation with the medial and lateral malleoli; the medial facet is comma-shaped and the lateral is triangular. These three articular surfaces are collectively known as the **trochlear surface** of the talus. The inferior surface of the body is concave and articulates with the posterior facet on the calcaneus. The posterior margin bears posterior and medial tubercles; the posterior gives attachment to the posterior talofibular ligament and the groove between the tubercles lodges the tendon of flexor hallucis longus.

The **neck** is constricted and inferiorly bears a deep groove, the sulcus tali. The **head** is hemispherical and is inclined medially. It has articular facets for (*a*) the navicular bone anteriorly, (*b*) the anterior and middle calcaneal facets inferiorly, and (*c*) the inferior calcaneonavicular (spring) ligament inferomedially. The facets are all in continuity.

Calcaneus—is an irregular bone roughly rectangular in shape; its posterior part forms the prominence of the heel. The upper surface has posterior, middle and anterior articular facets for the talus. The posterior facet is convex and covers the middle third of the bone; it receives the inferior concavity of the body of the talus. The middle and anterior facets articulate with the head of the same bone. The middle facet lies on a medial extension of the bone, the **sustentaculum tali;** it is separated from the posterior facet by a deep groove, the **sulcus calcanei.** (The sulcus calcanei and the sulcus tali together form a narrow tunnel, the **sinus tarsi,** which houses the strong interosseous talocalcaneal ligament.)

The inferior surface has an **anterior tubercle,** to which is attached the short plantar ligament, and medial and lateral **posterior tubercles** which give attachment to the long plantar ligament, some short muscles of the sole and the plantar aponeurosis. The inferior surface of the sustentaculum tali is grooved by the flexor hallucis longus tendon.

The lateral surface has a short ridge, the **peroneal tubercle,** which separates the peroneus longus and brevis tendons. The posterior surface gives attachment to the tendo calcaneus (Achilles' tendon) in its middle third, and the smaller anterior surface articulates with the cuboid bone.

Navicular—lies on the medial side of the foot between the talus and the cuneiform bones. Posteriorly it has a concave facet for the head of the talus and anteriorly three facets for the cuneiform bones. Its medial surface is extended downwards and medially to form the prominent navicular **tuberosity** to which the tendon of tibialis posterior and the calcaneonavicular (spring) ligament are attached.

Cuboid—lies on the lateral side of the foot. It is roughly wedge-shaped and narrower inferiorly. Posteriorly it articulates with the calcaneus, anteriorly with the bases of the 4th and 5th metatarsal bones, and medially with the lateral cuneiform and sometimes the navicular. The anterior part of the inferior surface has a prominent **groove** (for the peroneus longus tendon) situated between anterior and posterior ridges which give attachment to the long plantar ligament.

Flexor digitorum longus

Flexor digitorum brevis

Flexor hallucis longus

Peroneus longus

Tibialis anterior

Peroneus brevis

Tibialis posterior

Accessorius

FIG. 23.2
The bones of the foot, plantar aspect.

Cuneiforms—are three wedge-shaped bones. The medial is narrower superiorly and the intermediate and lateral bones narrower inferiorly. Posteriorly they articulate with the navicular and anteriorly with the bases of the medial three metatarsal bones. The medial is the largest and the intermediate the shortest. The base of the 2nd metatarsal is wedged between the medial and lateral bones. The lateral cuneiform bone has a lateral articular facet for the cuboid. Parts of the tendons of tibialis anterior, tibialis posterior and peroneus longus are attached to the medial cuneiform.

Metatarsal bones and phalanges (Figs. 23.1, 23.2)—These are long bones resembling the metacarpals and phalanges of the hand. However, (*a*) the metatarsals are longer and more slender than the metacarpals, (*b*) the base of the 1st metatarsal is not saddle-shaped, (*c*) the base of the 5th metatarsal bears a posterior projection from its lateral side, (d) the phalanges are shorter in the foot and the 5th toe frequently has only two.

THE ANKLE JOINT

This is a synovial joint of the hinge variety between the mortise formed by the inferior surface of the tibia and the facing surfaces of the medial and lateral malleoli and, inferiorly, the upper, medial and lateral surfaces of the talus.

LIGAMENTS

(a) Capsule: is attached to the articular margins except anteriorly where it extends on to the neck of the talus.

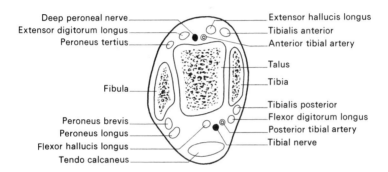

FIG. 23.3
Diagrammatic lay-out showing some of the main structures surrounding the left ankle joint.

(b) Capsular thickenings:
(i) **medial (deltoid) ligament**—is triangular in shape with its apex attached to the medial malleolus and its base to the navicular, the neck of the talus and the plantar calcaneonavicular ligament, the sustentaculum tali and the body of the talus from before backwards.
(ii) **lateral ligament**—is composed of three separate parts; anterior talofibular ligament passing from the lateral malleolus horizontally forwards to the neck of the talus, the calcaneofibular ligament passing backwards from the tip of the malleolus to the lateral side of the calcaneus, and the posterior talofibular ligament passing horizontally from the malleolar fossa on the lateral malleolus to the posterior tubercle of the talus.
(iii) **anterior and posterior ligaments**—are weak flat bands.
(c) Accessory ligaments: **inferior transverse tibiofibular ligament** is a thick band passing between the upper part of the malleolar fossa on the fibula and the posterior edge of the articular surface on the tibial malleolus. It forms part of the articular surface for the talus posteriorly.

INTRACAPSULAR STRUCTURES—the synovial membrane lines the non-articular surfaces of the joint.

247

FUNCTIONAL ASPECTS

Movement: the joint may be plantar flexed and dorsiflexed. Plantar flexion is downward movement of the foot. It is produced by gastrocnemius and soleus assisted by other muscles of the flexor and possibly the peroneal compartments of the leg. Dorsiflexion is upward movement of the foot. It is produced by tibialis anterior assisted by the other muscles of the extensor compartment.

When the foot is plantar flexed slight passive side to side movement of the talus is possible as its articular surface is narrower posteriorly.

Stability: this is a stable joint maintained by the mortise arrangement of its bones and the powerful ligaments. The joint is least stable in the plantar flexed position. The line of weight passes anterior to the joint and as the leg dorsiflexes on the grounded foot, the tibiofibular mortise firmly grips the wider anterior talar surface. Severe inversion or eversion injuries to the ankle frequently cause a fracture dislocation of the joint, the treatment of which is difficult and complex. Less severe strains may be associated with disabling tears of the medial or the lateral ligaments.

BLOOD AND NERVE SUPPLY: anterior and posterior tibial vessels and tibial and deep peroneal nerves.

RELATIONS (Fig. 23.3): medially and laterally the joint lies subcutaneously. Anteriorly it is crossed from medial to lateral by tendons of tibialis anterior and extensor hallucis longus, the anterior tibial vessels and deep peroneal nerve and the tendons of extensor digitorum longus and peroneus tertius. Posteromedially from medial to lateral it is crossed by the tendons of tibialis posterior and flexor digitorum longus, the posterior tibial vessels and tibial nerve and the tendon of flexor hallucis longus. The peroneus longus and brevis tendons cross the joint posterolaterally. All the tendons are surrounded by synovial sheaths. The joint is separated by a posterior pad of fat from the tendo calcaneus.

THE INTERTARSAL AND OTHER JOINTS

These comprise the subtalar (posterior talocalcaneal), the talocalcaneonavicular (including the anterior talocalcaneal joint), the calcaneocuboid, the smaller joints around the cuneiform and metatarsal bones and the phalanges.

Subtalar (posterior talocalcaneal) joint—is a synovial joint between the inferior concave facet on the body of the talus and the posterior convex facet of the calcaneus. The capsule is partly thickened by talocalcaneal bands but the main bond of union between the two bones is the **interosseous talocalcaneal ligament** lying in the sinus tarsi.

Talocalcaneonavicular joint—is a synovial joint of the ball and socket variety between the hemispherical head of the talus and the concavity formed by (*a*) the anterior and middle facets on the upper surface of the calcaneus posteriorly, (*b*) the concavity of the navicular anteriorly, and (*c*) the inner surface of the plantar calcaneonavicular (spring) ligament inferomedially. The capsule is reinforced by the spring ligament inferomedially, the deltoid ligament superomedially and the medial band of the bifurcate ligament (see below) laterally.

248

The **plantar calcaneonavicular (spring) ligament** is a strong thick band passing from the sustentaculum tali to the navicular tuberosity; it forms an articular surface for the head of the talus and is here covered by articular hyaline cartilage. It is an important factor in maintaining the medial longitudinal arch of the foot.

Calcaneocuboid joint—is a synovial joint of the saddle variety between the reciprocal concavoconvex facets of the two bones; the capsule is reinforced by the bifurcate ligament and the long and short plantar ligaments are accessory to the joint.

The **bifurcated ligament** is attached proximally to the anterior part of the upper surface of the calcaneus and divides distally to gain attachment to the adjacent surfaces of the cuboid and navicular bones. The **long plantar ligament** passes from the posterior calcaneal tubercles to the ridges on the cuboid and then on to the bases of the lateral metatarsals. The **short plantar ligament** passes from the anterior calcaneal tubercle to the adjacent surface of the cuboid.

FUNCTIONAL ASPECTS

The movements of inversion and eversion occur at these joints. In **inversion** the sole of the foot is turned to face inwards, thus raising its medial border; in **eversion** the sole is turned to face outwards, thus raising its lateral border. Both movements occur mainly at the subtalar and the talocalcaneonavicular joints. The calcaneus and the navicular, carrying the forepart of the foot with them, move medially on the talus by a combination of rotary and gliding movements. The combined movements produced at these joints are similar to those obtained at a saddle-shaped joint.

However, (*a*) the range of inversion and eversion is increased by movement at the midtarsal (talonavicular and calcaneocuboid) joint. (*b*) Inversion is increased during plantar flexion on account of a small amount of rocking of the narrower posterior end of the talar articular facet at the ankle joint. (*c*) Eversion is increased in dorsiflexion.

Inversion is produced by the tibialis anterior and posterior, and is limited by tension in the peroneal muscles and in the interosseous talocalcaneal ligament. Eversion is produced by the peroneal muscles, and limited by tension in the tibialis anterior and posterior and in the deltoid ligament.

The movements have been described when the foot is off the ground. The same movements occurring when the foot is on the ground adjust the foot and lower limb to uneven and sloping surfaces.

The **tarsometatarsal joints** and the remaining **intertarsal joints** are small plane synovial joints tightly bound together by interosseous ligaments of which those on the plantar aspect of the foot are the stronger. These joints are capable only of slight gliding movements.

Metatarsophalangeal and interphalangeal joints—resemble those of the fingers but are less mobile, the heads of the five metatarsals being bound together by deep transverse ligaments which unite the plantar thickenings of all the joint capsules. (In the hand, the thumb is freely opposable.) Plantar flexion and dorsiflexion occur at all these joints, and also a very limited amount of abduction and adduction at the meta-tarsophalangeal joints may be possible. Plantar flexion is produced by flexor hallucis longus and brevis and flexor digitorum longus and brevis. Flexor accessorius maintains the toes in a plantar flexed position when the ankle joint is being dorsiflexed. Dorsiflexion is produced by extensor hallucis longus and extensor digitorum longus and brevis muscles. Abductor hallucis and abductor digiti minimi may spread the toes, the interossei bring them together.

The first metatarsophalangeal joint in man is much larger than the others. Inferiorly a sesamoid bone is found in each tendon of flexor hallucis brevis, the tendons and bones being incorporated in the joint capsule. In the groove between the sesamoid bones, and so protected from pressure, is the tendon of the flexor hallucis longus. The natural angle between the long axis of the first metatarsal and that of the first phalanx may be accentuated by the wearing of poorly fitting shoes. A bursa is often present on the medial side of the joint and when it becomes inflamed, the condition is called a bunion.

THE ARCHES OF THE FOOT

The arched nature of the foot is a predominantly human charac-teristic and is present from birth, although masked in the baby by a large amount of subcutaneous fat. The arches allow the body's weight to be distributed over a larger area, and prevent crushing of the vessels and nerves crossing the sole.

The jointed pattern of the arch gives the foot a resilience well suited to absorb the impact of the body's weight when the foot comes into contact with the ground, while still allowing it to act as a semirigid lever for propelling the body forwards. The arched form comprises separate medial, lateral and transverse arches which, although to be considered individually, are collectively involved in the functions already enumerated.

The maintenance of each arch is dependent on bony, ligamentous and muscular factors which act in a complementary manner, it being unlikely that a single factor could maintain the arch for any length of time. The short ligaments and muscles tie the adjacent bones of the arch together and the long ligaments, the plantar aponeurosis and muscle tendons tie the two ends of the arch together. Some long tendons act in a sling-like manner, supporting the centre of the arch. The ligaments and muscles found on the plantar surface of the foot are stronger and more numerous than those on the dorsum.

The **medial longitudinal arch** extends from the medial tubercle of the calcaneus to the heads of the medial three metatarsals. The bones forming it are the calcaneus, talus, navicular, three cuneiforms and the medial three metatarsal bones. The arch is maintained by muscles and ligaments. The *muscular supports* are:

(i) the short muscles of the foot, especially abductor hallucis, flexor hallucis brevis and flexor digitorum brevis.

(ii) tibialis anterior attached near to the centre of the arch.

(iii) flexor hallucis longus and the medial part of flexor digitorum longus passing between the ends of the arch.

(iv) tibialis posterior tying together the posterior bones of the arch.

The *ligamentous supports* are:

(i) the plantar calcaneonavicular (spring) ligament supporting the head of the talus.

(ii) the interosseous ligaments.

(iii) the plantar aponeurosis tying together the ends of the arch.

The bony contribution is limited to the support given by the sustentaculum tali to the talus and to the wedge shape of some of the bones.

The **lateral longitudinal arch** is lower than the medial and extends from the lateral tubercle of the calcaneus to the heads of the 4th and 5th metatarsal bones. It is formed from the calcaneus, cuboid and 4th and 5th metatarsal bones. The arch is maintained mainly by ligaments.

The *ligamentous supports* are:

(i) the plantar aponeurosis.

(ii) the long and short plantar ligaments uniting the calcaneus to the cuboid and the bases of the 4th and 5th metatarsal bones.

(iii) the interosseous ligaments.

The *muscular supports* are:

(i) the short muscles of the foot, especially abductor digiti minimi and flexor digitorum brevis.

(ii) peroneus longus, passing below the cuboid and supporting the centre of the arch.

The **transverse arch** lies across the distal row of tarsal bones and the adjacent metatarsal bones and is formed by the cuneiform and cuboid bones and the metatarsal bases. The arch is maintained by the shape of the bones, the interosseous ligaments, and peroneus longus, tibialis posterior and adductor hallucis muscles.

THE SOLE OF THE FOOT

The skin over the weight-bearing areas of the heel and the 'ball' of the foot is thickened in its superficial layers and firmly attached to the deep fascia by fibrous, septa passing through the superficial fascia. The skin is thin in the flexure creases. The fatty superficial fascia insulates and cushions the deeper structures.

The deep fascia consists of a thickened central portion, the **plantar aponeurosis,** and thin medial and lateral portions. The aponeurosis is attached posteriorly to the back of the under-surface of the calcaneus and divides anteriorly into five digital expansions. These are continuous with the fibrous flexor tendon sheaths along the plantar aspect of the toes, and are also attached to the ligaments binding together the heads of the metatarsals. When the toes are dorsiflexed, the plantar aponeurosis is tightened and the longitudinal arch is accentuated.

Muscles of the Sole

The small muscles of the sole have a similar pattern of attachment to those of the hand. Short flexors, abductors, an adductor of the big toe, lumbrical and interosseous muscles are present but there is no opponens muscle. The small muscles help to maintain the arches and move the toes but have little abductor or adductor action. A large sesamoid bone is present on each side of the head of the 1st metatarsal. The sesamoids are embedded in the tendons of the short muscles passing to the big toe and the capsule of the 1st metatarsophalangeal joint. The sesamoids carry much of the weight and form a protective groove for the tendon of flexor hallucis longus.

The **flexor accessorius** has no counterpart in the hand. It is attached to the calcaneus posteriorly and to the lateral side of the tendons of flexor digitorum longus and flexor hallucis longus anteriorly. Tension in the digital tendons and flexion of the toes can be maintained by accessorius when the long flexors have to relax. This occurs when the leg is being pulled forwards over the ankle joint by tibialis anterior and the extensor muscles during the supporting phase of walking.

All the short muscles of the sole are supplied by the lateral plantar nerve except for abductor hallucis, flexor hallucis brevis, flexor digitorum brevis and the 1st lumbrical which are supplied by the medial plantar nerve. (Compare this distribution with that of the ulnar and median nerves in the palm.)

The long flexor tendons pass along the sole of the foot into the flexor tendon sheaths and are attached to the base of the terminal phalanges. The tendons of three large muscles are inserted close together on the medial side of the foot. The tendon of tibialis posterior is attached to the tuberosity of the navicular and then spreads out to all the other tarsal bones except the talus and to some metatarsal bases. The tendon of peroneus longus, having crossed the foot, is attached to the lateral side of the medial cuneiform and of the 1st metatarsal base. The tendon of tibialis anterior is attached to the medial side of the same two bones. These three muscles are strong supporters of the arches of the foot.

Plantar Vessels

1. Lateral plantar artery—is the larger terminal branch of the posterior tibial artery and arises deep to the flexor retinaculum. It runs in a superficial plane obliquely across the sole, to the base of the 5th metatarsal bone where it turns medially and passes deeply back across the foot to anastomose with the dorsalis pedis artery in the 1st metatarsal space, thus completing the plantar arch.

Branches
(i) digital branch to lateral side of 5th toe.
(ii) from the plantar arch—four plantar metatarsal arteries. They pass distally and divide into digital arteries supplying the sides of adjacent toes, and anastomose with the dorsal metatarsal branches of the dorsalis pedis artery by means of perforating branches which pass through the metatarsal spaces.

2. Medial plantar artery—is the smaller terminal branch of the posterior tibial artery. It passes anteriorly to supply the medial side of the great toe and anastomoses with the medial three plantar metatarsal arteries.

The veins accompany the arteries and anastomose with the dorsal venous arch.

Plantar Nerves

1. Lateral plantar nerve—is the smaller terminal branch of the tibial nerve. It begins under cover of the flexor retinaculum and, accompanied by its artery, passes obliquely across the sole, to the base of the 5th metatarsal bone where it divides into deep and superficial branches.

BRANCHES

(i) cutaneous branches—to the skin over the lateral side of the foot.

(ii) superficial terminal branch—gives muscular branches and then cutaneous branches to the lateral $1\frac{1}{2}$ toes.

(iii) deep terminal branch—this turns medially in company with the lateral plantar artery and supplies the small deep muscles.

2. Medial plantar nerve—begins under the flexor retinaculum and passes forwards accompanied by its vessels. It supplies some muscular branches and cutaneous branches to the medial part of the sole and the medial $3\frac{1}{2}$ toes.

THE FASCIA, VEINS, LYMPH DRAINAGE, NERVES, AND POSTURE

THE DEEP FASCIA

The deep fascia of the gluteal region and thigh forms a firm investing layer, the **fascia lata,** which surrounds the limb and provides medial and lateral intermuscular septa in the thigh. Superiorly, the fascia lata is attached, in a continuous line, to the pubic tubercle, inguinal ligament, iliac crest, back of the sacrum, sacrotuberous ligament, ischiopubic ramus, and the front of the body of the pubis as far as the pectineal line and pubic tubercle.

About 3 cm below and lateral to the pubic tubercle there is an oval deficiency, the **saphenous opening** (p. 223); it transmits the great saphenous vein and lymphatic vessels. The fascia lata is thickened on the lateral side of the thigh to form the **iliotibial tract** (p. 218). Gluteus maximus and tensor fasciae latae are attached to the iliotibial tract and so help extend and stabilise the knee joint. Over the popliteal fossa the deep fascia is reinforced by transverse bundles of fibres. It is pierced by the small saphenous vein.

The deep fascia of the lower leg ensheaths the muscles and forms anterior and posterior intermuscular septa which pass to the fibula and separate anterior, peroneal and posterior groups of muscles. Superiorly it is continuous with the fascia lata. It is attached to bone around the borders of the patella, the condyles of the tibia, the medial tibial surface (the shin), and inferiorly to both malleoli. It is thickened round the ankle to form the retinacula tethering the tendons entering the foot. On the dorsum of the foot the deep fascia is thin, but on the sole it is thickened to form the plantar aponeurosis.

The deep fascia is pierced by perforating veins joining the superficial and deep veins, and by cutaneous nerves, arteries and lymph vessels.

THE VENOUS DRAINAGE

As in the upper limb the veins may be divided into intercommunicating superficial and deep groups. Valves are present in the larger vessels including some communicating veins (Fig. 24.1).

The **superficial veins**—drain the subcutaneous tissues through two main longitudinal channels, the great and small saphenous veins:

(*a*) in the foot, communicating **dorsal and plantar venous arches** receive the digital and metatarsal veins of the sole and dorsum of the foot. The great and small saphenous veins originate from the medial and lateral ends respectively of the dorsal arch.

(*b*) The **great saphenous vein** originates from the medial end of the dorsal venous arch. It ascends just in front of the medial malleolus and subcutaneously along the medial side of the calf and thigh, accompanied in the calf by the saphenous nerve. It passes through the saphenous opening and enters the femoral vein.

FIG. 24.1
Venogram of the left leg. The three views show progression of the radiopaque material up the leg.

1. Soleal plexus of veins
2. Popliteal vein
3. Knee joint
4. Femoral vein
5. Valve

TRIBUTARIES
(i) communicating branches with the small saphenous vein and the deep veins of the calf and thigh.
(ii) subcutaneous branches draining the skin of the inguinal and pubic regions join it just prior to its passage through the saphenous opening.
(c) The **small saphenous vein** originates from the lateral end of the dorsal venous arch. It ascends behind the lateral malleolus, along the back of the calf, and ends by piercing the fascial roof of the popliteal fossa and entering the popliteal vein.

255

Its tributaries communicate with the great saphenous vein and the deep veins of the limb.

The **deep veins**—comprise the plantar, the soleal plexus of veins, the popliteal vein (p. 241) and the femoral vein (p. 225). They communicate with the superficial veins by tributaries, the valves of which are so arranged as to allow blood to pass only towards the deep veins.

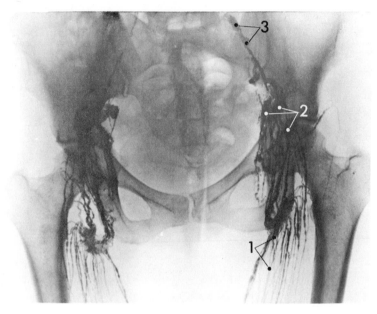

Fig. 24.2

Lymphangiogram of lower limbs. The radiopaque material has been introduced into a lymph vessel over the dorsum of each foot. (See also Fig. 15.2.)

1. Lymph vessels in upper thigh   3. Common iliac nodes
2. Femoral and external iliac nodes

Incompetence of these valves or blockage of the deep veins leads to varicosity of the superficial veins. Defective blood supply to the skin above the ankle may give rise to varicose ulcers. A blood clot from the deep veins may become dislodged and travel to the lungs—a pulmonary embolus.

THE LYMPH DRAINAGE (Fig. 24.2)

There are two main groups of lymph nodes in the lower limb—superficial and deep.

(*a*) The **superficial groups,** draining the skin, lie in three distinct situations:

(i) **upper superficial inguinal group**—lies just above the inguinal ligament and drains lymph from the lower part of the anterior abdominal wall, the perineum, external genitalia, anal canal and the gluteal region. Its efferent vessels pass to the lower superficial inguinal and deep inguinal groups of nodes.

(ii) **lower superficial inguinal group**—lies around the termination of the great saphenous vein and drains lymph from the previous group of nodes, and the skin over the thigh, medial part of the leg and foot. Its efferent vessels pass to the deep inguinal group through the saphenous opening.

(iii) **popliteal group**—this small group lies in the popliteal fossa around the termination of the small saphenous vein. It drains skin over the lateral side of the calf and foot. Its efferent vessels pass to the deep inguinal group of nodes.

(b) The vessels draining the **deep part** of the limb accompany the arteries and pass to the **deep inguinal nodes.** This group comprises one to three nodes lying in the femoral canal. It receives lymph from all superficial nodes and deep vessels from the entire limb. Its efferent vessels pass deep to the inguinal ligament to the external iliac group of nodes.

Maldevelopment of the lymph vessels or blockage of the lymph nodes by disease may produce swelling of the limb due to interference with lymph flow (lymphoedema).

NERVE SUPPLY

The cutaneous nerve supply is summarised in Figure 24.3.

Peripheral Nerve Injuries in the Leg

(i) **femoral nerve**—this produces loss of knee extension (quadriceps), some loss in hip flexion (iliacus and pectineus) and loss of sensation over the front and medial side of the thigh and leg (anterior and medial femoral cutaneous nerves and the saphenous nerve).

(ii) **obturator nerve**—some loss in the power of adduction (adductor magnus is partly supplied by the sciatic nerve) and no loss in sensation.

(iii) **sciatic nerve**—a proximal injury, e.g. following a posterior dislocation of the hip joint, produces an almost flail limb. A distal injury may spare the nerves supplying the hamstrings and allow the knee to be flexed.

(iv) **tibial nerve**—loss of plantar flexion and sensory loss over the sole of the foot. An injury near the ankle denervates the small muscles of the sole and the unopposed action of the long flexor and extensor muscles produces a highly arched foot. Injury proximal to the origin of the sural nerve produces also loss of sensation over the lateral side of the leg and foot.

(v) **common peroneal nerve**—this is the most frequent nerve to be injured in the leg, often associated with fractures of the neck of the fibula or a badly fitting leg plaster. The power of dorsiflexion (extensor muscles) and eversion (peroneal muscles) are lost—the foot drops and becomes inverted. There is sensory loss over the medial side of the dorsum of the foot.

Iliohypogastric nerve

Lateral branch 12th thoracic nerve

Lateral femoral cutaneous nerve

Posterior femoral cutaneous nerve

Lateral sural cutaneous nerve

Saphenous nerve

Sural nerve

Medial calcaneal branch of the tibial nerve

L1

L3

T12

L1

L2

L3

L4

L5

S1

S2

S3

Genitofemoral nerve

Ilio-inguinal nerve

Lateral femoral cutaneous nerve

Anterior femoral cutaneous nerve

Obturator nerve

Medial femoral cutaneous nerve

Saphenous nerve

Lateral sural cutaneous nerve

Superficial peroneal nerve

Sural nerve

Deep peroneal nerve

FIG. 24.3

Diagrammatic lay-out of the cutaneous innervation of the lower limb.

(vi) **superficial peroneal nerve**—the power of eversion (peronei) is lost and the foot becomes inverted. There is loss of sensation over the medial part of the dorsum of the foot.

(vii) **deep peroneal nerve**—the power to dorsiflex the toes is lost and there may be loss of sensation between the 1st and 2nd toes. The foot becomes inverted by the unopposed action of the tibialis posterior.

POSTURE IN STANDING AND WALKING

The body's weight is transmitted from the vertebral column through the pelvic girdle to both femoral heads. In each limb, the weight is transmitted through the bones, whose internal architecture is well adapted to withstand compressive stresses and strains, to the foot whose arched nature distributes the weight equally between the metatarsal heads and the tubercles of the calcaneus. The head of the 1st metatarsal normally takes more than a third of the total metatarsal load.

In the **normal stance** the line of weight passes through the centre of gravity which, in the anatomical position, is just in front of the 2nd piece of the sacrum. The line passes slightly behind the hip joint and just in front of the knee and ankle joints. The erect posture is maintained by a combination of muscular and ligamentous factors. Normally the effect of the body's weight is to cause hyperextension at the hip and knee joints. This is resisted at the hip by the anteriorly placed iliofemoral ligament and by contraction of iliopsoas. At the knee it is resisted by most of the ligaments and contraction of the hamstring muscles and gastrocnemius. At the ankle joint, the shape of the mortise between the tibia and fibula above and the talus below contributes more than the ligaments to the stability of this joint. Slight changes in posture may bring the line of weight behind the knee and flexion is then resisted by contraction of quadriceps femoris. The body's weight tends to dorsiflex the body over the foot but this is resisted by the calf plantar flexor muscles, especially soleus. The long digital flexors help by holding the toes firmly on the ground.

During **walking,** the cycles of movement of each limb can be divided into a stance (supporting) phase and a swing phase. Each cycle begins as the heel touches the ground and finishes as the same heel again touches the ground.

THE STANCE (SUPPORTING) PHASE

In this phase, the weight of the body is taken by the grounded leg, and muscle activity maintains or increases the forward momentum of the body. The phase starts as the heel touches the ground (heelstrike). At the hip joint, extension gives a forward thrust, and medial rotation maintains the correct direction of progress. Meanwhile, abduction at the hip joint by gluteus medius and minimus tilts the pelvis on the supporting leg and allows the swinging leg to move forwards. The knee joint is in the extended position, locked so that weight is not carried by the muscles but by the bones and ligaments. (At the end of this phase, the knee joint is unlocked by lateral rotation of the femur on the tibia.) At the ankle joint plantar flexion (partly passive as the foot goes on the ground) gives way to an active dorsiflexion which pulls the body weight over the ankle. The foot becomes slightly everted. The weight of the body is transferred forwards from the heel along the outer border of the foot to the metatarsal heads, especially the first.

THE SWING PHASE

In this, the leg swings through from a trailing to a leading position. At the hip joint, there is flexion, lateral rotation and adduction. At the knee joint, flexion occurs until the swinging foot has passed the supporting foot and then extension occurs, at the end of which some lateral rotation of the tibia may lock the knee joint in preparation for weight bearing. At the ankle joint, the foot is first dorsiflexed but becomes plantar flexed as the knee extends. The foot itself becomes inverted and the heel touches the ground (heelstrike) in readiness for the next supporting phase.

Starting to walk involves a forward tilting of the body thus advancing the centre of gravity and the line of weight. The supporting limb is extended, the pelvis is tilted on the supporting leg, and the heel is raised by the calf muscles. The opposite limb flexes and then extends until the heel touches the ground. Thus it becomes the supporting limb after a very short swing phase. Turning to left or right involves most of the trunk muscles as well as the rotators at the hip joint. They largely determine the route followed by the swinging leg and the position of the touch-down of the swinging heel. In running, the centre of gravity is usually further forward due to flexion of the vertebral column, thus altering the total posture. There is considerable time between the end of the stance phase and the heelstrike of the foot of the swinging leg, so that the body is clear of the ground (unsupported) for this time. In running, active plantar flexion at the ankle joint at the end of the stance phase increases the forwards momentum of the body.

Although described separately these movements merge into one another indistinguishably. Limitation of the movement at any joint results in a marked alteration in gait. The individuality of the gait depends on the length of the stride, the extent of pelvic rotation (swinging the hips) and the impetus at the end of the stance phase.

HEAD AND NECK

THE SKULL, SCALP AND FACE

THE SKULL

The skull consists of an upper part containing and protecting the brain, and a lower anterior part forming the facial skeleton. Its constituent bones, with the exception of the mandible, are united by immovable fibrous joints, the sutures.

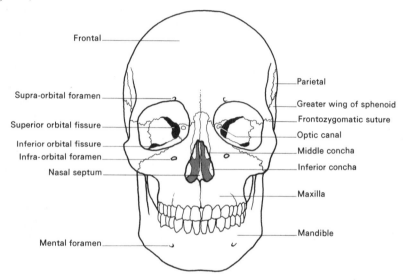

Fig. 25.1
The skull, frontal aspect.

The skull will be considered as viewed from above, in front, from the side, from below, and from behind, after which individual bones will be examined. The osteology of the intracranial region, and of the orbital, nasal and auditory cavities is considered under the relevant sections.

Superior aspect

The vault is crossed by three sutures. The **coronal suture** separates the frontal bone anteriorly from the two parietal bones posteriorly. The **sagittal suture** separates the parietal bones. Its junction with the coronal suture is known as the **bregma** and in the fetal skeleton, when the frontal bone is incompletely ossified, a diamond-shaped bony deficiency, the **anterior fontanelle,** is present. The anterior fontanelle closes at about 18 months. The **lambdoid suture** lies between the two parietal bones

262

and the occipital bone posteriorly; it meets the sagittal suture at the **lambda.** At the lambda there is, in the foetal skull, a triangular bony deficiency, the **posterior fontanelle.** It is usually closed by the 2nd or 3rd month after birth.

Anterior Aspect (Fig. 25.1)

This is formed superiorly by the smooth convexity of the frontal bone. The point of maximum convexity on each side is known as the frontal tuberosity. The inferior part is irregular and contains the openings of the orbital, nasal and oral cavities. Above the supra-orbital margins are rounded superciliary arches. The supra-orbital margin, which is formed by the frontal bone, possesses a supra-orbital notch or foramen (at the junction of its medial third and lateral two-thirds) which transmits the supra-orbital vessels and nerve. The lateral orbital margin is formed by the frontal and zygomatic bones (the zygomaticofrontal suture is palpable in the living). The medial orbital margin is formed by the frontal bone and the frontal process of the maxilla, the inferior margin by the maxillary bone medially and the zygomatic bone laterally. The prominence of the cheek, below and lateral to the orbital margin is produced by the zygomatic bone. On the maxilla 1 cm below the orbit, in line with the supra-orbital notch, is the infra-orbital foramen from which emerges the infra-orbital vessels and nerve. The pear-shaped nasal aperture is bounded superiorly by the nasal bones, and below and laterally by the maxillae. The alveolar margins of the maxillae and mandible surround the opening of the oral cavity and bear the sockets for the teeth. The mental foramen on the mandible is in line with the supra-orbital and infra-orbital foramina, and from it emerge the mental vessels and nerve.

Lateral Aspect (Fig. 25.2)

The temporal line curves upwards and backwards from the zygomatic process of the frontal bone across the parietal bone and downwards and forwards over the squamous temporal bone to end as the supramastoid crest above the external acoustic meatus. Below the temporal line and deep to the zygomatic arch is the temporal fossa. It is roofed in by the temporal fascia, itself attached to the temporal line and upper border of the zygomatic arch. The **zygomatic arch** is formed by the zygomatic process of the squamous temporal bone and the temporal process of the zygomatic bone. The medial wall of the fossa is the smooth convexity formed by the frontal, parietal, temporal and the greater wing of the sphenoid bones. Their H-shaped point of union, the **pterion,** lies about 3·5 cm behind and 1·5 cm above the zygomaticofrontal suture. This point indicates the position where the middle meningeal artery grooves, or runs through a canal in, the inner surface of the skull. The fossa is limited inferiorly by the infratemporal crest on the greater wing of the sphenoid and the squamous temporal bones. Below and medial to the crest is the **infratemporal fossa** which is limited medially by the lateral pterygoid plate. This fossa communicates medially with the pterygopalatine fossa through the pterygomaxillary fissure (between the pterygoid process and the back of the maxilla) and superiorly with the orbit through the inferior orbital fissure (between the greater wing of the sphenoid and the maxilla). The external acoustic meatus opens below the posterior end of the zygomatic

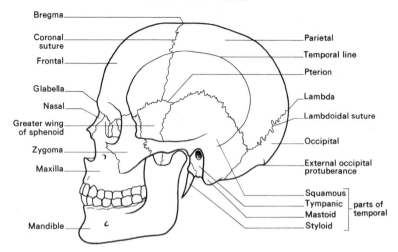

Bregma
Coronal suture
Frontal
Glabella
Nasal
Greater wing of sphenoid
Zygoma
Maxilla
Mandible

Parietal
Temporal line
Pterion
Lambda
Lambdoidal suture
Occipital
External occipital protuberance
Squamous ⎤
Tympanic | parts of
Mastoid | temporal
Styloid ⎦

FIG. 25.2
The skull, lateral aspect.

arch. The meatus is formed mainly by the tympanic plate of the temporal bone; the roof and upper part of the posterior wall are formed by the squamous temporal bone. The palpable mastoid process passes downwards behind the meatus.

Inferior Aspect (Fig. 25.3)

Anteriorly is the hard palate. It is formed from the palatine processes of the maxillae in front of the horizontal plates of the palatine bones. It is bounded anteriorly and laterally by the alveolar processes of the maxillae containing the sockets for the teeth. The rounded posterior part of the process on each side is called the maxillary tuberosity. Anteriorly a midline incisive foramen communicates with the nose and transmits the greater palatine arteries and nasopalatine nerves. Opening on to the posterolateral part of the palate are the greater and lesser palatine foramina; these convey the vessels and nerves of the same names from the pterygopalatine fossa. The posterior nasal apertures open above the palate. They are bounded superiorly by the body of the sphenoid bone, inferiorly by the horizontal plates of the palatine bones, and laterally by the medial pterygoid plates. The openings are separated in the midline by the vomer. The medial pterygoid plate projects downwards as the pterygoid hamulus, which gives attachment to the pterygomandibular raphé; the tensor veli palatini tendon hooks around the hamulus. The lateral and medial pterygoid plates enclose the pterygoid fossa. Behind the root of the lateral pterygoid process is the foramen ovale which transmits the mandibular nerve. Posterolateral to the foramen is the spine of the sphenoid and between them is the foramen spinosum which transmits the middle meningeal artery. The spine gives attachment to the sphenomandibular ligament. On the squamous temporal bone, lateral to the spine of the sphenoid, is the mandibular fossa for the condyle of the mandible. It is bounded anteriorly by the articular tubercle and posteriorly by the squamotympanic fissure and the tympanic plate of the temporal bone. The fissure is subdivided by a thin projection of the petrous temporal bone into a petrosquamous and a petrotympanic portion; the chorda tympani emerges through the latter. The irregular inferior surface of the petrous temporal bone projects anteromedially between the sphenoid and occipital bones; its apex is separated from them by the

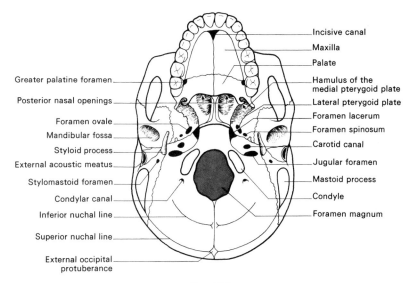

Incisive canal
Maxilla
Palate
Hamulus of the medial pterygoid plate
Lateral pterygoid plate
Foramen lacerum
Foramen spinosum
Carotid canal
Jugular foramen
Mastoid process
Condyle
Foramen magnum

Greater palatine foramen
Posterior nasal openings
Foramen ovale
Mandibular fossa
Styloid process
External acoustic meatus
Stylomastoid foramen
Condylar canal
Inferior nuchal line
Superior nuchal line
External occipital protuberance

FIG. 25.3
The skull, inferior aspect.

foramen lacerum. The bone contains the carotid canal whose inferior opening lies behind the spine of the sphenoid. The jugular foramen, transmitting the internal jugular vein, the inferior petrosal sinus, and glossopharyngeal, vagus and accessory nerves, lies immediately postero-lateral to the carotid opening. The styloid process projects downwards lateral to the jugular foramen. The stylomastoid foramen transmits the facial nerve and lies between the styloid and mastoid processes. Medial to the mastoid process are two grooves, the medial for the occipital artery and the lateral for the attachment of the posterior belly of digastric muscle. The occipital bone contains the large foramen magnum bounded on either side by the occipital condyles, each with two associated foramina. The anterior (hypoglossal foramen) transmits the hypoglossal nerve, and the posterior (condylar foramen) transmits an emissary vein and opens into a fossa behind the condyle.

Posterior Aspect

Behind the foramen magnum are the superior and inferior nuchal lines. A number of postvertebral muscles gain attachment to the rough-ened bone in this region. The superior line arches upwards from the mastoid process on each side, over the occipital bone to the palpable midline external occipital protuberance. The inferior line lies midway between the superior and the foramen magnum. Above the superior line, the bone is smooth.

DEVELOPMENT AND GROWTH OF THE SKULL (See also p. 23)

The bones of the vault of the skull and many face bones are formed in membrane while those of the base are developed mainly in cartilage (the chondrocranium).

At birth the face is relatively small. It increases in size with the appearance of the deciduous teeth and still more after the seventh year with the appearance of the permanent teeth and the enlargement of the nasal cavities and paranasal air sinuses. Growth in length of the base of the skull occurs mainly at the cartiliginous union between the body of the sphenoid and the basilar part of the occipital bone. Fusion of the two bones occurs after the appearance of the last molar teeth (17–25 years).

Although the bony protective characteristics of the skull have obvious advantages, its inextensibility means that an expanding space-occupying lesion, such as a tumour, or a haematoma from a bleeding intracranial vessel, will produce serious pressure effects on the brain. In particular, the midbrain may be compressed and vital centres become irreversibly damaged.

THE INDIVIDUAL BONES OF THE SKULL

Mandible (Fig. 25.4)

This bone is formed by the midline union of two halves. Each half has a horizontal body and a vertical ramus. The junction of the posterior border of the ramus and the lower border of the body forms the prominent **angle** of the mandible.

The **ramus** is flat and rectangular in shape; superiorly it forms two processes which are separated by the **mandibular notch.** The anterior **(coronoid process)** gives attachment to temporalis, and the posterior **(condylar process)** has an articular head and a narrower neck. The lateral pterygoid muscle is attached to the fossa on the front of the neck. The lateral surface of the ramus is roughened by the attachment of masseter. In the centre of the medial surface is the **mandibular foramen.** The sharp upward projecting inferior lip of the foramen is the **lingula;** it gives attachment to the sphenomandibular ligament. The medial pterygoid muscle is attached to the roughened area on the ramus below the foramen.

The **body** has a smooth rounded inferior border and an upper alveolar border containing the sockets for the teeth. The **mental foramen** is situated on the lateral surface at the level of the interval between the premolar teeth, and from it emerge the mental vessels and nerve. On the inner surface the **mylohyoid line** passes downwards and forwards from below the last molar tooth to the midline. It gives attachment to mylohyoid, and separates the sublingual fossa (for the sublingual gland) above from the submandibular fossa (for the submandibular gland) below.

Near the midline the digastric fossa for the anterior belly of digastric lies below the line and the **mental spine** is above it.

Each half of the mandible ossifies in membrane from a centre appearing in the sixth week of intra-uterine life. The centre lies lateral to Meckel's cartilage (the cartilage of the first pharyngeal arch) which becomes invaded and surrounded by the membrane bone. Secondary cartilages appear later for the condyle, the coronoid process and the region of the symphysis menti. They are ossified from the adjacent

Lateral pterygoid

Temporalis

Mandibular foramen

Medial pterygoid

Position of the sublingual gland

Genioglossus

Geniohyoid

Digastric

Position of the submandibular gland

Mylohyoid

Fig. 25.4
The mandible, medial aspect.

membrane bone. Bony union of the two halves takes place in the second year.

The length of the body is increased by absorption of the bone from the anterior border of the ramus and deposition along its posterior border. Vertical growth of the body is mainly by deposition of bone along the alveolar margin (associated with tooth eruption) and on the inferior border. The condylar secondary cartilage contributes to the height of the ramus. Loss of the teeth results in absorption of the alveolar bone. Thus the mental foramen, which lies midway between the upper and lower borders in adult life, is nearer the lower border at birth and the alveolar border in later life. Also associated with changes in the alveolar margin are changes in the angle of the jaw, it being about 140° at birth and in old age, and 110° in the adult.

Growth in size ceases at about the 25th year though moulding of the shape may continue. In fractures of the mandible, many of the related structures may be damaged.

Maxilla

Each maxilla consists of a body and four processes. The **body** contains the **maxillary air sinus** and has four surfaces. On the medial (nasal) surface there is a large opening which, in the articulated skeleton, is closed largely by other bones of the lateral wall of the nose. The anterior surface forms part of the facial skeleton and contains the **infra-orbital foramen.** The posterior surface is separated from the pterygoid process of the sphenoid by the pterygomaxillary fissure. The thin superior (orbital) surface forms the larger part of the orbital floor.

The **zygomatic process** extends laterally to the zygomatic bone. The **alveolar process** projects downwards and carries the upper teeth; a rounded posterior extension beyond the molars forms the **maxillary tuberosity.** The **horizontal (palatine) process** passes medially to contribute to the hard palate. The **frontal process** ascends to articulate with the frontal bone and forms part of the medial margin of the orbit.

The maxilla develops in membrane. The major part of the bone develops from a centre above the canine tooth. A second (premaxillary) centre forms that part of the bone carrying the incisor teeth. The infra-orbital nerve is usually damaged in fractures of the maxilla and gives rise to numbness over the cheek. An associated fracture of the zygomatic bone is common and then there may be difficulty in moving the temporomandibular joint. Injury to the orbital floor may give rise to double vision.

Sphenoid Bone

This consists of a central body from which two pairs of processes (the greater and lesser wings) extend laterally and two processes (the pterygoid processes) pass inferiorly.

The cube-shaped **body** encloses the paired sphenoidal air sinuses. It articulates anteriorly with the ethmoid bone, and posteriorly with the occipital bone. The inferior surface roofs in the nasopharynx. The superior surface is indented to form the **pituitary fossa,** anterior to which is the shallow **optic groove,** and posterior to which is the **dorsum sellae** projecting upwards and forwards over the fossa. At each end of the upper border of the dorsum sellae is a **posterior clinoid process.**

The **greater wing** has four surfaces. The upper surface is concave and supports the temporal lobe of the brain. The lower surface overlies the infratemporal fossa and carries the spine of the sphenoid. The lateral surface forms part of the medial wall of the temporal fossa and is separated from the lower surface by the infratemporal crest. The front of the wing is thickened to form an anterior surface which contributes to the lateral wall of the orbit. It is separated from the maxilla by the inferior orbital fissure. The root of the greater wing contains from before backwards the foramen rotundum, the foramen ovale and the foramen spinosum.

The **lesser wing** extends laterally from the anterior part of the body and forms the posterior limit of the floor of the anterior cranial fossa. The **anterior clinoid process** is the projecting medial end of the posterior free border. Between the lesser wing and the body is the optic canal and between the lesser and greater wings is the superior orbital fissure.

The **pterygoid process** extends downwards behind the maxilla. The process bears medial and lateral **pterygoid plates** which are united anteriorly.

The pterygoid process and the lateral part of the greater wing ossify in membrane, the remainder of the bone in cartilage.

Temporal Bone

Each consists of four parts: the squamous, petromastoid, tympanic and styloid.

The **squamous part** is a thin plate of bone on the lateral aspect of the skull articulating anteriorly with the greater wing of the sphenoid, superiorly with the parietal bone and posteriorly with the occipital bone. Its zygomatic process extends forwards from the lateral surface and contributes to the zygomatic arch. Below the process is the **mandibular fossa** for the condyle of the mandible. The fossa is continued anteriorly on to the **articular tubercle,** and posteriorly the squamotympanic fissure separates the articular surface (squamous temporal) from the nonarticular surface (tympanic plate). The squamous bone forms the roof and upper posterior part of the bony external acoustic meatus and lies lateral to the petrous part, forming the lateral wall of the middle ear.

The **petromastoid part** contains the middle and inner ears, and extends medially between the sphenoid and occipital bones. Its upper (intracranial) surface forms part of the floor of the middle and posterior cranial fossae. On the apex is a depression for the trigeminal ganglion, and lateral to this are openings for the greater petrosal nerve (posteriorly) and the lesser petrosal nerve (more anteriorly). The part forming the front of the posterior fossa is pierced by the **internal acoustic meatus** transmitting the facial and vestibulocochlear nerves. The irregular inferior surface contains the **carotid canal** for the internal carotid artery, and the **jugular fossa** opens between it and the occipital bone. The bony **auditory tube** opens anteriorly on to the inferior surface of the petrous temporal bone. The mastoid process extends down posteriorly and contains the tympanic antrum and mastoid air cells.

The **tympanic part** is a curved bony plate forming the anterior wall and floor of the bony external acoustic meatus. It also forms the nonarticular posterior wall of the mandibular fossa.

The **styloid process** is a slender downward projection from the petrous part. It is about 2 cm long. The **stylomastoid foramen,** between it and the mastoid process, transmits the facial nerve.

The squamous and tympanic parts of the temporal bone develop in membrane, the petromastoid and styloid parts in cartilage (the styloid from the cartilage of the second pharyngeal arch). The four parts do not fuse until after birth.

Occipital Bone

This has a basilar, a squamous and two lateral portions situated around the **foramen magnum.**

The **basilar portion** lies anterior to the foramen magnum and articulates with the body of the sphenoid bone. In the midline near the foramen is the **pharyngeal tubercle.**

The **squamous part** is a flat plate behind the foramen magnum extending at first backwards and then upwards to articulate with the parietal and squamous temporal bones. The lower part of the outer surface carries the superior and inferior **nuchal lines** and the midline **external occipital protuberance;** it gives attachment to the postvertebral muscles. The intracranial surface is grooved by the superior sagittal and transverse sinuses.

The **lateral parts** bear, on their inferior surface, the **occipital condyles** for articulation with the atlas. Lateral to each condyle there is a projecting jugular process which forms the posterior wall of the jugular foramen. Anteriorly, the **hypoglossal canal** carries the hypoglossal nerve and posteriorly, an emissary vein passes through the **condylar canal.**

The smooth upper portion of the squamous part of the bone develops in membrane, the remainder of the bone in cartilage.

Parietal Bone

These are two convex quadrilateral plates of bone forming the posterior part of the vault of the skull. They meet at the sagittal suture and articulate anteriorly with the frontal bone at the coronal suture, laterally with the temporal bone and posteriorly with the occipital bone at the lambdoid suture. The area of greatest convexity on each bone is called the parietal tuberosity.

The bone develops in membrane.

Frontal Bone

This has a domed superior portion forming the anterior part of the vault of the skull; the two areas of maximum convexity are called the frontal tuberosities. The inferiorly placed horizontal **orbital plates** contribute to the roof of each orbit. The bone articulates superiorly with the parietal bones at the coronal suture, and inferiorly with the greater wing of the sphenoid, the zygomatic, nasal and ethmoid bones and the frontal process of the maxilla. The orbital plates meet the lesser wings of the sphenoid posteriorly. The paired **frontal air sinuses** are situated in the bone above the nose and the medial part of the orbit.

The bone develops in membrane in two halves which fuse about the 5th year. The suture between the halves is known as the metopic suture when it persists in the adult.

Zygomatic Bone

These are irregular bones forming the prominence of each cheek.

The orbital surface forms the anterior part of the lateral wall of the orbit; the lateral surface forms the prominence of the cheek; the temporal surface forms the anterior limit of the temporal fossa.

The temporal process forms the anterior part of the zygomatic arch, the frontal process articulates with the frontal bone; the maxillary process articulates with the maxillary bone; the orbital process articulates with the greater wing of the sphenoid.

The bone ossifies in membrane.

Nasal Bone

The two nasal bones meet in the midline and form the skeleton of the upper part of the external nose. They articulate superiorly with the frontal bone, laterally with the frontal processes of the maxillae and inferiorly with the nasal cartilages. They are formed in membrane.

Ethmoid Bone

This consists of a midline **perpendicular plate** and a perforated horizontal **cribriform plate** uniting the upper extremities of two lateral portions, the ethmoidal labyrinths. The perpendicular plate forms part of the nasal septum. The cribriform plate transmits the olfactory nerves and bears a midline upward projection, the **crista galli.**

Each **ethmoidal labyrinth** is thin walled and contains the ethmoidal air cells. It separates the medial wall of the orbit from the upper part of the lateral wall of the nose, lies in front of the body of the sphenoid and is covered superiorly by the orbital plate of the frontal bone. The superior and middle nasal **conchae** project from its medial wall into the nasal cavity and below the middle concha it forms the **bulla ethmoidalis,** a bulge containing the middle ethmoidal air cells.

The bone develops in cartilage.

Lacrimal Bone

These are small thin bones possessing medial and lateral surfaces. Each forms, with the frontal process of the maxilla, a hollow for the lacrimal sac and the upper part of the nasolacrimal duct. It forms part of the medial wall of the orbit.

The bone develops in membrane.

Palatine Bone

Each consists of a horizontal and a vertical plate. The two plates unite at right angles and the posterior part of the union expands to form a **tubercle** which separates the maxilla from the pterygoid process of the sphenoid bone.

The **horizontal plates** form the posterior third of the hard palate. Each **vertical plate** overlies the medial wall of the maxilla enclosing a canal for the greater palatine vessels and the anterior palatine nerve. The upper end of the vertical plate forms a small process which contributes to the floor in the apex of the orbit, and medial to this there is a notch which meets the body of the sphenoid to form the **sphenopalatine foramen.**

The bone develops in membrane.

Inferior Concha Bone

Each is a thin plate of bone which curls downwards and medially from the lower part of the lateral wall of the nose. It forms the lower medial wall of the maxillary air sinus and of the nasolacrimal duct which opens below it.

The bone develops in membrane.

Vomer

This is a thin midline plate of bone forming the posterior part of the nasal septum. It is quadrilateral in shape articulating with the body of the sphenoid above, the hard palate below, and the perpendicular plate of the ethmoid anteriorly. It has a free posterior border.

The bone develops in membrane.

Hyoid Bone

This is a U-shaped bone situated below and behind the mandible and slung from the styloid process by the stylohyoid ligament which passes to its lesser horn.

The bone consists of an anterior horizontal midline bar, the body, from each end of which extend narrow greater and lesser horns. The greater horn projects backwards and the short lesser horn passes upwards and slightly backwards. The hyoid gives attachment superiorly to muscles passing to the tongue, mandible and base of the skull. Inferiorly, a membrane passes to the thyroid cartilage, and muscles pass to this cartilage, and to the sternum, clavicle and scapula.

The bone develops from the 2nd and 3rd pharyngeal arch cartilages.

THE SCALP

The scalp is the term given to the soft tissue over the vault of the skull. It consists of five layers.

(*a*) The skin is thick, containing many hair follicles and sweat glands.

(*b*) The superficial fascia is fibrous and adherent to the skin and underlying aponeurosis. It is richly supplied with vessels and nerves.

(*c*) The epicranial aponeurosis is a musculofibrous layer containing the **occipitalis** muscle behind and the **frontalis** muscle in front. The occipitalis is attached to the superior nuchal line. Laterally the aponeurosis is attached to the temporal fascia. Anteriorly the frontalis has no bony attachment but blends with the fibres of the orbicularis oculi muscles. The occipito-frontalis muscle draws the scalp backwards and forwards and raises the eyebrows; it is innervated by the facial nerve.

(*d*) A layer of loose areolar tissue allows free movement of the aponeurosis and adherent skin over the periosteum.

(*e*) The periosteum (pericranium) of the bones of the vault is continuous through the sutures with the endocranium.

The scalp is richly supplied by anastomosing branches of the external carotid artery (occipital, posterior auricular and superficial temporal) and of the ophthalmic artery (supra-orbital and supratrochlear). Scalp wounds bleed profusely. The veins pass with the arteries to reach the jugular vessels but may communicate with the diploic veins of the skull or through emissary veins with the intracranial venous sinuses.

The sensory innervation of the scalp is from the trigeminal, lesser and greater occipital nerves, and other branches of the dorsal rami of the upper three cervical nerves (see Fig. 30.2).

The lymph vessels pass to adjacent nodes in the circular chain around the base of the skull (see page 341).

THE FACE

The face contains the anterior openings of the mouth, nose and orbit. Its skin is thin and vascular, and closely bound down to the underlying superficial fascia and muscles. There is no deep fascia on the face.

FACIAL MUSCLES (Fig. 25.5)

These are the muscles of facial expression; they are arranged as sphincters and dilators around the openings of the mouth, nose and orbit.

The muscles are derived from the mesoderm of the 2nd pharyngeal arch and are supplied by the facial nerve.

1. Orbicularis oris—is the sphincter surrounding the mouth and forms the greater part of the substance of the lips. When it contracts it

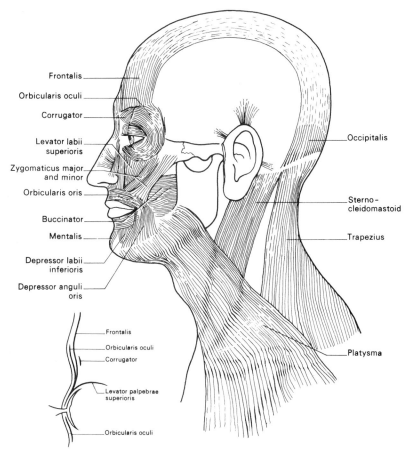

Frontalis

Orbicularis oculi

Corrugator

Levator labii superioris

Zygomaticus major and minor

Orbicularis oris

Buccinator

Mentalis

Depressor labii inferioris

Depressor anguli oris

Occipitalis

Sterno-cleidomastoid

Trapezius

Platysma

Frontalis

Orbicularis oculi

Corrugator

Levator palpebrae superioris

Orbicularis oculi

FIG. 25.5
The superficial muscles of the head and neck. Inset: the muscle relations in the eyelids.

produces a small orifice, as in whistling. Other muscles blend with and reinforce the orbicularis oris, particularly the buccinator and the levator and depressor muscles. These last muscles are attached to the angles of the mouth (anguli) and also to the middle of the lips (labii).

2. Buccinator—forms the greater part of the substance of the cheek. It has a continuous lateral attachment to the pterygomandibular raphé and the outer surfaces of the maxillae and mandible adjacent to the last molar teeth. (The buccinator and superior constrictor have a common attachment to the pterygomandibular raphé.) The fibres pass medially, decussate behind the angle of the mouth and enter the lips to blend with orbicularis oris. The muscle is used to keep food between the teeth in chewing, and also in forced blowing.

3. The compressor and dilator nares—muscles pass from the maxilla to the nasal cartilages.

4. Orbicularis oculi—surrounds the opening of the orbit and has palpebral and orbital portions. The central palpebral fibres lie within the eyelids and are attached by the medial palpebral ligament to the frontal process of the maxilla. The peripheral orbital fibres surround the orbital margin and are attached medially to the medial palpebral ligament and directly to the frontal process of the maxilla. The fibres blend with frontalis above the orbit.

The palpebral part closes the eyelids in sleep, winking and blinking; the orbital part produces more positive closure of the eyelids and is used in frowning (see p. 281).

5. Platysma—is a broad flat sheet of muscle situated in the superficial fascia on each side of the neck. Superiorly it passes over the mandible to blend with the muscles around the mouth; inferiorly it blends with the superficial fascia over the upper part of the chest. The muscle is a weak depressor of the jaw.

The attachments of the above muscles and also of the corrugator, zygomaticus major and minor, levator labii superioris and depressor labii inferioris and depressor anguli oris are shown in Figure 25.5.

Vessels and nerves
The face is supplied mainly by the facial and transverse facial arteries and is drained by the facial and retromandibular veins. Sensory nerves pass to the three divisions of the trigeminal nerve and, over the angle of the jaw, to the greater auricular nerve (see Fig. 30.2). Motor innervation is by the facial nerve. Paralysis leads to loss of protection for the cornea of the eye, difficulties in eating and speaking, and has obvious social implications. The lymph drainage of the chin is to the submental nodes, that of the medial part of the cheek and face to the submandibular nodes, and of the forehead and lateral part of the cheek to the parotid nodes.

Development of the face
The face develops from a median frontonasal process and paired maxillary and mandibular processes. The frontonasal process is formed between the roof of the mouth and the forebrain. Its upper part forms the forehead. Two thickenings, the nasal placodes develop on its anterior aspect and sink to form nasal pits. The two pits divide the frontonasal process into a median and two lateral nasal processes. The nasal pits deepen to form the nasal sacs which extend backwards through the head

mesoderm separated by a median nasal septum. The median nasal processes become the premaxilla which is largely submerged and forms the part of the upper jaw carrying the incisor teeth. The mandibular processes comprise the first pharyngeal arch structures (p. 301); they form the lower jaw. The maxillary processes of the mandibular arch pass medially below the nasal pits to fuse with each other near the midline and form the upper lip. The nasolacrimal duct develops along the line of fusion of the frontonasal process and the maxillary process of each side. Palatine processes from the two maxillary processes fuse in the midline to form the hard and soft palates.

CHAPTER 26

THE ORBIT, NOSE AND MOUTH

THE ORBITAL CAVITY AND EYEBALL

The two **orbital cavities** (Fig. 26.1) lie within the facial skeleton and contain the eyeballs, extra-ocular muscles, vessels, nerves, glands and fat. Each cavity is pyramidal in shape with the apex posterior. It has a roof, floor, and medial and lateral walls. Anteriorly the cavity opens on to the face.

The roof is formed mainly by the orbital plate of the frontal bone and, posteriorly, by the lesser wing of the sphenoid. It separates the orbit from

FIG. 26.1
Diagram indicating the relations of the extra-ocular muscles and the nerves in the right orbital cavity.

the anterior cranial fossa. The floor, formed largely by the maxilla and zygoma, separates the orbit from the maxillary air sinus and has an inferior orbital fissure posteriorly which passes forwards into the infra-orbital canal. The lateral wall is formed by the zygomatic bone and the greater wing of the sphenoid, and separates the orbit from the temporal fossa. The medial wall consists of the frontal process of the maxilla, the lacrimal bone, the orbital plate of the ethmoid, and the body of the sphenoid bone, from before backwards. It separates the orbit from the ethmoidal air sinuses and the nasal cavity.

There are three posterior openings in the cavity, the superior and inferior orbital fissures laterally and the optic canal medially. The

superior orbital fissure lies between the greater and lesser wings of the sphenoid and opens into the middle cranial fossa. It is divided by the common tendinous attachment of the extra-ocular muscles into a narrow lateral and a wider medial part. The lateral part transmits the lacrimal, frontal and trochlear nerves, and the medial part the abducent, the superior division of the oculomotor, the nasociliary, and the inferior division of the oculomotor nerves, all from lateral to medial. The **inferior orbital fissure** lies between the floor and lateral wall and opens into the pterygopalatine fossa medially and the infratemporal fossa laterally. The maxillary nerve and its zygomatic branch, together with communicating veins to the pterygoid venous plexus, pass through the fissure. The **optic canal** opens into the apex of the cavity from the middle cranial fossa; it transmits the optic nerve with the meningeal coverings and the ophthalmic artery.

Anteriorly a wide canal passes downwards from the inferomedial angle of the orbital cavity to the nose; it contains the nasolacrimal duct.

THE EYEBALL (Fig. 26.2)

The eyeball is the visual organ. It is situated in the anterior part of the orbital cavity and is roughly spherical in shape, being distorted by an anterior projecting clear area. The optic nerve leaves it posteriorly.

The walls of the sphere have three coats: an outer fibrous (supporting) layer, a middle choroid (vascular) and an inner retinal (nervous). The eyeball is modified anteriorly to allow light to enter.

The fibrous coat forms the dense white **sclera** posteriorly, and anteriorly the transparent **cornea**. The **choroid** is vascular and pigmented. Anteriorly it has a circular thickening, the **ciliary body,** which contains the smooth ciliary muscle. In front of the ciliary body the choroid thins to form the **iris** with its central aperture, the **pupil.** The iris contains the circularly placed sphincter pupillae and radially arranged dilator pupillae. They alter the size of the pupil.

The **retina** contains the light receptors from which information is passed eventually along the optic nerve. The retina consists of 10 layers as shown in Figure 26.3. To the medial side of the posterior wall there is a paler area, the **optic disc,** where the optic nerve leaves the eyeball. About 3 mm lateral to the disc, where the visual axis projects on to the retina, there is a small depression, the **fovea centralis.** The area around is called the **macula** and is used mainly in daylight vision.

The anteriorly placed biconvex **lens** divides the cavity of the eyeball into two parts. The posterior part is filled with a jelly-like **vitreous body,** the anterior with the more fluid **aqueous humor.** The iris further divides the anterior part into the anterior chamber between the iris and the cornea, and the posterior chamber between the iris and the lens. The two chambers are in continuity through the pupil.

The lens is held in position by the suspensory ligament (zonular fibres) which passes from the periphery of the lens to the ciliary body. Accommodation is the process by which near objects are focused on to the retina. The ciliary muscle contracts, draws forwards the ciliary body and relaxes the suspensory ligament, thus allowing the lens, because of its inherent elasticity, to become more convex.

BLOOD SUPPLY: the central artery of the retina is a branch of the ophthalmic artery. Ciliary branches of the ophthalmic artery pass forwards mainly in the choroid. The veins collect to form four venae vorticosae which leave the eyeball posteriorly and pass to the ophthalmic veins.

NERVE SUPPLY: the optic nerve carries sensory fibres from the retina. The long ciliary nerves (from the nasociliary) and short ciliary nerves

Vitreous body
Retina
Choroid
Fovea centralis
Sclera

Ciliary body
Iris
Cornea
Lens
Aqueous humor
Anterior ⎤
Posterior ⎦ chamber
Conjunctiva

FIG. 26.2
Horizontal section through the eyeball.

(from the ciliary ganglion) pierce the sclera posteriorly. They carry autonomic fibres (to the sphincter and dilator pupillae and the ciliary muscles) and sensory fibres.

EMBRYOLOGY: the optic nerve, retina, ciliary body and iris develop as an outgrowth of the primitive forebrain; the cornea, sclera and choroid are condensations of mesoderm; and the lens is derived from ectoderm. (See also page 31.)

Orbital (bulbar) fascia: the eyeball is closely surrounded, behind the cornea, by the orbital fascia which separates it from the orbital fat. The fascia is pierced by, and forms a sheath around, the muscles attached to the sclera. Thickenings of the fascia are attached to the lacrimal and zygomatic bones and form the medial and lateral **check ligaments** respectively. A thickening below the eyeball forms the **suspensory ligament.**

Extra-ocular (Bulbar) Muscles (Fig. 26.1)

1. Rectus muscles—superior, inferior, medial and lateral.

ATTACHMENTS
Anterior—the muscles pass forwards, in the positions implied by their names, to the sclera just in front of the equator.

Posterior—a common tendinous ring which surrounds the optic canal and the medial end of the superior orbital fissure.

ACTIONS: the superior rectus turns the pupil upwards and medially, and the inferior rectus, downwards and medially. The lateral and medial recti turn the pupil to the corresponding side.

FIG. 26.3
Diagram of the layers of the retina.

2. Superior oblique—is attached posteriorly above the common tendinous ring. It passes forwards and its tendon hooks around a fibrocartilaginous pulley, the trochlea, on the superomedial border of the front of the orbit. It then passes backward and laterally between the superior rectus and the eyeball to gain its posterolateral surface behind the equator.

ACTION: the muscle turns the pupil downwards and laterally.

3. Inferior oblique—is attached to the anteromedial aspect of the floor of the orbit. It passes backwards and laterally below the inferior rectus to gain the posterolateral surface of the eyeball behind the equator.

ACTION: the muscle turns the pupil upwards and laterally.

4. Levator palpebrae superioris—is attached posteriorly above the common tendinous origin and anteriorly to the conjunctiva and tarsal plate.

ACTION: it raises the upper eyelid.

279

NERVE SUPPLY: the lateral rectus is supplied by the abducent nerve, the superior oblique by the trochlear nerve, the remaining muscles by the oculomotor nerve.

The Ophthalmic Artery

This is a branch of the internal carotid artery. It arises in the middle cranial fossa, enters the orbit through the optic canal and ends behind the medial side of the upper eyelid by dividing into supratrochlear and dorsal nasal branches.

RELATIONS: in the middle cranial fossa, the artery lies above the cavernous sinus, medial to the anterior clinoid process, inferolateral to the optic nerve. It passes through the optic canal inferior to the optic nerve. In the orbit, it passes medially over the optic nerve (in company with the nasociliary nerve) and passes forwards along the medial wall of the cavity.

BRANCHES

(i) central artery of the retina—arises near the apex of the orbit and enters the optic nerve.

(ii) ciliary branches—to the eyeball.

(iii) muscular branches.

(iv) further branches—accompany the supra-orbital, supratrochlear, anterior and posterior ethmoidal and lacrimal nerves.

The Ophthalmic Veins

Superior and inferior ophthalmic veins drain the orbital contents and pass through the superior orbital fissure to the cavernous sinus. They communicate posteriorly, through the inferior orbital fissure, with the pterygoid venous plexus. Anteriorly, they communicate with the facial vein near the medial angle of the eye, and thus infection may pass from the face through the orbit to the cavernous sinus.

Nerves of the Orbit

The nerves are described more fully in Chapter 28. Their relations are best understood by appreciating their positions within the superior orbital fissure (Fig. 26.1). Nerves passing outside the common tendinous ring remain outside the cone of extra-ocular muscles and those within the ring remain inside the cone.

THE EYELIDS

The orbital cavity is limited anteriorly by two movable skin folds, the larger upper and smaller lower eyelids. They are united medially and laterally and limit the palpebral fissure at its medial and lateral angles. Within the medial angle there is a pinkish elevation, the **lacrimal caruncle.** On the medial end of the margin of each lid there is a small elevation, the **lacrimal papilla,** on the apex of which is the **lacrimal punctum** (the opening of the lacrimal canaliculus).

Each eyelid comprises five layers, from without inwards:

(*a*) Skin.

(*b*) Superficial fascia.

(c) Palpebral fibres of obicularis oculi and levator palpebrae superioris (Fig. 25.5).

(d) **Tarsal plate**—this is an elliptical plate of dense fibrous tissue which is attached to the margin of the orbit by the **medial** and **lateral palpebral ligaments.** On the deep surface of the plate lie the tarsal (Meibomian) glands which are modified sebaceous glands. Their ducts open on to the lid margin.

(e) **Conjunctiva**—this is a thin layer of stratified squamous epithelium which lines the inner surface of both lids and is reflected over the front of the eyeball, so that when the lids are approximated, it encloses a narrow sac containing a small amount of fluid. Upper and lower pouches between the lids and the eyeball are known as the superior and inferior conjunctival fornices. A crescentic fold of conjunctiva, the semilunar fold, lies lateral to the lacrimal caruncle on the surface of the eyeball.

The skin and conjunctiva are in continuity around the free border of the lids. The eyelashes emerge through the skin on the margin of the lids and numerous small sebaceous glands are associated with the hair follicles. The eyelids are closed by the action of orbicularis oculi and the upper lid is raised by levator palpebrae superioris.

THE LACRIMAL APPARATUS

The front of the eyeball with its conjunctival covering, is continually being washed by lacrimal secretions which are drained by blinking, when the increased intraconjunctival pressure, produced by the closed lids, forces the tears into the puncta. The structures concerned with the production of the lacrimal fluid and its subsequent passage to the nasal cavity are collectively called the lacrimal apparatus. This comprises: the lacrimal gland and its ducts, the conjunctival sac, the lacrimal canaliculi, the lacrimal sac and the nasolacrimal duct.

Lacrimal Gland

This is a serous gland situated in the superolateral angle of the orbit behind the upper lid. It is almond-shaped and has a palpebral process which descends between the conjunctiva and the tarsal plate. It has 6–12 ducts which open into the superior conjunctival fornix.

It is supplied by the lacrimal branch of the ophthalmic artery and innervated by the facial nerve through the pterygopalatine ganglion, postganglionic fibres passing in the zygomatic and lacrimal nerves. Its lymph drainage is to the parotid lymph nodes.

Lacrimal Canaliculi

Each canal is about 10 mm long and passes from the lacrimal punctum in each eyelid medially, deep to the medial palpebral ligament, to the lacrimal sac.

Lacrimal Sac

This is a thin fibrous sac situated on the medial side of the orbit in the lacrimal fossa. It receives the lacrimal canaliculi and continues downwards as the nasolacrimal duct. The lacrimal sac and canaliculi are lined by stratified squamous epithelium.

Nasolacrimal Duct

This descends, having the maxillary bone laterally and the lacrimal bone and inferior concha medially, and opens into the inferior meatus of the nose. The opening is guarded by a fold of mucous membrane which prevents air passing upwards when blowing the nose. The duct is lined by columnar epithelium which is ciliated in places.

THE NOSE

The nose comprises the external nose and the two nasal cavities. The **external nose**, a prominent feature of the face, bears the anterior nasal openings, (the nostrils, nares). It is pyramidal in shape but varies in width and in the direction of the anterior nares in different individuals. Its skeleton is formed superiorly by the nasal bones which articulate with the frontal bone, and the frontal processes of the maxillae. Inferiorly

Fig. 26.4
Diagram of the bones forming the lateral wall of the nasal cavity.

it is formed by several cartilages which articulate with the nasal and maxillary bones and surround the anterior nares. The skin covering the external nose is freely movable over the nasal bones but more firmly attached over the cartilages. The part of the nasal cavities just within the external nose is the **vestibule,** the expanded lateral wall of which is called the **ala** of the nose.

The **nasal cavities** form the first part of the respiratory passage and extend from the anterior nares to the nasopharynx. They are lined mainly by respiratory epithelium, but superiorly with olfactory epithelium. The cavities are separated by a midline septum and each possesses a roof, a floor, lateral and medial walls, and anterior and posterior apertures.

The narrow **roof** lies below the anterior cranial fossa, it is arched anteroposteriorly. It is formed from the nasal cartilages, the nasal and frontal bones, the cribriform plate of the ethmoid and the body of the sphenoid from before backwards.

The horizontal **floor** forms part of the roof of the oral cavity, and is formed by the palatine process of the maxilla and the horizontal plate of the palatine bone. Anteriorly, in the midline, the incisive canal transmits the greater palatine artery and nasopalatine nerve.

The **medial wall** of the cavity is the nasal septum. It is formed by the septal cartilage, the perpendicular plate of the ethmoid and the vomer from before backwards, with small peripheral contributions from the palatine, maxillary and sphenoid bones.

The **lateral wall** (Fig. 26.4) lies medial to the orbit, ethmoid and maxillary air sinuses and the pterygopalatine fossa. Its surface area is greatly increased by three horizontal bony projections, the superior, middle and inferior nasal **conchae,** and by a series of diverticulae, the **paranasal air sinuses.** The inferior concha is the largest and lies about 1 cm above the floor of the nose. The superior and middle conchae are united anteriorly. The space below each concha is called a **meatus** and the space above the superior concha the spheno-ethmoidal recess. The sphenoid air sinus opens into the spheno-ethmoidal recess; the posterior ethmoidal air cells open into the superior meatus; the nasolacrimal duct opens into the inferior meatus. The middle meatus possesses a domed bulge, the **bulla ethmoidalis,** containing the middle ethmoidal air cells which open on to it. A semicircular groove below the bulla, the **hiatus semilunaris,** receives the openings of the frontal, anterior ethmoidal and maxillary air sinuses, from before backwards.

The skeleton of the lateral wall is formed mainly by the maxillary and ethmoid bones. The labyrinth of the ethmoid, containing the ethmoidal air sinuses, lies superiorly; the superior and middle conchae are both part of this bone. The maxilla, containing the maxillary air sinus, is deficient medially but is overlapped by the bulla ethmoidalis, the lacrimal bone, the vertical plate of the palatine bone and the inferior concha. The sphenopalatine foramen, between the vertical plate of the palatine bone and the body of the sphenoid in the roof of the cavity, leads into the pterygopalatine fossa. The greater palatine canal descends from the fossa, between the palatine and maxillary bones to the greater palatine foramen. The nasolacrimal duct descends between the maxilla laterally and the lacrimal bone and inferior concha medially. The wall is completed anteriorly by the nasal bone and cartilages, and posteriorly by the medial pterygoid plate articulating with the vertical plate of the palatine bone.

NERVE SUPPLY: from branches of the maxillary nerve and the anterior ethmoidal branch of the ophthalmic nerve. The lateral wall may be divided into quadrants; the upper anterior quadrant is supplied by the anterior ethmoidal nerve, the upper posterior by the nasal nerves, the lower posterior quadrant by the greater palatine nerve and the lower anterior by the anterior superior alveolar nerve. The roof and upper anterior half of the nasal septum are innervated by the anterior ethmoidal nerve, the floor and lower posterior half of the septum by the naso-palatine nerve. The olfactory mucosa, in the upper part of the cavity, is also supplied by the olfactory nerves.

BLOOD SUPPLY: from the ophthalmic, maxillary and facial arteries. The names of the arteries largely correspond to the nerves, the anterior inferior part of the cavity receiving additional branches from the facial artery. The veins drain to the pterygoid venous plexus and the facial vein.

LYMPH DRAINAGE: the anterior part of the cavity drains to the submandibular nodes and the posterior part to the retropharyngeal nodes.

HISTOLOGY: the nose is lined by vascular mucoperiosteum. The superior concha, the roof and adjoining nasal septum are covered by yellow olfactory epithelium consisting of supporting cells around the endings of the bipolar olfactory cells. The rest of the cavity is lined by respiratory epithelium. The nose warms and moistens the inhaled air, some of which passes over the olfactory endings. Owing to its connection with the oropharynx, it modifies sounds produced by the larynx.

THE PARANASAL AIR SINUSES

Paired frontal, maxillary, ethmoidal and sphenoidal air sinuses are found within the corresponding bones. The sinuses develop as a series of diverticula from each nasal cavity and are lined by extensions of its mucoperiosteum. They are small at birth, enlarge mainly during the eruption of the second dentition and reach their adult size soon after puberty. They lighten the front of the skull and may increase the resonance of the voice. Their presence may be due to an overgrowth of the diploë. The sinuses are often the site of infection, drainage is poor and their lymph vessels pass mainly to the deeply placed retropharyngeal nodes.

1. Frontal—is situated above the medial end of the superciliary arch separated by a bony septum from its fellow. It lies anterior to the anterior cranial fossa and above the orbit. Each opens into the middle meatus of the nasal cavity through the long, narrow frontonasal duct which traverses the anterior ethmoidal air cells. The sinus is supplied by the supra-orbital vessels and nerves.

2. Ethmoidal—each ethmoidal labyrinth, lying between the orbit and the upper part of the nose, contains numerous air cells which are divided into anterior, middle and posterior groups. The anterior group drains into the anterior part of the hiatus semilunaris: the middle group opens on to the bulla ethmoidalis, within which the air cells are situated; the posterior group drains into the superior meatus. The sinuses are supplied by the anterior and posterior ethmoidal vessels and nerves.

3. Sphenoidal—are contained within the body of the sphenoid bone and usually communicate with each other through an incomplete bony septum. They lie below the sella turcica and the pituitary gland, medial to the cavernous sinus and its contents, and above the nasal cavity. Each sinus opens into the spheno-ethmoidal recess and is supplied by the posterior ethmoidal vessels and nerve.

4. Maxillary—is the largest of the paranasal air sinuses and is pyramidal in shape. Its base forms part of the lateral wall of the nose.

Its apex projects laterally into the zygomatic process of the maxilla. The roof separates the sinus from the orbit and transmits the infra-orbital vessels and nerve in a canal. The floor is the alveolar margin containing the molar teeth, the roots of which project into the cavity covered only by a thin layer of bone. The posterior wall contains the posterior superior alveolar nerve and lies in front of the infratemporal and pterygopalatine fossae. The anterior wall is the facial surface of the maxilla which is covered by the mucous membrane of the vestibule of the mouth. The medial wall (base) forms part of the lateral wall of the nose and is completed by the inferior concha and parts of the ethmoid, lacrimal and palatine bones (Fig. 26.4). The sinus opens into the hiatus semilunaris posteriorly. The opening is high on the base of the sinus and does not facilitate drainage. The mucoperiosteum is supplied by the anterior and posterior superior alveolar vessels and nerves. Its lymph vessels pass to the submandibular and retropharyngeal nodes.

In a healthy state the sinuses contain air but in the event of fluid formation, because of infection or a fracture, the fluid level may be demonstrated radiologically.

THE ORAL CAVITY

This is the first part of the alimentary tract and extends from the lips to the isthmus of the fauces. It contains the tongue, alveolar arches with the gums and teeth, and receives the openings of the salivary glands. Its mucous membrane is lined throughout by stratified squamous epithelium. The alveolar arches, gums and teeth divide the cavity into an outer vestibule and an inner mouth cavity proper.

The **vestibule** is a slit-like cavity limited externally by the lips and cheeks, and opens on to the face between the lips at the oral fissure. Internally it is limited by the gums and teeth. It communicates with the mouth cavity proper either between the teeth or, when the teeth are occluded, through the retromolar spaces behind the last molars. The cavity is limited superiorly and inferiorly by the mucous membrane passing from the lips and cheeks on to the alveolar margins. The parotid duct opens into the vestibule at the level of the crown of the second upper molar tooth.

The **mouth cavity proper** is limited anteriorly and laterally by the gums and teeth, and possesses a roof, a floor and a posterior opening. The roof is formed by the palate which separates the mouth from the nasal cavities. Much of the floor is occupied by the tongue from which the mucous membrane extends to the mandibular alveolar arch. A midline fold of mucous membrane, the **frenulum,** connects the under surface of the tongue to the floor. On each side of the base of the frenulum is a **sublingual papilla** on to which opens the submandibular duct. Passing backwards from the papillae, the **sublingual folds** of mucous membrane cover the sublingual glands. The posterior opening of the oral cavity is the **fauceal isthmus** which is bounded laterally by the palatoglossal fold (the anterior arch of the fauces), superiorly by the soft palate and inferiorly by the back of the tongue.

Gums

The gums surround the necks of the teeth and are composed of fibrous tissue covered with a vascular mucous membrane. They are firmly attached to the alveolar margins but less so to the necks of the teeth.

THE TEETH

Each tooth consists of a projecting crown, a neck surrounded by the gum and one or more roots embedded in the alveolar bone. It has a central cavity which opens on to the apex of the root and is filled with **pulp** (loose connective tissue containing vessels and nerves). The cavity is surrounded by **dentine,** a hard calcified material which forms the bulk of the tooth. The dentine of the crown is covered by **enamel,** a very hard inorganic layer, and that of the root by **cementum,** a bone-like material. The modified periosteum of the alveolar socket **(periodontal membrane)** holds the root in position.

The teeth are named, from in front laterally: incisors (I); canines (C); premolars (P) and molars (M). They vary in shape, size and function.

Crowns—incisors have sharp cutting edges used for biting food. Canines are large and conical. Premolars (bicuspid teeth) and molars (with three to five tubercles) are used in chewing.

Roots—the incisors, canines and premolars, with the exception of the 1st upper premolar, possess a single root; the 1st upper premolar and lower molars have two roots and the upper molars three roots.

Man has two sets of teeth which erupt at different times. The deciduous (milk) teeth appear between the 6th and 24th months; they are replaced by the permanent teeth which appear between the 6th and 25th years. Each half of each jaw contains five deciduous (I2, C1, M2) and eight permanent teeth (I2, C1, P2, M3).

The average eruption times of each half of the upper and lower jaws are:

	I		C	M		
DECIDUOUS:	7	8	18	12	24	MONTHS
	6	9	18	12	24	

	I		C	P		M			
PERMANENT:	7	8	12	9	10	6	12	18+	YEARS
	7	8	12	9	10	6	12	18+	

N.B. The first deciduous tooth is a lower central incisor, the first permanent tooth is a 1st molar. The lower permanent teeth appear slighly earlier than the upper. The wisdom teeth (3rd molars) appear between the 17th and 25th years.

NERVE AND BLOOD SUPPLY: the teeth of the upper jaw are innervated by the anterior and posterior superior alveolar nerves, the lower by the inferior alveolar nerve. The central incisors have a bilateral innervation. The blood supply is by the corresponding arteries.

The upper gums—the labial surface is supplied by the infra-orbital and posterior superior alveolar nerves, the palatine surface by the naso-palatine and greater palatine nerves.

The lower gums—the labial surface is supplied by the mental and buccal nerves, the lingual surface by the lingual nerve.

EMBRYOLOGY: an ectodermal fold grows from the mouth cavity into the mesoderm of the maxillary and mandibular alveolar arches. This is the primary dental lamina, and cup-shaped buds from it produce the enamel of each tooth. The mesoderm within the cup forms the dentine, cementum and pulp. Both deciduous and permanent teeth are formed in this manner and, after the formation of the latter, the primary dental lamina disappears. X-rays have shown many of the details of postnatal tooth development.

THE PALATE

This forms the roof of the mouth and separates the mouth from the nasal cavities. It consists of the hard palate anteriorly and the soft palate posteriorly.

Hard Palate

This is formed by the palatine processes of the maxillae and the horizontal plates of the palatine bones. The anterior midline **incisive foramen** transmits the nasopalatine nerve and the greater palatine artery. The greater and lesser palatine foramina are situated postero-laterally and transmit the greater and lesser palatine vessels and nerves. The hard palate is covered by a mucoperiosteum which is rich in mucous glands and is continuous anteriorly and laterally with the gums, and posteriorly with the mucous membrane over the soft palate. It is supplied by the greater and lesser palatine vessels and nerves except for the area behind the incisor teeth which is supplied by the nasopalatine nerve. Its lymph vessels pass to the deep cervical lymph nodes. The palate develops from the palatine process of the maxillary process on each side and the midline premaxillary process of the frontonasal process.

Soft Palate

This is a movable partition between the naso- and oro-pharynx. It consists of a number of paired muscles covered by a fold of mucous membrane. Anteriorly it is attached to the back of the hard palate. Its posterior free border has a midline conical projection, the **uvula.** On each side two vertical folds, the anterior and posterior arches of the fauces, pass from its anterior surface to the tongue and pharynx. They contain the palatoglossus and palatopharyngeus muscles respectively.

Muscles of the Soft Palate

1. Tensor veli palatini—is attached superiorly to the auditory tube and the base of the skull between the pterygoid fossa and the spine of the sphenoid. Its fibres converge on to a narrow tendon which hooks medially around the hamulus. In the palate the tendon fans out to join that of the opposite side and form the palatine aponeurosis. The aponeurosis, which is attached to the back of the hard palate, is the 'skeleton' of the palate and the other palatine muscles are attached to it.

2. Levator veli palatini—is attached superiorly to the auditory tube and the apex of the petrous temporal bone. It descends in the lateral wall of the nasopharynx to blend with the palate.

3. Palatoglossus—passes from the palate to the side of the tongue.

4. Palatopharyngeus—descends from the palate, blends with the inner surface of the constrictor muscles and gains attachment to the posterior border of the thyroid cartilage. Some of the fibres pass horizontally around the inner surface of the superior constrictor and form the palatopharyngeal sphincter.

Movement of these muscles plays an important role in swallowing (p. 302).

NERVE SUPPLY : the tensor palatini is innervated by the medial pterygoid branch of the mandibular nerve, and the other muscles by the vagus nerve via the pharyngeal plexus. The cell bodies lie in the nucleus ambiguus. The mucous membrane is innervated by the greater and lesser palatine branches of the maxillary nerve. Taste fibres may also be present in these nerves.

BLOOD SUPPLY : palatine branches of the maxillary, facial, and lingual arteries; the venous drainage is to the pharyngeal venous plexus.

LYMPH DRAINAGE : to the deep cervical lymph chain.

HISTOLOGY : the upper surface is covered by respiratory epithelium and the lower by stratified squamous. Numerous mucous glands are present on both surfaces.

THE TONGUE (Fig. 26.5)

This is a muscular organ situated in the floor of the mouth and oropharynx. It is the shape of an inverted shoe, attached mainly to the hyoid bone and the mandible, and resting on the geniohyoid and mylohyoid muscles. The tip is free and projects anteriorly. The upper surface (dorsum) is covered by mucous membrane and is divided by a V-shaped groove, the **sulcus terminalis,** into an anterior two-thirds and a posterior third. There is a small pit, the **foramen caecum,** at the apex of the sulcus. The two parts differ in their nerve supply, histology and development. The mucous membrane which is continued from the dorsum to the anterior surface of the epiglottis, is raised in a midline glosso-epiglottic fold. The fold separates two shallow fossae, the **valleculae,** which are limited laterally by the pharyngeal wall. The lower surface of the tongue is also covered by mucous membrane and attached by a midline fold of mucous membrane, the **frenulum,** to the floor of the mouth.

Muscles of the Tongue

Intrinsic and extrinsic muscles lie on each side of a midline fibrous septum. The fine intrinsic muscles are arranged in vertical, horizontal and transverse bundles. The coarse extrinsic muscles connect the tongue to the mandible, hyoid bone, styloid process and palate. The extrinsic muscles mainly alter the position of the tongue and the intrinsic muscles its shape.

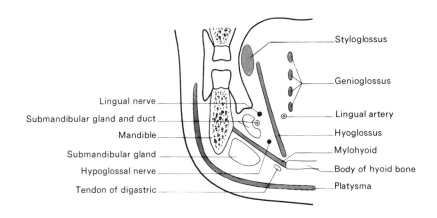

FIG. 26.5
Diagrammatic lay-out of the main structures seen in a coronal section at the level of the 2nd molar teeth.

1. Genioglossus—is attached to the mental spine on the mandible. The fibres pass backwards and fan out to be attached to the tip and the whole length of the dorsum of the tongue.

2. Hyoglossus—this thin quadrilateral muscle is attached to the body and greater horns of the hyoid bone, and passes upwards and forwards into the side of the tongue.

RELATIONS: medially from before backwards are the lingual artery, the middle constrictor, the stylohyoid ligament, the intrinsic muscles of the tongue and the glossopharyngeal nerve. Laterally, from above downwards, are styloglossus, the lingual nerve, the submandibular ganglion, the submandibular gland and its duct, the sublingual gland and the hypoglossal nerve. Lateral to these is the mylohyoid muscle.

3. Styloglossus (see page 301) and **palatoglossus** (see page 288).

BLOOD SUPPLY: lingual artery, whose dorsal lingual branch passes to the posterior third and whose deep branch passes to the tip and the rest of the tongue. The deep lingual vein passes along the inferior surface of the tongue, lateral to hyoglossus and then enters the lingual vein accompanying the lingual artery. The dorsal lingual vein is also a tributary of the lingual vein which then enters the internal jugular vein.

NERVE SUPPLY: the mucous membrane of the anterior two-thirds is supplied by the lingual nerve. Taste fibres leave the nerve in the chorda tympani and are then conveyed by the facial nerve to the nucleus of the tractus solitarius. The glossopharyngeal nerve carries both taste and common sensation from the posterior third. All the extrinsic and intrinsic muscles of the tongue, except palatoglossus, are supplied by the hypoglossal nerve. Palatoglossus is supplied by the vagus nerve, through the pharyngeal plexus.

LYMPH DRAINAGE: vessels from the tip of the tongue pass bilaterally to the submental lymph nodes. The sides drain to the ipsilateral submandibular lymph nodes, and the dorsum drains to these nodes and the jugulodigastric nodes of both sides. The posterior third drains to the retropharyngeal and jugulodigastric nodes of both sides. From all these nodes, efferent vessels pass to the jugulo-omohyoid and other nodes of the deep cervical lymph chain.

HISTOLOGY: the mucous membrane of the anterior part of the dorsum is thin and possesses numerous papillae. The papillae are of three types.

(a) Fungiform papillae—numerous small rounded projections mainly on the tip and margins of the tongue. They have a few taste buds.

(b) Filiform papillae—the most numerous, conical and arranged in rows.

(c) Seven to twelve circumvallate papillae lie just in front of the sulcus terminalis; they are surrounded by a moat, the walls of which have many taste buds and are innervated by the glossopharyngeal nerve.

Taste buds are found all over the dorsum and sides of the tongue (and also on the epiglottis and the soft palate). The mucous membrane of the inferior surface resembles that over the rest of the oral cavity and contains scattered small salivary glands. The mucous membrane over the posterior third of the tongue is thick and loose with numerous mucous glands and aggregations of lymphoid tissue, the **lingual tonsil.**

EMBRYOLOGY: the mucous membrane of the anterior two-thirds is formed of endoderm from the two lateral lingual swellings on the floor of the pharynx over the 1st arch. A midline swelling between the 1st and 2nd arches, the tuberculum impar, forms a small part of the tongue in front of the foramen caecum. The posterior third is formed from a midline swelling over the 3rd and 4th arches, the copula. The muscles of the tongue develop from suboccipital myotomes which migrate forwards around the pharynx carrying the hypoglossal nerve with them.

FUNCTION: the tongue is concerned in chewing, swallowing, talking and (in the infant) suckling.

Muscles of the Floor of the Mouth

1. Mylohyoid—the two mylohyoid muscles form a diaphragm across the floor of the mouth. Each is attached anterolaterally to the mylohyoid line on the mandible. Its fibres pass downwards and medially, the posterior to the body of the hyoid bone, the anterior to a midline raphé between the hyoid bone and the symphysis menti. It is supplied by the mylohyoid branch of the inferior alveolar nerve.

2. Geniohyoid—lies above the mylohyoid and passes from the mental spine on the mandible to the body of the hyoid bone. It is supplied by C.1 fibres carried in the hypoglossal nerve.

3. Digastric—consists of two fleshy bellies united by an intermediate tendon which is slung by a fibrous sheath to the greater horn of the hyoid bone. The posterior belly is attached to a groove on the medial side of the mastoid process and the anterior belly to the digastric fossa on the mandible. The posterior belly is supplied by the facial nerve, the anterior belly by the mylohyoid branch of the inferior alveolar nerve.

RELATIONS of the posterior belly: it crosses, from behind forwards, the transverse process of the atlas, the accessory nerve, the internal jugular vein, the hypoglossal nerve, the internal and external carotid arteries, the facial and lingual arteries, and hyoglossus. The posterior auricular artery runs along its upper border, the occipital artery along its lower. Stylohyoid splits around its upper border which grooves the lower part of the parotid gland.

ACTION: the three muscles on each side raise the hyoid bone in swallowing or when the hyoid bone is fixed, depress the mandible.

SALIVARY GLANDS

Comprise three paired glands—the parotid, submandibular and sublingual—and numerous smaller ones around the mouth cavity. Their secretions clean and moisten the mouth, assisting in chewing, digestion, swallowing and phonation. The duct systems of the parotid and submandibular glands can be demonstrated in the living by injecting a radio-opaque solution into the opening of the main ducts.

THE PAROTID GLAND (Figs. 26.6, 26.7)
This is the largest of the paired salivary glands. It is wedged between the ramus of the mandible in front, the mastoid process behind and the styloid process medially. Each of these bones has muscles attached to it. The gland has an irregular shape and is described as having anteromedial, posteromedial and superficial surfaces. The anterior border overlies the masseter and from it the duct passes forwards across the muscle to turn medially around its anterior border and pierce buccinator. The duct opens on to the mucous membrane of the cheek opposite the crown of the second upper molar tooth; it is about 5 cm long. A detached part of the gland, the accessory lobe, is often found lying on the masseter above the duct. The deep (investing) layer of cervical fascia covers the superficial surface of the gland. The fascia is less well defined deep to the gland but forms the stylomandibular ligament which separates the parotid and submandibular glands.

RELATIONS: the superficial surface is covered by skin and fascia. The superficial parotid lymph nodes are partly embedded in the surface. The anteromedial surface is wrapped around the ramus of the mandible and extends on to masseter laterally and medial pterygoid medially. The posteromedial surface lies on the mastoid process, sternocleidomastoid and the posterior belly of digastric. The deep medial part of the gland is separated by the styloid process and its attached muscles from the carotid sheath and the pharynx. The upper part of the gland lies between the temporo-mandibular joint and the external acoustic meatus. The inferior part lies on the posterior belly of digastric and the stylomandibular ligament. The gland is traversed by the external carotid artery deeply, the retro-mandibular vein, and the facial nerve, superficially.

FIG. 26.6
Left parotid sialogram. The duct system of the gland is outlined by the radiopaque substance injected through the cannula (1).

1. Cannula
2. Main parotid duct

3. Outline of gland as shown by duct system
4. Angle of mandible

BLOOD SUPPLY: branches of the external carotid artery. Venous blood passes to the retromandibular vein.

NERVE SUPPLY: sympathetic fibres from the superior cervical ganglion pass along the external carotid artery; parasympathetic fibres come from the glossopharyngeal nerve via the otic ganglion and the auriculotemporal nerve.

LYMPH DRAINAGE: superficial part to the parotid nodes, deep part to the retropharyngeal nodes.

HISTOLOGY AND EMBRYOLOGY: the gland is lobulated and consists of serous alveoli with cubical-lined collecting ducts. It develops as a tubular ectodermal outgrowth from the inside of the cheek.

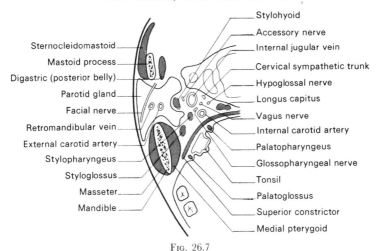

Sternocleidomastoid

Mastoid process

Digastric (posterior belly)

Parotid gland

Facial nerve

Retromandibular vein

External carotid artery

Stylopharyngeus

Styloglossus

Masseter

Mandible

Stylohyoid

Accessory nerve

Internal jugular vein

Cervical sympathetic trunk

Hypoglossal nerve

Longus capitus

Vagus nerve

Internal carotid artery

Palatopharyngeus

Glossopharyngeal nerve

Tonsil

Palatoglossus

Superior constrictor

Medial pterygoid

Fig. 26.7
Diagrammatic lay-out of the main structures seen in a oblique section
through the parotid gland and the palatine tonsil.

THE SUBMANDIBULAR GLAND (Fig. 26.5)

This is situated in the floor of the mouth and has a fibrous capsule. The gland is divided into superficial and deep parts which communicate round the posterior border of mylohyoid. The submandibular duct passes forwards from the deep part of the gland, between mylohyoid and hyoglossus, medial to the sublingual gland and opens on to the sublingual papilla in the floor of the mouth at the base of the frenulum. It is crossed laterally, from above downwards, by the lingual nerve which then turns up medial to it.

RELATIONS

Superficial part—superomedially are mylohyoid and the anterior belly of digastric; superolaterally are the body of the mandible and medial pterygoid; inferiorly are the deep investing layer of fascia of the neck, the submandibular lymph nodes, superficial fascia with platysma and skin. The facial artery, having grooved the posterior surface of the gland, passes laterally over it to reach the inferior border of the body of the mandible.

Deep part—is wedged between mylohyoid and hyoglossus. On the latter it is related to the lingual nerve and the submandibular ganglion above and the hypoglossal nerve below. Posteriorly it lies on the middle constrictor, where the hypoglossal nerve crosses the loop of the lingual artery.

BLOOD SUPPLY: facial and lingual arteries. Venous blood passes to the facial and lingual veins.

NERVE SUPPLY: sympathetic fibres from the superior cervical ganglion pass along the arteries of the gland; parasympathetic fibres from the facial nerve via the chorda tympani and the submandibular ganglion.

LYMPH DRAINAGE: to the overlying submandibular lymph nodes.

293

HISTOLOGY AND EMBRYOLOGY: the submandibular is a mixed salivary gland possessing both serous and mucous cells. The serous form darkly staining crescents opposite the openings of the alveolar ducts. The gland develops as a tubular endodermal outgrowth from the floor of the mouth.

THE SUBLINGUAL GLAND

This is situated below the mucous membrane of the floor of the mouth. Its secretions (mainly mucous) pass either into the submandibular duct or directly into the mouth cavity by 15–20 small ducts. It resembles the submandibular gland in its blood and nerve supply, lymph drainage, histology and development.

RELATIONS: superiorly—the sublingual fold of mucous membrane; inferiorly—mylohyoid; laterally—the body of the mandible; medially— the submandibular duct, the lingual nerve, and hyoglossus and genioglossus muscles.

CHAPTER 27

THE TEMPOROMANDIBULAR JOINT, PHARYNX AND LARYNX

THE TEMPOROMANDIBULAR JOINT

This is a synovial joint of a modified hinge variety between the condyle of the mandible and the mandibular fossa and articular tubercle of the squamous temporal bone. The hemicylindrical condyle is directed medially and slightly backwards, the temporal articular surface is concavo-convex from behind forwards, extending from the squamo-tympanic fissure to the front of the articular tubercle. The articular surfaces are lined by fibrocartilage, unlike most other synovial joints.

LIGAMENTS

(a) Capsular: attached around the neck of the mandible and to the articular margins on the temporal bone.

(b) Capsular thickenings: the **lateral ligament**—a strong band passing downwards and backwards from the inferior surface of the zygomatic arch to the back of the neck of the mandible.

(c) Accessory ligaments:

(i) **sphenomandibular ligament**—passes from the spine of the sphenoid to the lingula of the mandible.

(ii) **stylomandibular ligament**—a thickening of the deep layer of the cervical fascia passes from the styloid process to the posterior border of the ramus of the mandible.

INTRACAPSULAR STRUCTURES: a fibrocartilaginous disc, whose margins are attached to the capsule, completely divides the joint cavity into superior and inferior compartments each with its own synovial membrane. The disc has a concave undersurface and a concavo-convex upper surface. The lateral pterygoid tendon is attached to the anterior aspect of the capsule and to the disc.

FUNCTIONAL ASPECTS

Movement: the mandible may be depressed, elevated, protruded and retracted as in opening and closing the mouth, and moved from side to side as in grinding movements. However, movement at the joint has two components, each occurring in a separate compartment of the joint.

(a) Gliding occurs in the upper compartment. The condyle of the mandible and the articular disc move together over the articular surface.

(b) Hinge movement occurs in the lower compartment. The condyle of the mandible articulates with the undersurface of the articular disc.

In mandibular movements these components are never completely dissociated; in depression and elevation both are equally involved but in protrusion, retraction and grinding movements the gliding component is predominant. Some of these details may be demonstrated by radio-logical means.

Depression—takes place about an axis passing through the lingulae. The condyle is pulled forwards by lateral pterygoid and the body is pulled downwards by geniohyoid, digastric and mylohyoid acting from a fixed hyoid bone. The movement is assisted by gravity.

Elevation—is around the same axis and is produced by masseter, temporalis and medial pterygoid.

Protrusion is produced by lateral and medial pterygoid muscles.

Retraction is produced by the posterior fibres of temporalis.

Grinding movements are composed of alternating protrusion and retraction on the two sides and are brought about by the appropriate muscles. In chewing, the mandible is moved from side to side and at the same time is elevated by masseter and temporalis, the muscles of the tongue and cheek keeping the food between the teeth.

Stability: this varies with the position of the mandible. The joint is most stable when the mandible is fully elevated because (*a*) the condyle lies within the articular fossa, (*b*) occlusion of the teeth prevents further upward movement, (*c*) the lateral ligament is taut in this position, preventing posterior dislocation. Contraction of the muscles is important in maintaining this position, and under anaesthesia the jaw drops open. In the resting position the teeth are separated slightly.

When the mandible is depressed the above factors are absent. The condyle lies on the articular tubercle and the integrity of the joint is dependent on the tone of the muscles and the strength of the capsule. Forward dislocation is the commonest form of displacement.

BLOOD SUPPLY: superficial temporal and maxillary arteries.

NERVE SUPPLY: auriculotemporal and masseteric nerves.

RELATIONS

Laterally—skin and superficial fascia.

Medially—sphenomandibular ligament, auriculotemporal nerve, and the middle meningeal artery.

Anteriorly—lateral pterygoid.

Posteriorly—the parotid gland and related structures, the auriculotemporal nerve and the tympanic plate of the temporal bone.

The chorda tympani emerges from the petrotympanic fissure just behind the capsule of the joint.

Muscles of Mastication

These muscles are all supplied by the mandibular division of the trigeminal nerve.

1. Masseter

ATTACHMENTS

Superior—lower border of the anterior two-thirds of the zygomatic arch.

Inferior—the fibres descend to the lateral surface of the ramus and angle of the mandible.

ACTION: elevation of the mandible.

296

2. Temporalis

ATTACHMENTS

Superior—lateral surface of the temporal bone below the temporal line. *Inferior*—from their wide upper attachment, the fibres converge on to a narrow tendon which is attached to the coronoid process and the anterior border of the ramus of the mandible. The anterior fibres are vertical, the posterior are horizontal.

ACTION: the anterior fibres elevate and the posterior fibres retract the mandible.

Temporal fascia—a dense sheet covering temporalis muscle. It has a continuous attachment to the temporal line above and the zygomatic arch below, and is continuous with the epicranial aponeurosis.

3. Medial Pterygoid

ATTACHMENTS

Superior, by two heads which embrace the lower fibres of lateral pterygoid—the deep from the medial surface of the lateral pterygoid plate, and the superficial from the maxillary tuberosity.

Inferior—the medial surface of the ramus and angle of the mandible.

ACTION: elevation and protrusion of the mandible.

4. Lateral Pterygoid

ATTACHMENTS

Anterior, by two heads—the upper from the infratemporal surface of the greater wing of the sphenoid, and the lower from the lateral surface of the lateral pterygoid plate.

Posterior—the neck of the mandible, and the capsule and intra-articular disc of the temporomandibular joint.

ACTION: protrusion and depression of the mandible.

Infratemporal Fossa

This fossa lies below the base of the skull behind the maxilla and pterygoid plates of the sphenoid bone and in front of the carotid sheath. It is limited medially by the pharynx and laterally by temporalis and the ramus of the mandible. Inferiorly it is continuous with the fascial spaces of the neck.

The fossa contains the lateral and medial pterygoid muscles, the mandibular division of the trigeminal nerve and its branches, the maxillary artery and branches, the pterygoid venous plexus, and the spheno-mandibular ligament.

THE PHARYNX

This is a muscular tube extending from the base of the skull to the level of the 6th cervical vertebra where it is continuous with the oeso-phagus. It is about 14 cm long. It lies behind, and communicates with, the nose, mouth and larynx, from above downwards, and is corres-pondingly divided into the naso-, oro- and laryngo-pharynx. Posteriorly it lies on the prevertebral fascia and muscles. Laterally it is related from above downwards to the auditory tube, the styloid process and its muscles, the carotid sheath and its contents, and the thyroid gland.

The walls of the pharynx have mucous, submucous and muscular coats.

(*a*) The mucous coat is continuous with that of the nose, auditory tube, oral cavity, larynx and oesophagus; in the nasopharynx it is lined with respiratory epithelium, and in the remainder with stratified squamous epithelium.

(*b*) The submucosa is thickened superiorly, where the muscular coat is deficient, to form the **pharyngobasilar fascia** which is attached to the base of the skull.

(*c*) The muscular coat comprises the superior, middle and inferior constrictor muscles, and the salpingo-, stylo- and palato-pharyngeus muscles.

The **superior constrictor** is attached anteriorly to—(i) the hamulus of the medial pterygoid plate, (ii) the retromolar fossa on the mandible, and (iii) between these attachments, to the pterygomandibular raphé.

The **middle constrictor** is attached anteriorly to—(i) the lower part of the stylohyoid ligament, (ii) the lesser horn of the hyoid bone and (iii) the greater horn of the hyoid bone.

The **inferior constrictor** is attached anteriorly to—(i) the oblique line on the thyroid cartilage, (ii) the fascia over cricothyroid and (iii) the lateral aspect of the cricoid cartilage.

Each constrictor fans out from its anterior attachment, passing posteriorly around the pharynx to join its fellow of the opposite side in a fibrous midline raphé. The raphé extends from the pharyngeal tubercle on the basilar part of the occipital bone down to the oesophagus. Owing to the posterior spreading of the muscles, the pairs overlap. The inferior lies outside the middle, which is itself outside the superior.

The salpingopharyngeus, stylopharyngeus and palatopharyngeus muscles are attached superiorly to the auditory tube, the styloid process and the soft palate respectively. They descend to blend with the inner surfaces of the constrictors and gain attachment to the posterior aspect of the lamina of the thyroid cartilage.

The muscles of the pharynx are concerned in swallowing (see page 302). They are all supplied by the vagus nerve via the pharyngeal plexus, with the exception of stylopharyngeus (supplied by the glossopharyngeal nerve). The cell bodies are in the nucleus ambiguus.

Between the superior constrictor and the base of the skull, the pharyngobasilar fascia is pierced by the auditory tube; between the superior and middle constrictors, stylopharyngeus and styloglossus and the glosso-pharyngeal nerve enter the pharyngeal wall; between the middle and inferior muscles pass the internal laryngeal nerve and the superior laryngeal artery to supply the larynx. The recurrent laryngeal nerve enters the region by ascending deep to the inferior constrictor.

The Interior of the Pharynx

Nasopharynx—lies behind the two posterior nasal openings **(choanae).** On each lateral wall are the opening of the auditory tube and a ridge produced by levator palati; a small diverticulum behind the ridge is the pharyngeal recess. Longus capitus bulges into the posterior wall and a submucous aggregation of lymphoid tissue, the pharyngeal tonsil (adenoids), is present. Superiorly the cavity is limited by the base of the occipital bone and the body of the sphenoid. Below, it communicates with the oropharynx through the pharyngeal isthmus, a constriction which may be closed by the backward-projecting, movable soft palate.

Oropharynx—extends down to the level of the upper border of the epiglottis where it is continuous with the laryngopharynx. Anteriorly it communicates through the **faucial isthmus** with the oral cavity. Below the faucial isthmus is the tongue which lies partly in the pharynx and partly in the oral cavity. In the lateral wall of the faucial isthmus are two folds of mucous membrane, the anterior and posterior arches of the fauces. They are produced by palatoglossus (extending from the undersurface of the palate to the side of the tongue) and palatopharyngeus (extending from the undersurface of the palate to the lateral wall of the pharynx) respectively. The **palatine tonsil** is situated between the anterior and posterior arches.

Laryngopharynx—extends from the oropharynx to the oesophagus. Anteriorly are the opening of the larynx and the posterior surfaces of the arytenoid and cricoid cartilages. The cavity extends forwards on each side of the larynx and the recesses so formed are the **piriform fossae.** Each fossa is bounded laterally by the mucous membrane over the lamina of the thyroid cartilage and medially by the mucous membrane over the ary-epiglottic folds and the arytenoid and cricoid cartilages. The lumen of the pharynx is narrowest near its union with the oesophagus.

BLOOD SUPPLY: branches from the ascending pharyngeal, superior thyroid, lingual, facial and maxillary arteries. Venous blood passes through the pharyngeal venous plexus to the internal jugular vein.

NERVE SUPPLY: mainly through the **pharyngeal plexus** on the outer surface of the middle constrictor. The plexus is formed by:
(i) sensory fibres in pharyngeal branches of the glossopharyngeal and vagus nerves.
(ii) the pharyngeal branch of the vagus carrying motor fibres from the nucleus ambiguus to all pharyngeal muscles except stylopharyngeus. (The fibres to the stylopharyngeus pass from the nucleus ambiguus in the glossopharyngeal nerve.)
(iii) branches from the cervical sympathetic chain.
The nasopharynx receives an added sensory supply from the pharyngeal branch of the maxillary nerve (through the pterygopalatine ganglion) and the laryngopharynx receives sensory branches from the internal and recurrent laryngeal nerves.

LYMPH DRAINAGE: the nasopharynx drains to the retropharyngeal lymph nodes and the remainder of the pharynx to nodes in the deep cervical lymph chain.

THE TONSIL (Fig. 26.7)

The tonsil (palatine tonsil) is a mass of lymphoid tissue situated in a fossa on the lateral wall of the faucial isthmus. It is variable in size, being usually larger in children. It is oval in shape, possessing upper and lower poles. The pitted medial surface is covered by stratified squamous epithelium and there is usually a well marked intratonsillar cleft between the upper pole and the superior wall of the fossa. The deep surface of the tonsil has a fibrous capsule and by this it is firmly attached antero-inferiorly (where vessels enter it) to its fossa. The tonsil is related anteriorly to the palatoglossal arch, posteriorly to the palato-pharyngeal arch, superiorly to the soft palate and inferiorly to the tongue. Its medial surface projects into the oropharynx and the lateral surface lies on the superior constrictor which separates it from the facial artery and the carotid sheath.

BLOOD SUPPLY: tonsillar branches from the facial, lingual and ascending pharyngeal arteries. Venous blood passes to the pharyngeal venous plexus.

LYMPH DRAINAGE: to the deep cervical lymph chain especially the jugulodigastric node.

The palatine tonsil develops from the second pharyngeal pouch. Aggregations of lymph tissue surround the upper part of the pharynx: the palatine tonsil below the palate, the lingual tonsil in the posterior third of the tongue, the tubal tonsil around the opening of the auditory tube, and the pharyngeal tonsil (adenoids) beneath the mucous membrane of the roof and posterior wall of the nasopharynx. The palatine tonsils and adenoids are frequently enlarged in children as the result of recurrent throat infections. In some cases enlargment may interfere with breathing and phonation. Surgical removal is then indicated.

The Auditory Tube

This passes from the anterior wall of the middle ear to the lateral wall of the pharynx. It is about 4 cm long and is directed downwards, forwards and medially. The lateral third lies within the petrous temporal bone, the medial two-thirds is mainly cartilaginous but is completed inferiorly by fibrous tissue. The tube is lined by ciliated columnar epithelium with many mucous glands. It is supplied by the ascending pharyngeal artery and its veins pass to the pterygoid venous plexus. Its nerve supply is from the pharyngeal branch of the maxillary nerve and its lymph vessels pass to the retropharyngeal lymph nodes.

The tube serves to equalize the pressure on the two sides of the tympanic membrane. Salpingopharyngeus and tensor and levator veli palatini are attached to and pull on the medial part, and thus swallowing opens the tube. In the child the tube is wider and more horizontal, and infection is more likely to spread to the middle ear from the nasopharynx.

Styloid Muscles

The styloid process is a bony projection of the temporal bone; it gives attachment to three muscles and a ligament. The muscles are active in swallowing; they are described in their order of attachment from above downwards.

Stylopharyngeus descends between the internal and external carotid arteries and enters the pharynx between the superior and middle constrictors. It blends with the middle constrictor and is attached to the posterior border of the thyroid cartilage. It is supplied by the glossopharyngeal nerve. **Stylohyoid** descends to the hyoid bone, splitting around the intermediate tendon of digastric. It is supplied by the facial nerve. **Styloglossus** passes anteriorly between the internal and external carotid arteries and between the superior and middle constrictors to the side of the tongue. It is supplied by the hypoglossal nerve. The **stylohyoid ligament** passes from the tip of the styloid process to the lesser horn of the hyoid bone and gives attachment to the middle constrictor. It is a remnant of the 2nd pharyngeal arch cartilage.

DEVELOPMENT OF THE PHARYNX AND PHARYNGEAL ARCHES

In the walls of the primitive foregut, from which the pharynx develops, six pharyngeal arches are formed on each side. They are numbered from before backwards. The arches consist of a mesodermal mass lined internally with pharyngeal endoderm and covered externally with ectoderm. The furrows between the arches externally form the pharyngeal clefts and internally the pharyngeal pouches. Each arch is supplied by a cranial nerve and a central artery joins the ventral and dorsal aortae. Its mesoderm forms a cartilaginous bar and striated muscle. During early development the 5th arch is obliterated, while the others undergo considerable modification, contributing to the formation of the face, mouth, pharynx and larynx. The nerve of the 1st arch is the trigeminal; 2nd, the facial; 3rd, the glossopharyngeal; 4th, the superior laryngeal; and the 6th, the recurrent laryngeal nerves.

Arch Derivatives

1. ECTODERMAL: The 1st pharyngeal cleft forms the external acoustic meatus. The other clefts are obliterated by an ectodermal fold from the 2nd arch (the operculum) growing caudally over them. If it remains unfused, a cervical sinus develops.

2. MESODERMAL: (*a*) Cartilage: 1st arch—Meckel's cartilage, the sphenomandibular ligament, the malleus and the incus; 2nd arch—the stapes, styloid process, stylohyoid ligament and the lesser horn and upper part of the body of the hyoid bone; 3rd arch—the greater horn and the lower part of the body of the hyoid bone; 4th and 6th arches—cartilages of the larynx.

(*b*) Muscle: 1st arch—the muscles of mastication and the tensor veli palatini and tensor tympani; 2nd arch—the muscles of facial expression and other muscles supplied by the facial nerve; 3rd arch—stylopharyngeus; 4th and 6th arches—muscles of the pharynx, soft palate and larynx.

(*c*) Arteries: The arteries form the paired aortic arches uniting the ventral and dorsal aortae. The 1st and 2nd arches disappear; the 3rd forms part of the common and internal carotid arteries; the 4th forms the subclavian artery on the right and the aortic arch on the left. The 6th arch forms the pulmonary arteries; on the right the artery loses its connection with the dorsal aorta but this persists on the left as the ductus arteriosus of the fetus.

3. ENDODERMAL: The 1st pharyngeal pouch forms the auditory tube, the middle ear, and mastoid antrum; the 2nd pouch contributes towards the tonsil; the 3rd, the thymus and inferior parathyroid gland; and the 4th, the superior parathyroid gland and possibly part of the thyroid gland (C-cells which produce calcitonin).

Modifications in the ventral parts of the upper arches in the floor of the mouth give rise to the tongue (see page 290), the thyroid gland (see page 329) and the respiratory tube (see page 29).

DEGLUTITION

Swallowing (deglutition) is the act by which fluid or a bolus of food is passed from the mouth to the stomach. X-ray examination, using radio-

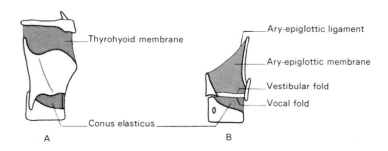

FIG. 27.1
The larynx: A, lateral aspect and B, lateral aspect after removal of right half of the thyroid cartilage and the hyoid bone.

opaque material, has greatly helped in understanding the processes involved in swallowing.

The first stage (oral phase) is voluntary and involves passage of food from the mouth to the oropharynx. The mandible is fixed, with the teeth occluded, by the muscles of mastication. The tongue is tensed, by its intrinsic muscles, and raised by the palatoglossus and muscles acting on the hyoid bone (genioglossus, mylohyoid, stylohyoid and digastric). The tongue is pressed against the hard palate from the tip backwards, forcing food into the oropharynx.

In the second stage (pharyngeal phase), which is largely involuntary, food is passed to the lower end of the pharynx. It is initiated by food touching the arches of the fauces, the soft palate, the posterior wall of the oropharynx or the epiglottis. It involves closing-off of the naso-pharynx, closing-off of the larynx, cessation of respiration and shortening of the pharynx.

The pharyngeal isthmus is closed by tensing and raising the soft palate with tensor and levator veli palatini, and simultaneous approxima-tion of the walls of the pharynx to the posterior free border of the palate. The latter movement is produced by contraction of palatopharyngeus and the upper fibres of superior constrictor.

The larynx is closed by the approximation of the epiglottis and arytenoid cartilages. Contraction of the ary-epiglottic muscles is assisted by passive bending back of the epiglottis by the bolus of food. Liquids pass round the sides of the epiglottis. The larynx is raised by contracting the palatopharyngeus, salpingopharyngeus, stylopharyngeus and thyrohyoid muscles. The mucous membrane also rises, and when the larynx drops back some of the mucous membrane lags behind, so helping to close the opening. The pharynx is shortened by the pharyngeal muscles raising the larynx. The vocal cords are adducted and respiration is inhibited.

Finally food is passed by the inferior constrictor into the oesophagus. This stage (oesophageal phase) is involuntary and is initiated by food stimulating the walls of the lower pharynx and oesophagus. Peristaltic waves pass food on to the stomach. The soft palate and larynx return to their initial positions and respiration is recommenced.

THE LARYNX (Fig. 27.1)

This is the part of the respiratory passage between the pharynx and the trachea. It forms a sphincter protecting the inlet of the trachea and includes the vocal folds. It is situated in the neck anterior to the laryngopharynx and opposite the 3rd–6th cervical vertebrae. A lobe of the thyroid gland and the carotid sheath lie on each side, and it is covered anteriorly by the infrahyoid muscles and the deep (investing) layer of fascia of the neck.

The skeleton of the larynx is formed of a number of cartilages which surround its lumen. These are the unpaired thyroid, cricoid and epiglottic and the paired arytenoid cartilages. Articulations occur at the cricothyroid and crico-arytenoid joints which are acted upon by the muscles of the larynx. The epiglottis and part of the arytenoid cartilages are yellow elastic cartilage, the rest are hyaline cartilage and tend to calcify in later adult life.

CARTILAGES

Thyroid cartilage—comprises two thin quadrilateral laminae united anteriorly at an angle of $120°$ in the female and $90°$ in the adult male. The angle forms the median subcutaneous **laryngeal prominence** and above this the laminae are separated by the palpable V-shaped **thyroid notch.** The free posterior border of each lamina extends superiorly and inferiorly as the superior and inferior horns respectively. On the outer surface of the lamina, an oblique line passes downwards and forwards from the superior horn to the inferior border. The inferior horn articulates with the cricoid cartilage.

The upper border of the cartilage gives attachment to the thyrohyoid membrane. The thyrohyoid, sternothyroid and inferior constrictor muscles are attached to the oblique line, and the palatopharyngeus, salpingopharyngeus and stylopharyngeus muscles to the posterior border. Cricothyroid is attached to the inferior horn and adjacent lower border of the lamina. To the posterior aspect of the laryngeal prominence are attached the epiglottic cartilage with the cricothyroid ligament and the thyroarytenoid muscles below it.

Cricoid cartilage—is situated at the lower border of the larynx and completely encircles it. It is the shape of a signet ring, possessing a broad posterior lamina and a narrow anterolateral arch. Each lateral surface has an articular facet for the inferior horn of the thyroid cartilage; the upper border of the lamina has two facets for the arytenoid cartilages.

To the upper border are attached the conus elasticus and the cricothyroid ligament; cricothyroid and lateral crico-arytenoid muscles are attached to the outer lateral surfaces; posterior crico-arytenoid muscle passes to the back of the lamina.

Epiglottic cartilage (epiglottis)—is a leaf-shaped cartilage. Its narrow inferior end is attached to the back of the laryngeal prominence of the thyroid cartilage and its free broad upper end projects upwards behind the tongue. The sides give attachment to the ary-epiglottic membrane and the thyro-epiglottic and ary-epiglottic muscles. It is covered on its upper anterior and all its posterior surfaces by mucous membrane.

Arytenoid cartilages—each arytenoid cartilage is the shape of a three-sided pyramid, possessing medial, posterior and anterolateral surfaces; the base is inferior and articulates with the lamina of the cricoid. It projects anteriorly as the vocal process and laterally as the muscular process. The anterior border gives attachment to the ary-epiglottic membrane; the muscular process to the lateral and posterior crico-arytenoid muscles; the vocal process, to the vocal ligament; the anterolateral surface, to the thyro-arytenoid muscle. The ary-epiglottic muscle passes to the apex and continues downwards and medially to the back of the cartilage of the opposite side as the oblique arytenoid muscle. The transverse arytenoid muscle passes between the posterior surfaces of the two cartilages.

JOINTS, MEMBRANES AND LIGAMENTS

Cricothyroid joints—are plane synovial joints between the inferior horns of the thyroid cartilage and the lateral aspect of the cricoid. They possess a lax capsule. Rotary movement of the thyroid cartilage about the transverse axis through the two joints, and some anteroposterior gliding occur.

Crico-arytenoid joints—are plane synovial joints between the base of the arytenoid cartilages and the facets on the upper border of the cricoid lamina. Rotation and gliding of the arytenoid cartilages occur; lateral gliding is accompanied by downward displacement because of the obliquity of the joint.

Conus elasticus—this ligament is formed of yellow elastic tissue. Each half is triangular in shape, having an upper free border deep to the thyroid lamina, a lower border attached to the cricoid cartilage, and an anterior border continuous with the ligament of the opposite side. The upper free border extends from the back of the laryngeal prominence of the thyroid cartilage to the vocal process of the arytenoid cartilage and is thickened to form the vocal ligament. This is covered with mucous membrane and forms the **vocal fold** (true vocal cord). The union of the anterior borders is reinforced to form the **cricothyroid ligament.**

304

Ary-epiglottic membrane—extends from the side of the epiglottis to the anterior border of the arytenoid cartilage. The free superior border forms the ary-epiglottic ligament and the free inferior border the vestibular ligament. The lower thickening is in the **vestibular fold** (false vocal cord).

Thyrohyoid membrane—is a fibrous membrane uniting the upper border of the thyroid cartilage to the posterior surface of the body and greater horns of the hyoid bone. Between the hyoid bone and the membrane is a midline bursa. The lateral extremities of the membrane are thickened to form the lateral thyrohyoid ligaments. The membrane is pierced by the superior laryngeal artery and the internal laryngeal nerve.

MUSCLES
With the exception of the transverse arytenoid these are paired muscles.

Cricothyroid—extends from the inferior horn and adjacent lower border of the thyroid cartilage to the outer anterolateral surface of the cricoid.

Posterior crico-arytenoid—passes from the posterior surface of the lamina of the cricoid to the muscular process of the arytenoid.

Lateral crico-arytenoid—passes from the outer lateral surface of the cricoid arch to the muscular process of the arytenoid.

Transverse arytenoid—is attached to the posterior surface of both arytenoid cartilages.

Ary-epiglottic—passes from the lateral border of the epiglottis along the upper border of the ary-epiglottic membrane to the apex of the arytenoid cartilage. The muscle continues to the back of the arytenoid of the opposite side and is here called the oblique arytenoid muscle.

Thyro-arytenoid—passes from the back of the laryngeal prominence along the outer surface of the conus elasticus to the anterolateral surface of the arytenoid cartilage. Some fibres are attached to the free border of the ligament and form the **vocalis muscle,** others pass upwards to the side of the epiglottis forming the **thyro-epiglottic muscle.**

INTERIOR OF THE LARYNX
The superior opening of the larynx is bounded anteriorly by the epiglottis, laterally by the ary-epiglottic folds, and posteriorly by the apices of the arytenoid cartilages and the transverse arytenoid muscle. Within the larynx two pairs of parallel horizontal folds are present in the lateral walls. The upper is the vestibular fold (false vocal cord), the lower is the vocal fold (true vocal cord). The gap between the vocal folds is known as the **rima glottidis.** A lateral recess of mucous membrane between the vestibular and vocal folds is known as the **sinus** of the larynx.

BLOOD SUPPLY: laryngeal branches of the superior and inferior thyroid arteries and their accompanying veins.

NERVE SUPPLY: the mucous membrane is supplied by the internal laryngeal nerve above the vocal folds and the recurrent laryngeal nerve below. The former enters the larynx by piercing the thyrohyoid membrane, the latter by ascending posterior to the cricothyroid joint and deep to the inferior constrictor muscle. Cricothyroid is supplied by the external laryngeal nerve, the other intrinsic muscles by the recurrent laryngeal nerve.

LYMPH DRAINAGE: efferent vessels pass to both upper deep cervical and pretracheal nodes.

HISTOLOGY: the vocal folds are lined by stratified squamous epithelium, the larynx above and the lower part of the larynx are lined by respiratory epithelium.

EMBRYOLOGY: the pulmonary diverticulum arises ventrally in the pharyngeal floor just behind the 6th arches. It passes caudally in front of the oesophagus. The larynx develops from the cartilages and muscles of the 4th and 6th pharyngeal arches. The cricoid may be a modified tracheal ring.

MOVEMENTS OF THE LARYNX

During vocalisation movements of the thyroid and arytenoid cartilages alter the length, tension and position of the vocal folds. In swallowing the whole larynx is raised and then lowered, and the epiglottis is approximated to the arytenoid cartilages.

(*a*) Movements of the thyroid cartilage—forward rotation at the cricothyroid joints lengthens the vocal folds and is produced by crico-thyroid; the movement is reversed by thyro-arytenoid.

(*b*) Movements of the arytenoid cartilages—occur at the crico-arytenoid joints, and are gliding and rotatory:
(i) gliding—lateral gliding separates the cartilages, thus abducting the vocal folds and producing a ∧-shaped rima glottidis. The combined action of the lateral and posterior crico-arytenoid muscles are involved, and counteracted by the transverse arytenoid muscle.
(ii) rotation—lateral rotation separates the vocal processes and thus abducts the vocal folds. In this case a <>-shaped rima glottidis is produced. The movement is produced by posterior crico-arytenoid and counteracted by lateral crico-arytenoid. The posterior crico-arytenoid is the only muscle which, acting alone, abducts the vocal folds.

(*c*) Vocalis increases the tension in the vocal fold.

(*d*) Raising and lowering of the larynx: the larynx is raised by palato-pharyngeus, salpingopharyngeus, stylopharyngeus and thyrohyoid. It is lowered by the infrahyoid muscles aided by gravity.

(*e*) Approximation of the epiglottis to the arytenoid cartilage may be produced by the ary-epiglottic muscles but probably occurs passively in swallowing.

The larynx functions as a sphincter and in vocalisation. Direct visualisation of the region is possible with the help of a laryngoscope. The sphincter action prevents food entering the trachea and also serves to close the larynx when increasing intrathoracic pressure (e.g. before coughing) and intra-abdominal pressure (e.g. in micturition). Sound is produced by columns of air passing through the larynx usually in expiration. The frequency of the sounds emitted varies with the movement, length and tension of the vocal folds, and the intensity with the volume of air expired. The resonance of the sound is increased by the large spaces in the lungs, pharynx, mouth and nose.

CHAPTER 28

EAR, INTRACRANIAL REGION AND CRANIAL NERVES

EAR

The ear is the organ of hearing and balance. It is divided into an external ear directing sound waves to the tympanic membrane, a middle ear relaying the vibrations of the membrane to the internal ear, and the internal ear which translates these vibrations into nervous impulses and also includes the organ of balance.

THE EXTERNAL EAR

This consists of the auricle and the external acoustic meatus.

The **auricle** is formed of an irregularly-shaped piece of fibrocartilage covered by firmly adherent skin. It has a dependent lobule and an anterior tragus which overlaps the opening of the meatus. To the auricle are attached three vestigial muscles supplied by the facial nerve. They are of little functional value in man. The **external acoustic meatus** is cartilage laterally and bone medially. It passes nearly horizontally from the tragus to the tympanic membrane and is about 4 cm long. The cartilaginous lateral third is continuous with the cartilage of the auricle. The bony medial two-thirds is formed mainly by the tympanic plate of the temporal bone completed posterosuperiorly by the squamous temporal bone. The direction of the canal is slightly posterior in the lateral portion; slightly anterior in the medial portion. The canal is lined with skin richly endowed with wax-secreting (ceruminous) glands. It receives its blood supply from the maxillary and superficial temporal arteries and is innervated by the auriculotemporal nerve anteriorly and the vagus nerve posteriorly.

The translucent **tympanic membrane** (ear drum) separates the external ear from the middle ear. It is oval in shape and lies obliquely with its lateral surface facing downwards and forwards. It consists of an incomplete fibrous layer covered laterally by modified skin and medially by modified mucous membrane of the middle ear. The handle of the malleus, attached to the medial surface, can be seen through the drum extending upwards from the centre to the superior flaccid part of the membrane where the fibrous layer is deficient. The lower end of the handle produces a small elevation on the drum and on inspection with an auroscope, a cone of light is seen passing downwards and forwards from this point.

THE MIDDLE EAR (TYMPANIC CAVITY)

The middle ear lies within the temporal bone and may be likened to a narrow room. The height and length are about 15 mm. The lateral and medial walls curve inwards and are about 2 mm apart at the middle and about 6 mm apart at the roof. The cavity is lined in places by ciliated columnar epithelium and contains three small bones (auditory ossicles).

The **lateral wall** is formed mainly by the tympanic membrane. The chorda tympani passes forwards between the membrane and the handle of the malleus laterally and the incus medially. Above and behind the membrane there is an upward extension of the cavity, the **epitympanic recess** which accommodates the head of the malleus and body of the incus.

The **medial wall** has a central bulge, the **promontory,** formed by the first turn of the cochlea. Above and behind the bulge is the **fenestra vestibuli** (oval window) and below and behind it the **fenestra cochleae** (round window), both foramina leading into the inner ear. The fenestra vestibuli is closed by the footplate of the stapes and the fenestra cochleae by a fibrous disc. The facial nerve, in a bony canal, crosses the medial wall superiorly from before backwards and then descends on the posterior wall.

The **anterior wall** has two openings inferiorly, separated by a bony shelf. The upper transmits tensor tympani whose tendon turns laterally around a projection of the bony shelf and is attached to the handle of the malleus. The lower is the opening of the auditory tube through which the cavities of the middle ear and nasopharynx are in continuity.

High on the **posterior wall** is the **aditus,** the opening into the mastoid (tympanic) antrum. Below it there is a projection of bone, the pyramid, out of which the tendon of the stapedius muscle passes to the stapes. Lateral to this there is a small foramen out of which passes the chorda tympani. The canal for the facial nerve passes down the medial side of the wall.

The **roof** is covered by a thin plate of the petrous temporal bone (the tegmen tympani) which separates the cavity from the middle cranial fossa. The bony **floor** separates the cavity from the carotid canal in front and the jugular foramen behind.

The middle ear contains three small ossicles, the malleus, the incus and the stapes; they extend in line from the tympanic membrane to the fenestra vestibuli and transmit the vibrations of the membrane to the inner ear. The **malleus** has a handle which is attached to the tympanic membrane, and a rounded superior head which lies in the epitympanic recess and articulates with the body of the incus. The **incus** has a body and two processes; one process rests on the posterior wall of the middle ear, the other articulates with the **stapes,** the footplate of which occupies the fenestra vestibuli. The malleus and incus develop from the cartilage of the 1st pharyngeal arch, the stapes from the 2nd. Decreased mobility of the ossicles in middle and old age produce degrees of conductive deafness.

Two small muscles, the **tensor tympani** (supplied by the mandibular nerve) and the **stapedius** (supplied by the facial nerve) are attached to the malleus and the stapes respectively; they modify the transmission of the sound waves.

The middle ear receives its blood supply from the internal carotid and maxillary arteries and is innervated by the glossopharyngeal nerve through the tympanic plexus. Lymph passes to the retropharyngeal lymph nodes.

Mastoid (tympanic) antrum—is a cavity within the mastoid part of the petrous temporal bone. It communicates with the cavity of the middle ear through the aditus. At birth the antrum is small and lies very superficially. As the mastoid process enlarges, the antrum becomes more deeply placed and mastoid air cells develop as diverticula around it. Posteromedially the antrum is separated by a thin plate of bone from the posterior cranial fossa and the sigmoid venous sinus. Superiorly it is related to the temporal lobe of the brain. Laterally are the muscles attached to the mastoid process.

The communication of the middle ear with the nasopharynx along the auditory tube provides a pathway for infection to pass from the throat to the mastoid antrum and mastoid air cells. Here an abcess may develop and this is of serious consequence for it is clearly related to the temporal lobe of the brain and the cerebellum being separated from them only by thin plates of bone. Meningitis and brain abscess are thus occasional complications of a mastoid infection.

THE INTERNAL EAR

The internal ear lies within the petrous temporal bone. It consists of a complicated membranous sac (the membranous labyrinth) filled with a clear fluid (endolymph) and contained within a larger bony cavity (the bony labyrinth). The space between the membranous and bony labyrinths is filled with fluid (perilymph).

The **bony labyrinth** comprises the cochlea anteriorly, the vestibule in the middle and the semicircular canals posteriorly. The cavities are in continuity. The **cochlea** is a spirally coiled bony tube of $2\frac{3}{4}$ turns, around a central bony pillar, the **modiolus.** The medial wall of the coil has a narrow plate of bone, the **spiral lamina,** which projects into the cavity and partly divides it. The basal turn of the cochlea opens into the **vestibule** which lies lateral to the internal acoustic meatus. The lateral wall of the vestibule opens on to the middle ear at the vestibular and cochlear foramina. The anterior, posterior and lateral **semicircular canals** each form two-thirds of a circle and open at either end into the vestibule; as the anterior and posterior canals have a conjoined medial end, there are only five openings into the vestibule. The lateral end of each canal posses a dilatation, the ampulla. The canals lie in three planes at right angles to one another; the anterior and posterior canals are set vertically, the lateral horizontally.

The **membranous labyrinth** (Fig. 28.1) comprises the duct of the cochlea, the saccule, the utricle and the three semicircular ducts from before backwards; all are in continuity. The **duct of the cochlea** lies within the bony cochlea placed between the projecting edge of the spiral lamina and the opposite wall. It divides the cavity into three: an upper **scala vestibuli** containing perilymph, a middle **scala media** (the cavity of the duct) containing endolymph, and a lower **scala tympani** containing perilymph. The scala vestibuli extends from the fenestra vestibuli to the apex of the coil where it communicates by a small opening, the **helicotrema,** with the scala tympani. The latter extends to the fenestra

310

cochleae. Lying on the basilar membrane which separates the scala media and scala tympani, are hair cells supporting the **membrana tectoria.** The hair cells are stimulated by the disturbance of perilymph in the scala vestibuli and scala tympani set up by movement of the stapes at the fenestra vestibuli. The **spiral organ** (end organ of hearing) consists of the hair cells and the tectorial membrane (Fig. 28.2).

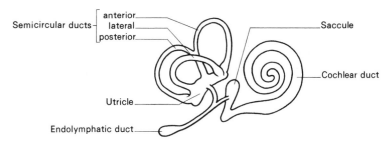

Semicircular ducts — anterior / lateral / posterior

Saccule

Cochlear duct

Utricle

Endolymphatic duct

Fig. 28.1
Diagrammatic lay-out of the membranous labyrinth.

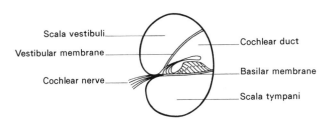

Scala vestibuli

Vestibular membrane

Cochlear nerve

Cochlear duct

Basilar membrane

Scala tympani

Fig. 28.2
Diagrammatic lay-out of a section through one of the coils of the cochlea.

The **saccule** and **utricle** are two sacs within the vestibule; they are united by the narrow Y-shaped endolymphatic duct. The saccule is joined to the duct of the cochlea by the narrow ductus reuniens, the utricle receives the five openings of the semicircular ducts. Both sacs possess a small thickened area of columnar cells with projecting hairs. These are the **maculae,** the end organs of static balance.

The narrow **semicircular ducts** lie within their respective bony canals. They each have a dilated ampulla containing a sensory area, the **crista.** The cristae are similar to the maculae but are the end organs of kinetic balance. The hairs of the maculae and cristae are stimulated by small calcium carbonate crystals (otoliths) within the endolymph.

Blood is supplied by the labyrinthine branch of the basilar artery. Venous blood passes to the superior and inferior petrosal sinuses. The maculae and cristae are innervated by the vestibular division of the eighth cranial nerve, the hair cells of the cochlea by the cochlear division of the nerve. The cochlear ganglion is in the modiolus and the vestibular ganglion is in the internal acoustic meatus.

INTRACRANIAL REGION

The cranial cavity contains the brain and its membranes. The vault of the skull covers the hemispheres superiorly, and inferiorly the base of the skull forms the anterior, middle and posterior cranial fossae which contain the frontal lobes, temporal lobes and hindbrain respectively.

The **vault** is formed from the frontal, parietal, squamous temporal and occipital bones. There are two foramina for the parietal emissary veins near the vertex. The inner surface shows shallow impressions for the cerebral gyri and is grooved in the sagittal plane by the superior sagittal sinus as far back as the internal occipital protuberance. On either side of the groove are pits for the **lateral recesses** containing the **arachnoid granulations.** The lateral side of the vault shows markings for the anterior and posterior branches of the middle meningeal vessels.

The **anterior cranial fossa** is formed by the orbital plates of the frontal bone, the cribriform plate of the ethmoid bone with its upward midline projection, the **crista galli,** and the lesser wings of the sphenoid which projects posteromedially to form the anterior clinoid processes. The fossa houses the frontal lobes of the brain and overlies the nasal and orbital cavities. The cribiform plates underlie the olfactory bulbs and the foramina transmit bundles of the olfactory nerves with their meningeal coverings and the anterior ethmoidal vessels and nerves. The orbital plates of the frontal bone show markings for the orbital gyri of the frontal lobes and contain the posterior parts of the frontal air sinuses

The **middle cranial fossa** has a median portion and two larger lateral compartments. The median part is formed by the body of the sphenoid which is hollowed out to form the **pituitary fossa** (the sella turcica). Anteriorly a transverse ridge, the **tuberculum sellae,** separates the fossa from the shallow optic groove which leads to the optic canal on each side. Posteriorly a plate of bone, the dorsum sellae, projects upwards and forwards; its two corners are the posterior clinoid processes. On each side of the fossa a shallow carotid groove leads posteriorly to the foramen lacerum. The body of the sphenoid contains the sphenoidal air sinuses, lies under the pituitary gland and cavernous venous sinuses, and above the nasopharynx. Each **optic canal** transmits the optic nerve with its meningeal coverings and the ophthalmic artery. The **foramen lacerum** lies between the occipital bone behind, the greater wing of the sphenoid bone in front, and the apex of the petrous temporal laterally. It is irregular in shape, and in life it is filled with fibrocartilage. The cartilage in the foramen forms the floor of the medial end of the carotid canal. The internal carotid artery, and the greater petrosal and deep petrosal nerves pass medially over the cartilage.

The lateral compartments are formed, from before backwards, by the lesser and greater wings of the sphenoid, and the squamous and petrous parts of the temporal bone. They support the temporal lobes of the brain, separating them from the temporal and infratemporal regions. One fissure and three foramina are found towards the medial side of each compartment.

1. The **superior orbital fissure** lies between the greater and lesser wings of the sphenoid. It opens into the orbit and transmits the oculomotor, trochlear, branches of the ophthalmic, and abducent nerves and the ophthalmic veins.

2. The **foramen rotundum** is in the greater wing of the sphenoid behind the medial end of the superior orbital fissure. It opens into the pterygopalatine fossa and transmits the maxillary nerve.

3. The **foramen ovale** is also in the greater wing and is about 1·5 cm behind the foramen rotundum. It opens into the infratemporal fossa and transmits the mandibular nerve, the lesser petrosal nerve and an accessory meningeal artery.

4. The **foramen spinosum** lies just posterolateral to the foramen ovale. It transmits the middle meningeal vessels and meningeal branches of the mandibular nerve. The vessels groove the bone as they pass laterally and divide into anterior and posterior branches. The anterior branch lies deep to the pterion.

The anterior surface of the petrous temporal bone has a depression near its apex for the trigeminal ganglion. Further laterally the surface has an elevation, the **arcuate eminence,** produced by the anterior semicircular canal. Anterior and lateral to the eminence a thin plate of bone, the **tegmen tympani,** overlies the mastoid antrum, the middle ear and the auditory tube. Grooves for the greater and lesser petrosal nerves are found medial to the eminence.

The **posterior cranial fossa** is the largest and deepest of the three fossae. It is formed from the sphenoid, temporal, occipital and parietal bones. Anterolaterally the fossa is limited by the dorsum sellae and the upper border of the petrous temporal bones. Posterolaterally the grooves for the transverse venous sinus on the occipital and parietal bones form the upper limit of the fossa. The fossa contains the cerebellum, pons and medulla. It is roofed in by the tentorium cerebelli on which lie the occipital lobes of the cerebral hemispheres. The following foramina are present:

1. The **foramen magnum** is large and lies in the midline in the floor of the fossa, bounded on each side by the occipital condyles. It transmits the spinal cord with its coverings, the vertebral and spinal arteries, and the accessory nerves.

2. The **jugular foramen** lies between the occipital and petrous temporal bones. It is irregular in outline and contains the upper bulb of the internal jugular vein, and transmits the inferior petrosal sinus and the glossopharyngeal, vagus and also accessory nerves.

3. The **internal acoustic meatus** lies on the posterior aspect of the petrous temporal bone. Each is directed laterally and transmits the facial and vestibulocochlear nerves and the labyrinthine artery, all surrounded by a meningeal sheath. The ganglion of the vestibular nerve lies in the meatus.

4. The **hypoglossal canal** lies above and anterior to the occipital condyle; it transmits the hypoglossal nerve.

5 & 6. The **condylar canal** (behind the condyle) and the **mastoid foramen** transmit emissary veins.

The posterior surface of the petrous temporal bone is grooved above by the superior petrosal sinus, medially by the inferior petrosal sinus and laterally by the sigmoid part of the transverse sinus. The internal occipital protuberance lies at the point of union of the two transverse sinuses in the midline posteriorly.

CRANIAL NERVES

The 12 pairs of cranial nerves originate in the brain and leave the cranial cavity through its basal foramina. The nerves have motor and sensory components of the somatic, visceral and special visceral (branchial) varieties in varying proportions. The olfactory and optic nerves are not usually included in this classification. The central connections of nerves 3–12 are outlined in Chapter 33.

The somatic motor component supplies muscles derived from somitic mesoderm and is present in the oculomotor, trochlear, abducent and hypoglossal nerves. The general somatic sensory component supplies the skin of the face by the trigeminal nerve. The special somatic sensory component supplies the organs of balance and hearing by the vestibulo-cochlear nerve. The general visceral (parasympathetic) motor components are in the oculomotor, facial, glossopharyngeal and vagus nerves. The special visceral motor component supplies muscles derived from pharyngeal arch mesoderm and is present in the trigeminal, facial, glossopharyngeal, and vagus nerves. The special visceral sensory component provides taste fibres in the facial and glossopharyngeal nerves. The general visceral sensory (reflex) components are in the glossopharyngeal and vagus nerves.

The course of the sensory nerves (the olfactory, optic and vestibulo-cochlear) will be described as approaching the brain, and motor and mixed nerves as leaving it.

1. Olfactory Nerves

They supply the olfactory mucous membrane in the upper part of the nasal cavity. The nerve fibres originate in the bipolar olfactory cells of the mucosa and join to form 15–20 olfactory bundles which pass through the cribiform plate of the ethmoid bone to reach the olfactory bulb. (For central connections see page 355.)

2. **Optic Nerve** (Figs. 26.1, 26.2, 26.3)

It is the sensory nerve of the retina. Its fibres originate in the ganglion layer and converge on the posterior part of the eyeball. The nerve passes backwards through the orbit and optic canal into the middle cranial fossa where it unites with the nerve of the opposite side to form the **optic chiasma.**

RELATIONS: within the orbit—the nerve is enclosed in a meningeal sheath containing cerebrospinal fluid, and surrounded by the cone of extra-ocular muscles embedded in fat. The ciliary ganglion lies on its lateral side and the ophthalmic artery and nasociliary nerve pass forwards and medially above it. The central artery of the retina (a branch of the ophthalmic artery) enters the substance of the nerve in this part of its course. In the optic canal—the nerve with its meningeal sheath is accompanied by the ophthalmic artery. The short intracranial portion—lies on the sphenoid bone and is medial to the internal carotid artery. (For central connections see page 381.)

3. Oculomotor Nerve (Figs. 26.1, 36.8)

This nerve has somatic motor and general visceral (parasympathetic) motor fibres. The somatic fibres supply the bulbar muscles, except superior oblique and lateral rectus. The parasympathetic fibres synapse in the ciliary ganglion and supply the sphincter pupillae and ciliary muscle.

The nuclei of the nerve are situated in the upper midbrain in the peri-aqueductal grey matter. The nerve fibres pass forwards through the midbrain and leave it between the cerebral peduncles. The nerve passes through the posterior and middle cranial fossae and divides into superior and inferior divisions near the superior orbital fissure.

RELATIONS: in the posterior cranial fossa—the nerve passes between the posterior cerebral and superior cerebellar arteries, then medial to the trochlear nerve and lies near the edge of the tentorium cerebelli. In the middle crainal fossa—it pierces the cerebral layer of dura to pass forwards on the lateral wall of the cavernous sinus where it is at first above but later descends medial to the trochlear nerve.

BRANCHES

(i) the superior division passes through the superior orbital fissure within the tendinous ring of the extra-ocular muscles and supplies superior rectus and levator palpebrae superioris.

(ii) the inferior division also passes through the tendinous ring and supplies the medial and inferior recti and inferior oblique. The nerve to inferior oblique gives the parasympathetic branch to the ciliary ganglion (see page 340).

Because of its close relationship to the free edge of the tentorium cerebelli the oculomotor nerve may be damaged by a lateral shift of the brain. One of the earliest localising signs of rapidly increasing intracranial pressure may be dilatation of the pupil due to damage of the parasympathetic fibres passing to the ciliary ganglion.

4. Trochlear Nerve (Figs. 26.1, 36.8)

This is the somatic motor nerve supply to the superior oblique. Its nucleus lies in the lower midbrain in the peri-aqueductal grey matter. The fibres pass posteriorly and undergo a dorsal decussation with the nerve of the opposite side caudal to the inferior colliculi. The nerve then passes forwards through the posterior and middle cranial fossae, enters the orbit through the superior orbital fissure and supplies superior oblique.

RELATIONS: in the posterior cranial fossa—the nerve passes forwards around the midbrain, then between the posterior cerebral and superior cerebellar arteries, following the edge of the tentorium, lateral to the oculomotor nerve. In the middle cranial fossa—it pierces the cerebral layer of dura and lies between the oculomotor and ophthalmic nerves in the lateral wall of the cavernous sinus. The oculomotor later descends medial to it. It passes through the superior orbital fissure outside the tendinous ring and passes medially between levator palpebrae superioris and the roof of the orbit to reach the superior oblique.

5. Trigeminal Nerve (Figs. 26.1, 26.5)

This nerve has general somatic sensory and special visceral motor fibres. The sensory fibres supply the anterior part of the dura and scalp, the face, the nasopharynx, the nasal and oral cavities, and the paranasal air sinuses. The motor fibres supply the muscles of mastication. The nerve has four nuclei: the spinal (in the medulla), the mesencephalic (in the midbrain), and the superior sensory and motor (in the pons). The first three are sensory in function.

The nerve arises in the pons and emerges at the junction of the pons and the middle cerebellar peduncle as a large sensory and smaller motor root. It passes forwards to the trigeminal ganglion on the apex of the petrous temporal bone in the middle cranial fossa. The ganglion is semilunar in shape and lies on the anterior aspect of the petrous temporal bone lateral to the cavernous sinus. It is partly surrounded by a dural sheath carried forwards by the nerve. The ophthalmic, maxillary and mandibular divisions emerge from the anterior border of the ganglion. The motor root of the nerve passes medial to the ganglion and joins the mandibular division.

Ophthalmic division—is the smallest division; it passes forwards on the lateral wall of the cavernous sinus below the oculomotor and trochlear nerves and above the maxillary division. Near the superior orbital fissure it divides into the lacrimal, frontal and nasociliary nerves which pass through the fissure into the orbit.

(*a*) **Lacrimal nerve**—passes through the lateral part of the superior orbital fissure, outside the tendinous ring and above lateral rectus to reach the lacrimal gland. It then enters the upper eyelid to supply the skin and conjunctiva on the lateral side. A communicating branch from the zygomaticotemporal nerve conveys parasympathetic fibres from the pterygopalatine ganglion to the lacrimal gland.

(*b*) **Frontal nerve**—passes through the superior orbital fissure just outside the tendinous ring and then forwards between levator palpebrae superioris and the roof of the orbit. In the orbit it divides into supra-orbital and supratrochlear nerves. The former leaves the orbit through the supra-orbital notch and its branches supply the upper eyelid, the frontal sinuses and the scalp as far back as the vertex. The latter passes forwards above the trochlea for the superior oblique tendon, and supplies the skin of the upper eyelid and the medial part of the forehead.

(*c*) **Nasociliary nerve**—passes through the superior orbital fissure within the tendinous ring, and forwards and then medially above the optic nerve to end on the medial wall of the orbit as the anterior ethmoidal and infratrochlear nerves.

316

BRANCHES

(i) anterior ethmoidal nerve—passes through a foramen on the medial wall of the orbit to enter the anterior cranial fossa. It then descends through the cribriform plate, passes through the nasal cavity, and emerges between the nasal bone and the nasal cartilages as the external nasal nerve. It supplies the dura of the anterior cranial fossa, the anterior ethmoidal air cells, the upper anterior part of the nasal cavity and the skin over the external nose.

(ii) posterior ethmoidal nerve—supplies the posterior ethmoidal and sphenoidal air sinuses.

(iii) infratrochlear nerve—passes forwards below the trochlea and supplies the medial part of the upper eyelid, conjunctiva and adjacent part of the nose.

(iv) long ciliary nerves—two or three branches pass to the eyeball. They also convey sympathetic fibres to the dilator pupillae from the internal carotid plexus.

(v) branches via the ciliary ganglion to the eyeball.

Maxillary division—passes forwards through the middle cranial fossa, the foramen rotundum, the pterygopalatine fossa and the inferior orbital fissure where it becomes the infra-orbital nerve.

RELATIONS: in the middle cranial fossa the nerve lies for a short distance in the lateral wall of the cavernous sinus below the ophthalmic division; it leaves the fossa through the foramen rotundum. In the pterygopalatine fossa the pterygopalatine ganglion is suspended from it and it is related to the terminal branches of the maxillary artery.

BRANCHES

(a) Fibres to the **pterygopalatine ganglion,** through which they pass without synapsing to the nose, palate and nasopharynx, via the nasal and nasopalatine nerves (passing through the sphenopalatine foramen into the nose), the greater and lesser palatine nerves (descending between the maxillary and palatine bones to the palate), and the pharyngeal nerve (passing backwards to the nasopharynx).

(b) **Zygomatic nerve**—passes forwards on the lateral wall of the orbit and divides into temporal and facial branches which pass through small foramina in the zygomatic bone to supply the skin over the temple and cheek. In the orbit a communication with the lacrimal nerve carries parasympathetic fibres from the pterygopalatine ganglion to the lacrimal gland.

(c) **Posterior superior alveolar nerve**—three or four branches descend through foramina in the posterior aspect of the maxilla to the upper molar and premolar teeth.

(d) **Infra-orbital nerve**—is the continuation of the maxillary nerve out of the orbit. It lies in the infra-orbital groove and canal and emerges at the infra-orbital foramen on to the face where its leash of terminal branches supply the lower eyelid and conjunctiva, the side of the nose and the upper lip. Its **anterior superior alveolar branch,** given off in the canal, supplies the canine and incisor teeth, the lower part of the lateral wall of the nose and the maxillary air sinus.

Mandibular division—carries the motor root of the trigeminal nerve. It leaves the middle cranial fossa through the foramen ovale and soon divides into its branches. The nerve lies between tensor veli palatini and lateral pterygoid and has the otic ganglion on its medial side.

1. Motor branches to the muscles of mastication, tensor tympani and tensor veli palatini. The fibres to the tensor muscles leave the nerve to medial pterygoid and pass through the otic ganglion without synapsing.

2. Sensory branches have a wide distribution.

(a) **Meningeal branch**—a small twig which passes through the foramen spinosum to supply the dura of the middle cranial fossa.

(b) **Buccal nerve**—passes forwards between the two heads of lateral pterygoid and medial to the mandible. It gives off cutaneous branches then pierces buccinator and supplies the mucous membrane of the cheek.

(c) **Auriculotemporal nerve**—passes laterally between the spheno-mandibular ligament and the neck of the mandible, and above the parotid gland. It then ascends behind the joint, with the superior temporal artery, to the temporal region of the scalp. The nerve carries sensory fibres to the anterior part of the tympanic membrane, external acoustic meatus and the auricle, to the joint and to the temporal region of the scalp. It conveys parasympathetic fibres to the parotid gland from the otic ganglion and sympathetic fibres to the gland from the plexus on the middle meningeal artery, around which the nerve often divides.

(d) **Inferior alveolar nerve**—descends to the mandibular foramen where it enters the mandibular canal. It lies between the medial pterygoid and the ramus of the mandible, and the sphenomandibular ligament lies medial to it as it enters the foramen.

BRANCHES

(i) mylohyoid nerve—leaves the nerve before it enters the mandibular foramen, passes forwards close the the mandible to supply mylohyoid and the anterior belly of digastric.

(ii) dental branches—arise in the mandibular canal and supply adjacent gums and teeth.

(iii) incisor nerve—supplies the canine and incisor teeth and the central incisor of the opposite side.

(iv) mental nerve—emerges through the mental foramen and supplies the skin and mucous membrane of the lower lip and chin, and the gum above the foramen.

(e) **Lingual nerve**—arises anterior to the previous nerve and passes forwards along the side of the tongue to reach and supply its anterior two thirds. The nerve supplies sensory branches to the anterior two-thirds of the tongue, the floor of the mouth and the lingual gum. It receives the chorda tympani branch of the facial nerve about 3 cm below the base of the skull. The chorda tympani carries parasympathetic and taste fibres; the former synapse in the submandibular ganglion and supply the submandibular and sublingual salivary glands (p. 340). The latter are from the anterior two-thirds of the tongue.

RELATIONS: the nerve lies between four pairs of structures from above downwards—(a) tensor veli palatini and lateral pterygoid, (b) medial pterygoid and ramus of the mandible, (c) mucous membrane of the mouth and the root of the 3rd lower molar tooth, (d) hyoglossus and mylohyoid. Between the last pair of muscles the nerve is overlapped by the submandibular gland and then passes from lateral to medial below the submandibular duct.

6. Abducent Nerve (Figs. 26.1, 36.8)

It is a somatic motor nerve supplying lateral rectus. Its nucleus is situated in the lower pons. The nerve leaves the inferior border of the pons near the midline, passes forwards through the posterior and middle cranial fossae, the cavernous sinus and the orbit, to reach and supply lateral rectus.

RELATIONS: in the posterior cranial fossa the nerve lies between the pons and the basilar part of the occipital bone. It pierces the inner layer of dura covering the dorsum sellae, passes over the apex of the petrous temporal bone and through the cavernous sinus lateral to the internal carotid artery. It enters the orbit through the superior orbital fissure within the tendinous ring and supplies lateral rectus. This long thin nerve is prone to damage in patients with increased intracranial pressure.

7. Facial Nerve (Figs. 26.7, 33.8)

This nerve carries special visceral motor, special visceral sensory, and general visceral (parasympathetic) motor fibres. The special visceral motor fibres arise in the facial nucleus in the lower pons and upper medulla, and are distributed to the muscles of the face region. The special visceral sensory fibres carry taste sensation from the anterior two-thirds of the tongue to the nucleus of the tractus solitarius in the medulla. The cell bodies of the fibres are in the geniculate ganglion of the facial nerve. The parasympathetic fibres are secretomotor to the submandibular and sublingual glands (synapses are in the submandibular ganglion) and to the lacrimal gland and the mucous membrane of the nose, pharynx and mouth (synapses are in the pterygopalatine ganglion). The preganglionic parasympathetic fibres arise in the upper part of the salivary nucleus in the medulla. (Intracranially the sensory and parasympathetic fibres may be gathered together in a separate root.)

The nerve leaves the lower lateral surface of the pons and passes laterally, with the vestibulocochlear nerve, through the internal acoustic meatus to the facial (geniculate) ganglion. It here turns sharply posteriorly through a bony canal on the medial wall of the middle ear and then downwards behind the same cavity to emerge from the temporal bone at the stylomastoid foramen. The nerve then runs forward into the parotid gland where it divides into a number of branches. The geniculate ganglion contains the cell bodies of the taste and other sensory fibres.

BRANCHES

(a) **greater petrosal nerve**—carries secretomotor fibres to the pterygopalatine ganglion. It leaves the facial nerve at the geniculate ganglion, and passes through the petrous temporal bone into the middle cranial fossa. It traverses the fossa to reach the foramen lacerum and join the deep petrosal nerve (a sympathetic branch from the internal carotid plexus) to form the nerve of the pterygoid canal. The nerve passes through its canal in the sphenoid bone to the pterygopalatine ganglion in the pterygopalatine fossa. Some sensory fibres may be present in the nerve and have their cell bodies in the geniculate ganglion.

(b) nerve to stapedius muscle.

(c) **chorda tympani**—arises just above the stylomastoid foramen, passes forwards through the middle ear between the tympanic membrane and the handle of the malleus laterally and the incus medially. It emerges from the petrotympanic fissure of the temporal bone and joins the lingual nerve about 3 cm below the base of the skull. It contains taste fibres from the anterior two-thirds of the tongue (the cell bodies are in the geniculate ganglion) and parasympathetic fibres which synapse in the submandibular ganglion.

(d) nerves to the posterior belly of digastric and stylohyoid, and the posterior auricular nerve to occipitalis and the auricular muscles arise just below the stylomastoid foramen.

(e) within the parotid gland the temporal, zygomatic, buccal, mandibular and cervical motor branches are formed; they supply the muscles of facial expression and also buccinator and platysma muscles.

Lower motor neurone facial paralysis may result from virus infections, from trauma, e.g. during surgical removal of a parotid tumour, or from neoplastic infiltration.

8. Vestibulocochlear Nerve (Figs. 28.2, 33.4, 33.8)

This is a special somatic sensory nerve consisting of two parts, the vestibular nerve concerned with balance and the cochlear nerve concerned with hearing. The nerve is formed in the internal acoustic meatus by the union of the two parts, and passes medially to enter the cerebello-medullary angle of the brain stem. Fibres from the cochlear duct pass to the bipolar cells of the spiral ganglion within the modiolus and the central connections pass to the dorsal and ventral cochlear nuclei in the upper medulla. Vestibular fibres pass from the semicircular ducts, saccule and utricle to the bipolar cells of the vestibular ganglion in the internal acoustic meatus, and the central fibres pass to the vestibular nuclei in the floor of the 4th ventricle. (For central connections see pages 367 and 382.)

9. Glossopharyngeal Nerve (Fig. 26.7)

This has general and special visceral sensory, special visceral motor and general visceral motor (parasympathetic) fibres. The general visceral sensory fibres come from the pharynx, posterior third of the tongue and the carotid sinus and carotid body. The special visceral sensory fibres (taste) come from the posterior one-third of the tongue. Their cell bodies are in the ganglion of the glossopharyngeal nerve and their central fibres enter the medulla (nucleus of the tractus solitarius). The parasympathetic (secretomotor) fibres arise in the salivary nucleus (lower part), synapse in the otic ganglion and supply the parotid gland. The special visceral motor fibres arise in the nucleus ambiguus and supply stylopharyngeus. The nerve rootlets leave the medulla lateral to the olive. The nerve passes through the jugular foramen medial to the vagus and accessory nerves and the internal jugular vein and lateral to the inferior petrosal sinus. It passes forwards between the internal and external carotid arteries. enters the pharyngeal wall between the superior and middle constrictor muscles and ends in the posterior one-third of the tongue. The nerve has two small sensory ganglia situated in the jugular foramen.

BRANCHES

(a) tympanic nerve—passes to the tympanic plexus on the promontory of the middle ear and supplies the mucous membrane of this cavity. The lesser petrosal nerve arises from the plexus and conveys the parasympathetic fibres to the parotid gland via the otic ganglion (p. 341).

(b) nerve to stylopharyngeus.

(c) sensory branches to the mucous membrane of the oropharynx, tonsil, soft palate and posterior one-third of the tongue (including the vallate papillae).

(d) sensory branches to the carotid body and carotid sinus.

10. Vagus Nerve (Figs. 6.1, 6.3, 6.4, 26.7, 29.1)

This nerve has general visceral motor (parasympathetic), special visceral motor, general and special visceral sensory, and somatic sensory fibres. The parasympathetic fibres supply the heart, lungs and alimentary canal nearly to the splenic flexure. The special visceral motor fibres innervate the striated muscles of the larynx, pharynx and palate. The general visceral sensory fibres come from the mucous membrane of the palate, pharynx and larynx, and from the heart, lungs and alimentary canal. The special visceral sensory (taste) fibres come from the valleculae and epiglottis. The somatic sensory fibres supply the posterior part of the external acoustic meatus and the tympanic membrane. The nuclei, which lie in the medulla, are the dorsal motor and sensory (parasympathetic), the nucleus ambiguus (special visceral motor) and nucleus of the tractus solitarius (visceral sensory). The somatic sensory fibres probably pass to the sensory nucleus of the trigeminal nerve.

The nerve emerges from the medulla lateral to the olive as rootlets and leaves the skull through the jugular foramen with the inferior petrosal sinus and the glossopharyngeal nerve medially and the accessory nerve and internal jugular vein laterally. It descends through the neck and thorax to the oesophageal plexus where it joins with its fellow of the opposite side to form the anterior and posterior vagal trunks. Near the base of the skull the vagus has superior and inferior sensory ganglia.

RELATIONS (in the neck): The nerve lies deeply in the carotid sheath, between the internal jugular vein laterally and the internal and common carotid arteries medially. It lies on the prevertebral fascia and muscles. In the root of the neck the right nerve passes forwards in front of the subclavian artery and enters the thorax. The left nerve runs between the common carotid and subclavian arteries as it enters the thorax.

BRANCHES (in the neck)

(a) auricular nerve—supplies the posterior part of the external acoustic meatus and the tympanic membrane.

(b) pharyngeal nerves—pass between the internal and external carotid arteries to reach the pharyngeal plexus and supply the muscles and mucous membrane of the pharynx and soft palate.

(c) **superior laryngeal nerve**—descends between the pharynx medially and the internal and external carotid arteries, and divides below the hyoid bone into internal and external branches. The internal nerve pierces the thyrohyoid membrane to supply the mucous membrane of the larynx above the vocal folds. The external nerve descends on the larynx to supply cricothyroid muscle.

(d) cervical cardiac branches—on each side they descend to the cardiac plexuses.

(e) **right recurrent laryngeal nerve**—looks around the right subclavian artery and then ascends in the groove between the oesophagus and trachea. It enters the larynx and supplies the intrinsic muscles except cricothyroid, and the mucous membrane below the vocal folds.

Vagus nerve, in the thorax (see page 68).

11. Accessory Nerve (Fig. 26.7)

This has somatic motor fibres which supply sternocleidomastoid and trapezius and have their nuclei in the upper five cervical segments of the spinal cord.

The nerve arises in the vertebral canal; it ascends behind the ligamenta denticulata and through the foramen magnum into the posterior cranial fossa. It then leaves the fossa through the jugular foramen and below the skull it passes laterally in front of the internal jugular vein and the transverse process of the atlas into the substance of sternocleidomastoid. It crosses the posterior triangle of the neck lying on levator scapulae to reach the deep surface of trapezius.

Inside the skull, fibres from the nucleus ambiguus join the accessory nerve but quickly return to the vagus. (These special visceral fibres are called the cranial root of the accessory nerve.)

12. Hypoglossal Nerve (Figs. 26.5, 26.7)

This nerve is the somatic motor supply to all the intrinsic and extrinsic muscles of the tongue, except palatoglossus. Its nucleus is situated in the medulla in the floor of the 4th ventricle.

The nerve emerges from the medulla between the pyramid and the olive, and leaves the posterior cranial fossa through the hypoglossal canal. It descends behind the carotid sheath before passing forwards around the pharynx to reach the tongue.

RELATIONS: Below the base of the skull the nerve lies behind the internal carotid artery and the vagus nerve on the prevertebral fascia. It passes forwards between the internal carotid artery and the internal jugular vein and crosses in turn the internal and external carotid arteries, the loop of the lingual artery on the middle constrictor muscle and then hyoglossus. As it runs forwards it is covered laterally by the posterior belly of digastric, the submandibular gland and the mylohyoid. Anterior to hyoglossus, the nerve turns medially to ramify in the substance of the tongue.

The hypoglossal nerve receives fibres from the ventral ramus of the 1st cervical nerve near the base of the skull. It conveys some of them to geniohyoid and thyrohyoid, and then forms the superior root of the ansa cervicalis which (with the inferior root from the 2nd and 3rd cervical nerves) supplies the infrahyoid group of muscles.

CHAPTER 29

THE NECK

FASCIA OF THE NECK

The **superficial fascia** is a fatty areolar layer between the skin and the more obvious deep fascia. It contains the platysma muscles and the external jugular veins and their tributaries. In an older person the fat is lost and the anterior edges of platysma show clearly through the skin. The **deep fascia** consists of: (1) the cervical fascia, (2) the prevertebral fascia, (3) the pretracheal fascia, (4) the carotid sheath (Fig. 29.1).

The **cervical fascia** forms an investing sleeve around all the deep structures of the neck. It splits to enclose sternocleidomastoid and trapezius, and posteriorly it is attached to the ligamentum nuchae. Superiorly it gains attachment to the superior nuchal lines, the mastoid processes and the inferior border of the body of the mandible. Between the mastoid and mandible it splits into two layers which form a sheath for the parotid gland; the superficial layer is attached above to the zygomatic arch. Inferiorly the fascia is attached to the manubrium sterni, the clavicles, the acromial processes and spines of the scapulae and between the scapulae it descends over the posterior vertebral muscles. Above the manubrium, a split in the fascia contains the jugular venous arch. The infrahyoid group of muscles is embedded in the deep surface of this fascia.

The **prevertebral fascia** lies in front of the vertebral column, the prevertebral muscles and the cervical and brachial plexuses. Laterally it turns backwards covering the postvertebral muscles on the floor of the posterior triangle and blends with the cervical fascia. Superiorly it is attached to the base of the skull and inferiorly it blends with the anterior longitudinal ligament in front of the body of the 4th thoracic vertebra. Medial to scalenus anterior, the fascia is deficient and the subclavian artery here passes deep to it. Laterally, the subclavian artery carries the fascia into the arm to form the axillary sheath. The cervical sympathetic trunk is embedded in the prevertebral fascia.

The **pretracheal fascia** is attached superiorly to the hyoid bone and the oblique lines on the thyroid cartilage. It splits around the thyroid gland to provide a sheath, and below the gland the fascia passes downwards to blend with the carotid sheaths.

The **carotid sheath** is a condensation of fascias of the neck, and encloses the internal jugular vein laterally, the common and internal carotid arteries medially and the vagus nerve posteriorly. Above, it is attached to the base of the skull and below it fuses with the fibrous pericardium.

MUSCLES OF THE NECK AND BACK

The Triangles of the Neck

Classically each side of the neck is divided for descriptive purposes into anterior and posterior triangles by sternocleidomastoid. It must be remembered that many important structures lie deep to this muscle.

The posterior triangle is bounded by sternocleidomastoid anteriorly, trapezius posteriorly and the clavicle inferiorly. The roof is formed by the

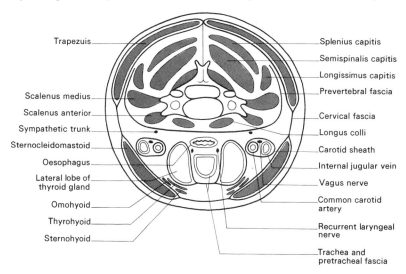

Labels (left side, top to bottom):
Trapezuis
Scalenus medius
Scalenus anterior
Sympathetic trunk
Sternocleidomastoid
Oesophagus
Lateral lobe of thyroid gland
Omohyoid
Thyrohyoid
Sternohyoid

Labels (right side, top to bottom):
Splenius capitis
Semispinalis capitis
Longissimus capitis
Prevertebral fascia
Cervical fascia
Longus colli
Carotid sheath
Internal jugular vein
Vagus nerve
Common carotid artery
Recurrent laryngeal nerve
Trachea and pretracheal fascia

Fig. 29.1
Diagram showing some of the principal structures seen in a horizontal section of the neck at the level of the 6th cervical vertebra.

cervical fascia, the floor by the prevertebral fascia over splenius capitis, levator scapulae, and scalenus medius from above downwards. The triangle is crossed by the posterior belly of omohyoid and contains the accessory nerve, branches of the cervical plexus, the upper and middle trunks of the brachial plexus, and the transverse cervical, suprascapular and subclavian arteries.

The anterior triangle is bounded laterally by sternocleidomastoid, superiorly by the body of the mandible and anteriorly by the midline. It contains structures related to the floor of the mouth, the larynx, the trachea and the pharynx.

Sternocleidomastoid—lies on the anterolateral aspect of the neck enclosed in the cervical fascia.

Attachments
Inferiorly by two heads:
(i) the upper anterior surface of the manubrium sterni.
(ii) the upper surface of the medial one-third of the clavicle.

Superiorly—the lateral surface of the mastoid process and the lateral half of the superior nuchal line.

ACTION

(i) each muscle turns the chin to the opposite side and laterally flexes the neck to its own side, as in looking under a table.

(ii) together, the two muscles flex the head against resistance but extend the neck as in jutting out the chin.

(iii) when the head is fixed the muscles may be used as accessory muscles of respiration.

NERVE SUPPLY: the spinal accessory nerve and a branch from the 2nd and 3rd cervical nerves.

Trapezius—see p. 175.

The Muscles of the Back

These comprise muscles attaching the shoulder girdle to the trunk (see page 174) and a group which extends the head and vertebral column.

The latter group forms a large composite mass, lying deep to trapezius and the other girdle muscles and extending from the back of the neck to the base of the skull. They may be subdivided from without inwards into: (a) the superiorly placed splenius capitis and cervicis, (b) the erector spinae muscles including longissimus, iliocostalis, spinalis and semispinalis and (c) the deep short muscles—levator costae, multifidus, rotatores, interspinous and intertransversus. These short muscles are replaced between the axis and the base of the skull by the suboccipital muscles.

Splenius capitis—passes upwards and laterally from the ligamentum nuchae and the spines of the upper thoracic vertebrae to the mastoid process and the lateral part of the superior nuchal line deep to the sternocleidomastoid.

Semispinalis—passes upwards and medially from the transverse processes to the spines above. The upper part of the muscle, semispinalis capitis, is attached to the occipital bone between the superior and inferior nuchal lines.

ACTION: the muscles of the back for the most part maintain the upright position of the body. When standing at rest, the centre of gravity lies just in front of the 2nd piece of the sacrum. Movement of the body frequently carries the centre of gravity much further forwards and this large mass of muscles is required to restore the upright position. The muscles attached to the skull produce extension, lateral flexion and rotation of the head.

NERVE SUPPLY: all these muscles are supplied by the dorsal rami of the spinal nerves.

Suboccipital Muscles

Rectus capitis posterior major—passes from the spine of the axis to the occipital bone below the inferior nuchal line.

326

Rectus capitis posterior minor—lies anteromedial to the major and passes from the posterior tubercle of the atlas to the occipital bone behind the foramen magnum.

Obliquus capitis superior—passes from the tip of the transverse process of the atlas to the occipital bone betwen the superior and inferior nuchal lines, lateral to semispinalis capitis.

Obliquus capitis inferior—passes from the tip of the transverse process of the atlas to the spine of the axis.

The suboccipital muscles extend the skull at the atlanto-occipital joints and rotate it at the atlanto-axial joints. Accurate positioning of the head is necessary for stereoscopic vision. They are all supplied by the dorsal ramus of the 1st cervical nerve.

The **suboccipital triangle** is bounded laterally by the superior oblique, medially by the rectus capitis posterior major and inferiorly by the inferior oblique. Its floor is formed by the posterior atlanto-occipital membrane and the posterior arch of the atlas. The vertebral artery, with the dorsal ramus of the 1st cervical nerve below it, passes deep to the membrane. The roof is crossed by the greater occipital nerve and covered by semispinalis capitis and longissimus capitis. The triangle is filled with fat and the suboccipital plexus of veins which drains to the vertebral veins.

Ligamentum Nuchae

In animals possessing a protruding head and neck this is a powerful midline elastic ligament passing from the occipital bone to all the cervical spines. In man it is smaller, mainly fibrous tissue and has little supporting action.

Prevertebral and Scalene Muscles

These muscles lie in front of all the cervical and the upper thoracic vertebrae. They are covered anteriorly by the prevertebral fascia.

Prevertebral muscles (rectus capitis anterior and lateralis, longus capitis and longus colli)—pass between the skull and vertebrae, and between vertebrae.

Scalenus anterior—is attached superiorly to the anterior tubercles of the 3rd–6th cervical vertebrae and inferiorly to the scalene tubercle on the 1st rib.

RELATIONS: the anterior surface is crossed obliquely by the phrenic nerve and separated by the prevertebral fascia with the sympathetic trunk from the carotid sheath and its contents, the transverse cervical and suprascapular arteries and the subclavian vein. The posterior surface lies on the scalenus medius (separated from it by the ventral rami of the lower cervical nerves), the dome of the pleura and the subclavian artery.

Scalenus medius—is attached superiorly to the posterior tubercles of the 2nd–7th cervical vertebrae and inferiorly to the upper surface of the 1st rib behind the groove for the subclavian artery.

Scalenus posterior—is the part of the previous muscle which is attached to the 2nd rib.

ACTIONS: these muscles are weak flexors of the head and neck; the scalene muscles also raise and fix the upper two ribs.

NERVE SUPPLY: all are supplied by the ventral rami of the cervical nerves.

Infrahyoid Muscles

There are four pairs of 'strap' muscles lying anteriorly in the neck and enclosed in a fascial sheath which is adherent to the deep surface of the cervical fascia:

Sternohyoid—is attached superiorly to the body of the hyoid bone and inferiorly to the back of the manubrium sterni and the medial end of the clavicle.

Omohyoid—has superior and inferior bellies united by an intermediate tendon which is held to the medial end of the clavicle by a fascial sling. Superiorly the muscle is attached to the body of the hyoid bone and inferiorly to the lateral end of the superior border of the scapula.

Thyrohyoid—is attached superiorly to the back of the body and greater horns of the hyoid bone and inferiorly to the oblique line on the thyroid cartilage.

Sternothyroid—is attached superiorly to the oblique line on the thyroid cartilage and inferiorly to the back of the manubrium sterni and 1st costal cartilage. The muscle lies deep to sternohyoid.

These muscles fix or depress the hyoid bone in swallowing and speech. They are supplied by the ventral rami of the upper three cervical nerves (via the superior or inferior roots of the ansa cervicalis, the ansa, or the hypoglossal nerve).

THE THYROID GLAND (Fig. 29.1)

This is a bilobed endocrine gland situated on each side of the trachea and oesophagus, with a communicating isthmus anterior to the trachea. It is enclosed in pretracheal fascia. Each lobe is about 5 cm long and extends from the oblique line of the thyroid cartilage to the 6th tracheal ring. Occasionally a pyramidal lobe is found arising from the upper border of the isthmus which lies on the 2nd and 3rd tracheal rings.

RELATIONS
Superficial—three strap muscles, deep investing layer of cervical fascia and sternocleidomastoid.

Medial—larynx and trachea and, more posteriorly, the pharynx and oesophagus. The recurrent laryngeal nerve lies between the trachea and oesophagus. The external laryngeal nerve descends to reach cricothyroid.

Posterior—contents of carotid sheath and the parathyroid glands.

BLOOD SUPPLY: superior and inferior thyroid arteries lying close to the external and the recurrent laryngeal nerves respectively as the vessels approach the gland. Venous blood passes via the superior and middle thyroid veins to the internal jugular vein and via the inferior thyroid veins by a common trunk to the left brachiocephalic vein.

NERVE SUPPLY: sympathetic nerves from plexuses around superior and inferior thyroid arteries.

LYMPH DRAINAGE: to pretracheal, paratracheal and inferior deep cervical nodes.

HISTOLOGY: cubical epithelium lines follicles which are filled with amorphous colloid. Interfollicular vascular connective tissue contains many lymphocytes.

EMBRYOLOGY: the gland develops from a midline ventral diverticulum between 1st and 2nd pharyngeal arches which grows caudally to meet an outgrowth of the 4th pharyngeal pouch. The lower end of the diverticulum proliferates to form the glandular tissue. The rest of the diverticulum (the thyroglossal duct) atrophies, but remnants may persist. The contribution from the 4th pouch may be responsible for the production of calcitonin. The main part of the gland produces thyroxine, a vital regulator of cellular metabolism, under the humoral control of the pituitary gland.

THE PARATHYROID GLANDS

These are four small endocrine glands situated behind the lateral lobes of the thyroid gland within its capsule. There is a superior and an inferior pair. Each gland is oval in shape, about 3–6 mm across and may be mistaken for a fat lobule. They have a rich blood supply from the superior and inferior thyroid arteries. They consist of columns of chief cells separated by blood spaces. The cells have dark-staining nuclei and a chromatin network. Around puberty, eosinophil-staining cells appear.

The superior and inferior glands develop from the 4th and 3rd pharyngeal pouches respectively. The glands play an important role in calcium metabolism.

During operations on the thyroid gland the recurrent and external laryngeal nerves are at risk and may be damaged. Reduction of the blood supply to the closely-applied parathyroid glands or inadvertent removal of the glands may produce postoperative hypoparathyroidism and tetany.

THE TRACHEA (Fig. 29.1)

The trachea is a part of the respiratory passage. It descends from the larynx at the level of the 6th cervical vertebra, through the neck and thorax to its bifurcation into the two bronchi at the level of the lower border of the 4th thoracic vertebra. It is about 10 cm long and 2 cm in diameter. It is covered by the pretracheal fascia. (See also page 324).

The walls of the trachea are formed of fibrous tissue reinforced by 15–20 incomplete cartilaginous rings united behind by fibrous tissue and smooth muscle where the trachea rests on the oesophagus. It is lined internally with respiratory epithelium. The rings are of hyaline cartilage.

RELATIONS (in the neck): the trachea lies anterior to the oesophagus with the recurrent laryngeal nerve laterally in the groove between. It lies behind the cervical fascia and the infrahyoid muscles, and is crossed anteriorly by the isthmus of the thyroid gland and the jugular venous arch. Laterally are the lateral lobe of the thyroid gland, the inferior thyroid artery and the carotid sheath.

RELATIONS (in the thorax): see page 69.

BLOOD SUPPLY: the inferior thyroid vessels.

LYMPH DRAINAGE: to the pre- and paratracheal and tracheobronchial nodes.

NERVE SUPPLY: branches of the sympathetic trunk; parasympathetic branches from the vagus nerve via the recurrent laryngeal nerve and the pulmonary plexuses. Sensory fibres enter the recurrent laryngeal nerves.

In upper respiratory tract obstruction a tracheostomy (opening into the trachea) may be required. Usually the preferred site is at the 3rd and 4th tracheal rings and the isthmus of the thyroid gland often has to be divided.

THE OESOPHAGUS (Fig. 29.1)

This is a part of the digestive tube. It begins just behind the cricoid cartilage at the level of the 6th cervical vertebra as a continuation of the pharynx. It descends through the neck, thorax and diaphragm, inclining slightly to the left, to enter the stomach at the level of the 11th thoracic vertebra. Its upper end is about 15 cm from the incisor teeth and it is about 25 cm long. (See also pages 69 and 95.)

RELATIONS (in the neck): the oesophagus lies anterior to the prevertebral fascia and muscles and posterior to the trachea, with the recurrent laryngeal nerves in the grooves between. Laterally are the lateral lobe of the thyroid gland and the common carotid artery. The thoracic duct ascends for a short distance along the left side.

RELATIONS (in the thorax and abdomen): see pages 69 and 95.

BLOOD SUPPLY: branches from the inferior thyroid artery, the aorta and the left gastric artery. Venous blood passes to the inferior thyroid, azygos and left gastric veins. The communication of the azygos and left gastric veins in the walls of the oseophagus forms an important portal-systemic anastomosis (p. 111).

LYMPH VESSELS: pass to the deep cervical lymph chain, the posterior mediastinal lymph nodes and along the left gastric artery to the coeliac nodes.

NERVE SUPPLY: sympathetic—thoracic sympathetic chains and greater splanchnic nerves; parasympathetic—from the vagus nerve via the oesophageal plexus; recurrent laryngeal nerves to the upper part.

HISTOLOGY: The oesophagus has four coats. An inner mucosa of stratified squamous epithelium with numerous mucous glands which extend into the vascular submucous coat except at the upper and lower ends. The muscular coat contains inner circular and outer longitudinal layers; it is composed of striated muscle in its upper one-third and smooth muscle below. The outer fibrous coat is a layer of areolar tissue with many elastic fibres. Peritoneum covers part of the abdominal oesophagus.

CHAPTER 30

THE VESSELS, NERVES AND LYMPH DRAINAGE

VESSELS

THE SUBCLAVIAN ARTERY (Fig. 30.1)

On the right side the artery is formed from the brachiocephalic artery behind the sternoclavicular joint. It passes laterally behind scalenus anterior and the prevertebral fascia, arches over the apex of the lung and crosses the 1st rib, at the outer border of which it becomes the axillary artery. On the left side the artery arises from the arch of the aorta and ascends through the mediastinum to arch over the lung and enter the arm.

RELATIONS of the *right* artery: medial to scalenus anterior it lies behind the right common carotid artery, vagus nerve and internal jugular vein, and in front of the right pleura and lung. The right recurrent laryngeal nerve and ansa subclavia hook around it. Behind scalenus anterior, which separates it from the phrenic nerve, the artery lies on the cervical pleura. Lateral to the muscle, the artery lies on the 1st rib with its vein and the clavicle in front, and the lower trunk of the brachial plexus and scalenus medius behind.

RELATIONS of the *left* artery: in the thorax, the artery lies behind the left common carotid artery and the left vagus and left phrenic nerves. The oesophagus, trachea and left recurrent laryngeal nerve lie medial to it, and the left pleura and lung lie lateral to it. In the root of the neck its relations differ from those of the right, in that (*a*) the thoracic duct and phrenic nerve cross anterior to it, (*b*) the left recurrent laryngeal nerve does not hook around it (Fig. 6.1).

BRANCHES

The vertebral, internal thoracic and thyrocervical branches arise in the root of the neck medial to scalenus anterior. On the right, the costocervical trunk is formed behind the muscle; on the left it usually arises medial to the muscle.

(i) **vertebral artery**—passes upwards and medially to reach the transverse process of the 6th cervical vertebra. It ascends through the foramen transversarium of the upper six vertebrae, turns medially behind the lateral mass of the atlas and pierces the dura to enter the skull through the foramen magnum. It unites with its fellow of the opposite side in front of the brain stem to form the basilar artery.

RELATIONS: the artery is surrounded by a sympathetic plexus derived from the inferior cervical ganglion. In the lower part of the neck the artery lies on the prevertebral fascia and crosses over the inferior cervical ganglion. It lies behind the common carotid artery and is crossed over by the inferior thyroid artery and the thoracic duct or right lymph trunk.

FIG. 30.1

Arteriogram of aortic arch and its main branches. Note also the vertebral arteries and their loop round the lateral mass of the atlas.

1. Aortic arch
2. Brachiocephalic trunk
3. R & L subclavian arteries
4. R & L vertebral arteries

5. R & L common carotid arteries
6. R & L external carotid arteries
7. R & L internal carotid arteries
8. R & L vertebral loops

Within the vertebrae it is accompanied by the vertebral vein. As it winds around the lateral mass of the atlas, in the groove on the posterior arch, it crosses the floor of the suboccipital triangle and passes below the edge of the posterior atlanto-occipital membrane. The dorsal ramus of the 1st cervical nerve emerges between the artery and the atlas.

BRANCHES: (i) in the neck it supplies the spinal cord and vertebral muscles. Its branches within the posterior cranial fossa supply the upper part of the spinal cord and the hindbrain (see page 390).

(ii) **internal thoracic artery**—see page 47.

(iii) **thyrocervical trunk**—is a short vessel which soon divides into inferior thyroid, transverse cervical and suprascapular arteries. The **inferior thyroid artery** passes upwards and medially to reach the inferior pole of the thyroid gland. It lies behind the common carotid artery and sympathetic trunk and in front of the vertebral artery and prevertebral fascia. It supplies the thyroid gland, the trachea, oesophagus, larynx and pharynx. The **transverse cervical** and **suprascapular arteries** pass laterally over the scalene muscles, the phrenic nerve and prevertebral fascia to join the anastomosis around the scapula and supply the muscles of the shoulder girdle.

(iv) **costocervical trunk**—passes backwards over the dome of the pleura to reach the neck of the 1st rib where it divides into **deep cervical** and **highest intercostal arteries.** The former passes above the neck of the rib to supply the postvertebral muscles. The latter descends behind the pleura, in front of the neck of the rib and gives rise to the 1st and 2nd posterior intercostal arteries.

THE SUBCLAVIAN VEIN

This is the continuation of the axillary vein and extends from the outer border of the 1st rib to the medial border of scalenus anterior, where it joins the internal jugular vein to form the brachiocephalic vein. Lateral to scalenus anterior the vein lies in front of its artery; it then passes in front of the muscle, crossing over the phrenic nerve. The vein lies behind the clavicle. Its main tributary is the external jugular vein. A bicuspid valve is usually present just lateral to the entry of this vein.

THE COMMON CAROTID ARTERY (Fig. 29.1)

On the right side the artery arises from the brachiocephalic artery behind the sternoclavicular joint. It ascends through the neck and divides into internal and external carotid arteries at the level of the upper border of the thyroid cartilage. On the left, the artery arises from the aortic arch and ascends through the thorax and neck to bifurcate at the same level. The carotid sinus is a dilatation of the upper end of the artery and is sensitive to blood pressure changes. The carotid body is a small neurovascular structure on the posterior wall of the sinus; it functions as a chemoreceptor. Both structures are richly innervated by the glossopharyngeal nerve. The bifurcation of the common carotid artery is a common site for degenerative arterial disease to occur and local thrombosis or an embolus from this region can have serious effects on cerebral function.

RELATIONS, in the *neck*, of the right and left arteries: each artery lies within the carotid sheath with the vagus nerve behind and internal jugular vein laterally. The sheath is covered anterolaterally by the infrahyoid and sternocleidomastoid muscles. Posteriorly the artery lies on the right subclavian artery at its origin, and then on the prevertebral fascia and muscles. Medially at first are the trachea and the oesophagus (with the recurrent laryngeal nerve between) and then the larynx and pharynx. The thyroid gland and its vessels may be anterior or medial to the artery.

RELATIONS, in the *thorax*, of the left artery: the artery lies anterior to the vagus and phrenic nerves and the left subclavian artery, to the left of the trachea and brachiocephalic artery, and is covered anterolaterally by the left pleura and lung (Fig. 6.1).

BRANCHES: none, other than its terminal branches.

THE EXTERNAL CAROTID ARTERY

This artery supplies the structures in the upper part of the neck and the face. It arises from the bifurcation of the common carotid artery at the level of the upper border of the thyroid cartilage and ascends to reach and pass through the parotid gland. The artery ends behind the neck of the mandible by dividing into maxillary and superficial temporal arteries.

RELATIONS: in the neck the artery lies on the lateral wall of the pharynx, at first anteromedial and then lateral to the internal carotid artery, separated from it by styloglossus and stylopharyngeus, the glosso-pharyngeal nerve and the pharyngeal branches of the vagus nerve. It lies deep to sternocleidomastoid and is crossed from above downwards by stylohyoid, the posterior belly of digastric, the hypoglossal nerve, and the lingual and facial veins. Within the parotid gland the artery lies medial to the retromandibular vein and the facial nerve.

BRANCHES (in order of origin):

Superior thyroid artery—descends with the external laryngeal nerve to the upper pole of the thyroid gland. Its superior laryngeal branch pierces the thyrohyoid membrane to supply the larynx and further branches supply the pharynx, thyroid gland and infrahyoid muscles.

Ascending pharyngeal artery—ascends on the lateral wall of the pharynx and gives branches to the pharynx, tonsil, soft palate and auditory tube.

Lingual artery—arises at the level of the hyoid bone and passes forwards deep to hyoglossus into the substance of the tongue and then to its tip.

RELATIONS: before reaching hyoglossus, it lies on the middle constrictor and here forms an upward loop which is crossed by the hypoglossal nerve. The artery supplies the suprahyoid muscles, the tonsil, the soft palate, the submandibular and sublingual glands and the tongue.

Facial artery—arises just above the lingual and arches over the submandibular gland. It then turns around the inferior border of the mandible (4 cm in front of the angle) and takes a tortuous course across the face to the medial angle of the eye.

RELATIONS: medial to the submandibular gland, the artery lies on the middle and superior constrictor muscles, separated by the latter from the tonsil. Lateral to the gland it is related to the body of the mandible. On the face, the artery lies between the superficial and deeper muscles.

BRANCHES: in the neck the artery supplies the tonsil, soft palate and submandibular gland, and on the face it supplies the upper and lower lips and the facial musculature.

Occipital artery—arises opposite the facial artery and passes backwards along the lower border of the posterior belly of digastric, and medial to the mastoid process. It turns upwards over the back of the skull to reach the vertex.

RELATIONS: with digastric it crosses the carotid sheath and lies in the medial of the two grooves on the medial side of the mastoid process. To reach the back of the skull it passes between semispinalis and splenius capitis and pierces trapezius. The greater occipital nerve lies medial to it on the back of the skull. The artery supplies the upper part of the neck and the back of the scalp.

Posterior auricular artery—passes backwards along the upper border of the posterior belly of digastric, then lateral to digastric and on to the lateral aspect of the scalp. It supplies the auricle and adjacent scalp.

Superficial temporal artery—is formed behind the neck of the mandible in the parotid gland and ascends over the posterior end of the zygomatic arch on to the lateral aspect of the scalp, where it divides into anterior and posterior branches. It supplies the face (by its transverse facial branch), the auricle and the scalp.

Maxillary artery—arises behind the neck of the mandible in the parotid gland. It passes forwards through the infratemporal fossa and pterygomaxillary fissure to enter the pterygopalatine fossa where it divides into terminal branches.

RELATIONS: it lies at first between the neck of the mandible and the sphenomandibular ligament and is crossed by the inferior alveolar nerve. It then usually passes on to the lateral surface of lateral pterygoid, lying deep to temporalis, and runs forwards on lateral pterygoid to reach the pterygomaxillary fissure and fossa. In the pterygopalatine fossa it is related to the maxillary nerve and the pterygopalatine ganglion.

BRANCHES
(i) to the ear.
(ii) **middle meningeal artery**—ascends through the foramen spinosum into the middle cranial fossa where it divides into anterior and posterior branches. The anterior branch passes medial to the pterion (p. 263) and often grooves the bone. It may be damaged in fractures of the skull and bleed intracranially, so producing an extradural clot with a life-threatening rise in intracranial pressure. The surface marking of the middle meningeal artery is 3·5 cm behind and 1·5 cm above the zygomaticofrontal suture and surgical access to the vessel can be achieved via a craniotomy centred over this spot, the pterion. The artery supplies the dura and bone of the middle cranial fossa and the vault of the skull. (An accessory meningeal artery may pass through foramen ovale.)
(iii) **inferior alveolar artery**—passes through the mandibular canal and is distributed to the gums and teeth.
(iv) branches to the muscles of mastication.
(v) terminal vessels accompany the branches of the pterygopalatine ganglion and supply the nose, palate and pharynx. The infra-orbital branch gives off the superior alveolar arteries to supply the upper teeth.

THE INTERNAL CAROTID ARTERY

This supplies the greater part of the brain and the contents of the orbit. It arises from the bifurcation of the common carotid artery at the level of the upper border of the thyroid cartilage. It ascends to the base of the skull and enters the middle cranial fossa by passing through the carotid canal in the petrous temporal bone. In the fossa it passes upwards and forwards through the cavernous sinus, pierces the roof of the sinus, and turns backwards on itself before dividing into anterior and middle cerebral arteries, medial to the anterior clinoid process.

RELATIONS: the artery is surrounded by a sympathetic plexus formed from fibres of the superior cervical ganglion. In the neck the artery lies within the carotid sheath with the internal jugular vein laterally, and the vagus nerve behind. The pharynx lies medially, and the prevertebral fascia and muscles posteriorly. The external carotid artery is at first anteromedial to it and then lateral, separated from it by styloglossus and stylopharyngeus, the glossopharyngeal nerve and the pharyngeal branches of the vagus. Laterally, the artery is crossed by stylohyoid, the posterior belly of digastric and the hypoglossal nerve.

In the petrous temporal bone the artery lies in the floor of the middle ear and, as it enters the middle cranial fossa, passes over the foramen lacerum.

Within the cavernous sinus, it lies in the carotid groove of the body of the sphenoid, covered by the venous endothelium of the sinus. On its lateral side it is crossed by the abducent nerve and further laterally the oculomotor, trochlear, ophthalmic and maxillary nerves lie in the lateral wall of the sinus. It pierces the roof of the sinus medial to the anterior clinoid process and here lies lateral to the optic chiasma and nerve.

BRANCHES
- (i) to the **pituitary gland** and the **meninges.**
- (ii) **ophthalmic** and **posterior communicating arteries.**
- (iii) **anterior** and **middle cerebral arteries** (p. 389).

VENOUS DRAINAGE OF THE HEAD AND NECK

This may be subdivided into: (1) Veins of the brain and the intracranial venous sinuses (p. 392). (2) Veins of the face and scalp. (3) Veins of the neck. The arrangement of the veins is more variable than that of the arteries but most vessels are tributaries of the jugular system.

THE VEINS OF THE FACE AND SCALP

The **facial vein** is formed at the medial angle of the eye by the union of the supra-orbital and supratrochlear veins draining the scalp. It passes obliquely backwards in the superficial fascia of the face, posterior to the facial artery, to be joined by the anterior branch of the retromandibular vein below the mandible. The facial vein drains the anterior part of the scalp and the superficial structures of the face. It communicates with the cavernous sinus by the ophthalmic veins, with the pterygoid venous plexus by the deep facial vein and with the diploic veins.

The **pterygoid venous plexus** is situated around the lateral pterygoid muscle and drains via the maxillary vein to the retromandibular vein. The plexus drains the infratemporal region and communicates with the cavernous sinus, and the ophthalmic and facial veins.

The **retromandibular vein** is formed behind the neck of the mandible by the union of the superficial temporal and maxillary veins. It descends through the parotid gland lateral to the external carotid artery and medial to the facial nerve. Below the gland it divides into anterior and posterior divisions. The anterior joins the facial vein below the angle of the mandible, the posterior joins the posterior auricular vein to form the external jugular vein. The veins of the back of the scalp drain into the suboccipital venous plexus.

The **superficial temporal** and **posterior auricular veins** drain the lateral aspect of the scalp and the external acoustic meatus; they accompany their corresponding arteries.

THE VEINS OF THE NECK

The **internal jugular vein** drains blood from the intracranial region, the head and neck. It arises at the jugular foramen on the base of the skull as a continuation of the sigmoid venous sinus, passes downwards through the neck and, behind the medial end of the clavicle, is joined by the subclavian vein to form the brachiocephalic vein. The vein has a dilatation at each end, the superior and inferior jugular bulbs, and a fairly constant pair of valves above the lower bulb. In patients with heart failure the jugular venous pressure is raised, and by careful positioning of the patient the height and wave form of the pulse in the internal jugular vein can be observed in the neck.

RELATIONS: the vein lies within the carotid sheath with the vagus nerve behind and the internal or common carotid arteries medially. The deep cervical lymph nodes lie around it. At the base of the skull it lies lateral to the last four cranial nerves. Posteriorly it lies on the sympathetic chain, prevertebral fascia and muscles, the phrenic nerve and, inferiorly, the subclavian artery. It is crossed over laterally by the accessory nerve passing downwards and laterally, then by the posterior belly of digastric passing upwards and backwards, and the omohyoid muscle passing downwards and backwards. Further laterally are the styloid process and its muscles, the sternocleidomastoid muscle and the medial end of the clavicle from above downwards.

TRIBUTARIES
(i) **inferior petrosal sinus.**
(ii) branches from the **pharyngeal plexus** of veins.
(iii) **facial vein** having drained blood from the face and scalp, passes backwards and downwards over the external and internal carotid arteries and the hypoglossal nerve to enter the internal jugular vein opposite the hyoid bone.
(iv) **lingual vein.**
(v) **superior** and **middle thyroid veins.**
(vi) on the left the **thoracic duct** may enter the vein and on the right the **right lymph duct.**

The **external jugular vein,** a superficial vein, is formed behind the angle of the mandible by the union of the posterior auricular and the posterior branch of the retromandibular vein. It descends over sternocleidomastoid, pierces the cervical fascia above the midpoint of the clavicle and enters the subclavian vein. The vein can be used to assess venous pressure.

The **anterior jugular vein** begins below the hyoid bone near the midline and passes downwards and laterally deep to sternocleidomastoid to enter the external jugular vein behind the clavicle. The **jugular arch** unites the two anterior veins just above the sternum.

NERVE SUPPLY

The **cutaneous nerve supply** is summarised in Figure 30.2.

THE CERVICAL PLEXUS OF NERVES

This is formed from the ventral rami of the upper four cervical nerves. The plexus lies on scalenus medius and is covered anteriorly by scalenus anterior, the prevertebral fascia and the internal jugular vein.

BRANCHES

(i) **lesser occipital nerve** (C2 & 3) is distributed to the skin over the posterior aspect of the auricle and mastoid region.

(ii) **great auricular nerve** (C2 & 3) supplies the skin over the inferior part of the auricle and the parotid region of the face.

(iii) **transverse cervical nerve** (C2 & 3) supplies the skin over the anterior and lateral parts of the neck.

(iv) **supraclavicular nerves** (C3 & 4) supply the skin above and below the clavicle.

(v) **communications** with the hypoglossal nerve—fibres from C1 are carried by the hypoglossal nerve to geniohyoid and thyrohyoid, and also form the superior root of the ansa cervicalis. The superior root descends on the internal carotid artery and forms a communicating loop (the ansa cervicalis) with the inferior root (from C2 & 3) which descends on the internal jugular vein. The ansa supplies the infrahyoid muscles.

(vi) other muscle branches—supply the prevertebral muscles, sternocleidomastoid, trapezius and levator scapulae.

(vii) **phrenic nerve** (C3, 4 & 5, mainly 4)—descends through the neck and thorax to supply the diaphragm.

RELATIONS (in the *neck*): the phrenic nerve winds around the lateral border of scalenus anterior on to the anterior surface. It is here covered by the prevertebral fascia and crossed by the internal jugular vein, the transverse cervical and suprascapular arteries, and the subclavian vein. On the left, the nerve is more medially placed in the root of the neck and crosses the subclavian artery. The nerves pass in front of the internal thoracic arteries as they enter the thorax.

RELATIONS (in the *thorax*): see page 67.

Because the phrenic and supraclavicular nerves come from the same segments of the cord, pain which originates in the region of the diaphragm may be referred by the brain to the point of the shoulder.

The Brachial Plexus: see page 179.

THE AUTONOMIC NERVOUS SYSTEM OF THE HEAD AND NECK

Sympathetic

The cervical sympathetic trunks pass vertically upwards to the base of the skull, lying on the prevertebral fascia and muscles, over the trans-

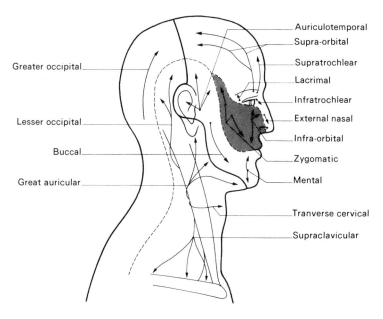

Greater occipital

Lesser occipital

Buccal

Great auricular

Auriculotemporal
Supra-orbital
Supratrochlear
Lacrimal
Infratrochlear
External nasal
Infra-orbital
Zygomatic
Mental
Tranverse cervical
Supraclavicular

FIG. 30.2
Diagrammatic lay-out of the cutaneous innervation of the head and neck.

verse processes of the cervical vertebrae and deep to the carotid sheath. Each trunk has three ganglia and is continuous below with the thoracic ganglionated trunk. Preganglionic fibres arise in the upper four thoracic spinal segments.

The **superior cervical ganglion** lies opposite the 2nd and 3rd cervical transverse processes and behind the angle of the mandible. Its postganglionic fibres pass—

(i) with the external carotid artery and its branches.
(ii) with the internal carotid artery and its branches.
(iii) to the pharyngeal plexus.

339

(iv) to the upper four cervical nerves—rami communicantes.
(v) in a cardiac branch to the cardiac plexus.

The **middle cervical ganglion** lies at the level of the 6th cervical vertebra and cricoid cartilage. Postganglionic fibres pass—
(i) with the inferior thyroid artery.
(ii) to the 5th and 6th cervical nerves—rami communicantes.
(iii) in a cardiac branch to the cardiac plexus.

The **inferior cervical ganglion** is a small ganglion lying opposite the 7th cervical vertebra. It may combine with the 1st thoracic ganglion to form the stellate ganglion lying on the neck of the 1st rib. Postganglionic fibres pass—
(i) with the vertebral artery.
(ii) to the 7th and 8th cervical nerves—rami communicantes.
(iii) in a cardiac branch to the cardiac plexus.

There is a fine communication, the ansa subclavia, between the middle and inferior ganglia. It hooks around the subclavian artery.

Parasympathetic

Preganglionic fibres pass in the oculomotor, facial, glossopharyngeal and vagus nerves and synapse either in four small ganglia in the head (the ciliary, pterygopalatine, submandibular and otic) or in the walls of the organs they supply in the neck, thorax and abdomen. The named ganglia, as well as containing parasympathetic synapses, give uninterrupted passage to sympathetic and somatic fibres.

The **ciliary ganglion** lies in the orbit, lateral to the optic nerve. The parasympathetic fibres are derived from the oculomotor branch to inferior oblique. Postganglionic fibres pass to the sphincter pupillae and ciliary muscles. Sympathetic fibres come from the superior cervical ganglion via the plexus on the ophthalmic artery and are distributed to the eyeball. Sensory fibres from the eyeball pass to the nasociliary nerve.

The **pterygopalatine ganglion** lies in the pterygopalatine fossa, connected to the maxillary nerve by small branches. The parasympathetic fibres are from the facial nerve via the greater petrosal branch which becomes the nerve of the pterygoid canal. Postganglionic fibres supply the lacrimal gland (through the zygomatico-temporal and lacrimal · nerves) and glands of the nose, palate and nasopharynx (through nasal, palatine, and pharyngeal branches of the ganglion).

Sympathetic fibres come from the superior cervical ganglion via the plexus on the internal carotid artery. The deep petrosal nerve (sympathetic) joins the greater petrosal nerve to form the nerve of the pterygoid canal which enters the ganglion. The fibres are distributed to the nose, palate and nasopharynx. Sensory fibres from the nose, palate and nasopharynx may pass in the branches of the ganglion to the maxillary nerve.

The **submandibular ganglion** lies lateral to hyoglossus suspended from the lingual nerve by small branches. Its parasympathetic fibres come from the facial nerve via its chorda tympani branch and then along the lingual nerve to the ganglion. Postganglionic fibres supply the submandibular and sublingual glands and other glands in the floor of the mouth.

Sympathetic fibres come from the superior cervical ganglion along the facial artery and pass to the glands in the floor of the mouth. Taste fibres may pass through the ganglion.

The **otic ganglion** lies on tensor veli palatini medial to the mandibular nerve. The parasympathetic fibres come from the glossopharyngeal nerve via the tympanic plexus and its branch, the lesser petrosal nerve. Post-ganglionic fibres pass with the auriculotemporal nerve to the parotid gland. Sympathetic fibres come from the superior cervical ganglion along the middle meningeal artery and pass to the parotid gland. Motor branches from the mandibular nerve pass through the ganglion, without synapsing, to supply tensor veli palatini and tensor tympani.

Parasympathetic fibres from the glossopharyngeal nerve supply directly, or through the pharyngeal plexus, the glands of the oropharynx and the posterior one-third of the tongue. Parasympathetic fibres from the vagus supply the glands of the laryngopharynx, larynx, oseophagus and trachea. In all these situations, the ganglion cells are on the viscus.

THE LYMPH DRAINAGE OF THE HEAD AND NECK

The lymph nodes of the head and neck are divided into two groups,
(a) the circular chain around the base of the skull.
(b) the deep and superficial cervical chains—the deep around the internal jugular vein and the superficial around the external and anterior jugular veins.

The **circular chain** consists of seven named groups of lymph nodes:

(i) **occipital**—around the occipital artery; drain the posterior part of the scalp and adjacent part of the neck.

(ii) **retro-auricular**—on the mastoid process; drain external acoustic meatus, the back of the auricle and adjacent scalp.

(iii) **superficial parotid**—in front of the tragus; drain the external acoustic meatus, the front of the auricle and the adjacent scalp.

(iv) **deep parotid**—deep to the parotid fascia and within the gland; drain the anterior half of the scalp, infratemporal region, the orbit, the lateral part of the eyelids, the upper molar teeth, the external acoustic meatus and the parotid gland.

(v) **retropharyngeal**—between the pharynx and the atlas; drain the upper part of the pharynx and related structures.

(vi) **submandibular**—between the mandible and the submandibular gland; drain the anterior nasal cavities, the tongue, teeth and gums, submandibular and sublingual glands and all the face except the lateral part of the eyelids and the medial part of the lower lip and chin.

(vii) **submental**—behind the chin and on mylohyoid; drain the tip of the tongue, the floor of the mouth, the lower lip and chin.

Efferent vessels from all these groups, except the superficial parotid nodes, pass to the deep cervical lymph chain. The superficial parotid group pass to the superficial cervical lymph nodes.

The **deep cervical lymph chain** lies around the internal jugular vein. The upper part of the chain is extended medially towards the retropharyngeal group of nodes. The lower part of the chain is extended laterally above the clavicle. Other named nodes of the chain are the jugulodigastric, jugulo-omohyoid, pretracheal and paratracheal:

(i) **jugulodigastric node**—behind the angle of the mandible above the posterior belly of digastric; drains the tonsil and lateral part of the tongue.

(ii) **jugulo-omohyoid node**—lies in the angle between the internal jugular vein and the superior belly of omohyoid; drains the tongue via the submental and submandibular nodes.

(iii) **para- and pre-tracheal nodes**—lie along the inferior thyroid vessels and drain the trachea and thyroid gland: efferent vessels may descend to the tracheobronchial nodes in the mediastinum.

The deep cervical lymph chain drains most of the circular chain of nodes and receives direct efferents from the salivary and thyroid glands, tongue, tonsil, nose, pharynx and larynx. Their efferents form the jugular lymph trunk which joins the thoracic duct on the left, and on the right it either joins the right lymph duct or opens separately into the internal jugular or subclavian veins. The clinician must be constantly aware that the first sign of cancer arising in the oropharynx, middle ear and buccal cavity is frequently a hard enlargement of the lymph nodes in the upper deep cervical group.

The **superficial lymph chains** lie along the external and anterior jugular veins. The former drains the superficial parotid nodes and the side of the neck and joins the subclavian lymph trunk. The latter drains the superficial structures on the front of the neck and joins the external jugular chain or the lower deep cervical chain directly.

CENTRAL NERVOUS SYSTEM

CHAPTER 31

INTRODUCTION

The central nervous system consists of the brain and spinal cord. The emerging cranial and spinal nerves pass through the surrounding meninges and cerebrospinal fluid; they form the peripheral nervous system. The autonomic nervous system overlaps both central and peripheral nervous systems and is concerned with the innervation of smooth muscle, cardiac muscle and glands.

The brain is situated within the cranium and comprises a forebrain (prosencephalon), a midbrain (mesencephalon) and a hindbrain (rhombencephalon). The last is continuous through the foramen magnum with the spinal cord. The forebrain is subdivided into a telencephalon consisting of the two cerebral hemispheres, and a diencephalon composed mainly of the two thalami and the hypothalamus. The hindbrain is subdivided into the pons, medulla and cerebellum.

The midbrain, pons and medulla are collectively known as the **brain stem**; they form a central axis connecting the diencephalon to the spinal cord and give attachment posteriorly to the cerebellum.

The nervous system is made up of innumerable nerve cells (**neurons**), each with its branches (the **dendrites**) and an **axon.** Most of the neurons in the central nervous system are found in the cortex of the cerebrum and cerebellum, and in aggregations called **nuclei.** Some neurons found outside the brain and spinal cord are grouped into **ganglia.** Many of the axons are myelinated and when massed together in the central nervous system form the tracts of the white matter.

ATTACHMENTS OF CRANIAL NERVES

The olfactory nerves (1) send bundles into the olfactory bulb, and optic nerves (2) lead back to the optic chiasma. (Both olfactory bulbs and tracts, and the optic nerves are part of the primitive forebrain.) The oculomotor nerve (3) emerges from the interpeduncular fossa behind the mamillary bodies. The trochlear nerve (4) emerges dorsally below the inferior colliculus and winds around the cerebral peduncles, lying between the temporal lobe and the peduncle. The trigeminal nerve (5) is attached to the lateral surface of the pons—motor and sensory roots may be distinguished. The abducent nerve (6) emerges between the pyramid and pons, the facial (7) and vestibulocochlear (8) nerves emerge in the cerebellopontomedullary angle. The glossopharyngeal (9), vagus (10) and cranial accessory (11) nerves emerge between the olive and the inferior cerebellar peduncle, the hypoglossal nerve (12) emerges between the olive and pyramid.

DEVELOPMENT OF THE CENTRAL NERVOUS SYSTEM
(See page 31, Figs. 2.2 and 31.1)

The nervous system develops from a dorsal longitudinal **neural plate** of ectoderm. The lateral margins of the plate become raised and its central part is depressed to form a **neural groove.** The groove deepens and the margins of the plate meet and fuse dorsally, forming the **neural tube.** The cephalic part of the tube is wider and forms the brain, the remainder becomes the spinal cord. Incomplete closure of the tube occurs

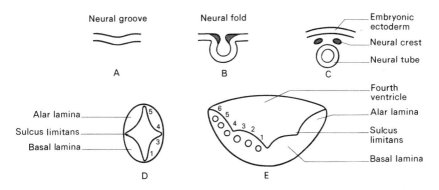

FIG. 31.1

The development of the central nervous system. A, B, C show the formation of the neural tube and the neural crest, D shows the arrangement of the alar (sensory) and basal (motor) laminae in the spinal cord and the lower medulla, E shows the re-arrangement of the alar and basal laminae in the floor of the 4th ventricle. (Nuclei: 1, somatic efferent; 2, special visceral efferent; 3, general visceral efferent; 4, general and special visceral afferent; 5, general somatic afferent; 6, special somatic afferent.)

occasionally in the lower part, giving rise to a condition known as spina bifida and is associated with the nonfusion of the neural arch of the related developing vertebrae. Also the tissues over them may not develop properly. More rarely the tube fails to close in the cerebral regions.

The junctional zone between neural ectoderm (forming the neural plate) and the embryonic ectoderm gives rise to the **neural crest tissue.** As the neural tube is separated from the embryonic ectoderm the neural crest tissue is also drawn in and forms a longitudinal plate of tissue on each side of the neural tube. From these longitudinal plates develop, amongst other things, the spinal and autonomic ganglia and the medulla of the suprarenal gland.

The ectodermal plate shows a marked increase in the number of its cells as the groove and tube are formed. Differentiation occurs into an **ependymal layer** lining the cavity of the tube, an intermediate **mantle layer** with numerous neuroblasts, and an outer **marginal layer** composed largely of fibres derived from the neuroblasts. The ependyma remains as the lining of the cavities of the central nervous system, the mantle layer becomes the future grey matter and the marginal layer the white matter.

Regional proliferation of neuroblasts causes changes in the size and shape of the tube. Two constrictions around the neural tube in the brain region divide it into three separate parts, the **primitive vesicles** of the forebrain, midbrain and hindbrain.

The tube becomes ventrally flexed at the junction of the brain and spinal cord (cervical flexure) and also in the midbrain region (mesencephalic flexure). Later a dorsal (pontine) flexure develops in the hindbrain region. The dorsal wall of the hindbrain vesicle is much attenuated and forms the inferior part of the roof of the fourth ventricle. The **cerebellum** develops from the rostral (cranial) edge of the roof of the hindbrain vesicle, at first growing into the vesicle cavity but later becoming everted and undergoing external enlargement. Rapid multiplication of the neurons ventral to the hindbrain vesicle produces the pons.

In the spinal region the wall of the neural tube becomes thinned dorsally and ventrally, and an internal lateral longitudinal furrow, the **sulcus limitans,** divides each lateral wall into **basal** (ventral) and **alar** (dorsal) **laminae** (plates). From the basal laminae develop neurons subserving motor function and from the alar, sensory neurons.

The neurons of the spinal cord are arranged in four longitudinal columns around the central canal. The most anterior is the somatic motor column which forms the **anterior horn of grey matter.** Behind this, also in the basal lamina and bordering the sulcus limitans, is the visceral motor column. The alar lamina also possesses visceral and somatic sensory columns, the latter forming the **posterior horn of grey matter.** The visceral sensory column together with the visceral motor column form the **lateral horn of grey matter,** found in the thoracic and sacral regions. The nerve fibres form motor and sensory tracts but their dorsoventral arrangement is not so well defined as that of the basal and alar lamina from whose neurons they are derived.

In the region of the pontine flexure of the hindbrain the dorsal part of the neural tube is thin, and the two alar laminae are more widely separated and lateral to the corresponding basal laminae. The columnar arrangement of the neurons remains although any one column may be absent or ill-defined in parts. In the region of the brain stem additional special visceral (branchial) efferent and afferent columns are formed, each lying between a somatic and a visceral column. The special visceral efferent column is motor to the muscles derived from the pharyngeal arch mesoderm and the afferent column carries the sensation of taste (Fig. 31.1).

DEVELOPMENT OF THE FOREBRAIN

The basal plate is absent in the forebrain which is derived from a continuation of the alar plate. The tissue surrounding the midline part of the forebrain vesicle becomes the diencephalon, the cavity becomes the third ventricle, its rostral wall being the thin lamina terminalis.

Two large outgrows develop from the sides of the vesicle, each destined to become a cerebral hemisphere with its cavity, the lateral ventricle. The lateral wall of the diverticulum undergoes considerable thickening and the lateral ventricle comes to lie near the midline. The communication between it and the third ventricle is known as the interventricular foramen. Masses of neurons in the wall of the diencephalon form the thalamus and hypothalamus, and in the hemisphere, the neurons on the floor of the ventricle form the basal nuclei. Many neurons migrate to the surface of the hemisphere and form the cortex (grey matter).

The medial surface of the developing hemisphere dorsal to the interventricular foramen becomes the hippocampus and that ventral to it the piriform cortex. The hippocampus and the piriform cortex are known as the allocortex (the neurons are usually covered by a thin layer of fibres). The rest of the cortex is called isocortex (the neurons being near the surface).

The hemisphere enlarges laterally and caudally and then ventrally, the lateral ventricle thus becoming elongated and C-shaped. The hippocampus curves around its convexity and the basal nuclei lie in its concavity. Fibres projecting from the isocortex to lower centres form part of a well defined bundle, the internal capsule, which passes through the tissue in the concavity of the ventricle and splits the basal nuclei into a lateral part (lentiform nucleus) and a medial part (caudate nucleus), the latter lying adjacent to the thalamus. The internal capsule also contains fibres passing from the thalamus to the cortex.

Commissural fibres between the temporal poles (piriform cortex and some neocortex) pass through the lamina terminalis forming the ventrally placed anterior commissure. Dorsally in the lamina the fornix commissure develops between the two hippocampal areas. The large neocortical commissure, the corpus callosum, develops in the fornix commissure and soon overshadows it, overhanging the roof of the diencephalon. As the corpus callosum increases in size the dorsally placed hippocampus becomes much attenuated and remains only as a thin layer of cells on top of the corpus callosum. That part of the hippocampus carried backwards and then ventrally persists in the adult, and lies in the floor of the inferior horn of the lateral ventricle.

The roof of the diencephalon remains thin ependyma and is invaginated by the choroid plexus of the third ventricle. The medial wall of the hemisphere, between the hippocampus and the interventricular foramen also remains thin ependyma and is invaginated by the choroid plexus of the lateral ventricle. As the hemisphere grows the line of invagination follows the C-shaped pattern of the lateral ventricle already described and forms the choroid fissure.

Small forward diverticula from the diencephalon form the optic stalks, giving rise to the optic nerves and part of the eyeball. The pineal body grows dorsally from the diencephalon, and the infundibular contribution to the pituitary gland grows downwards.

Sources of information on the structure and function
of the central nervous system

Some of the functions of component parts of the central nervous system will be considered under their relevant sections. However, the evidence on which these conclusions are based is drawn from five main sources:

1. Pathological—studying the effects of disease or operative removal of any region.
2. Recording electrodes—demonstrating resting electrical activity and any changes in this activity associated with changes elsewhere in the nervous system or in the body at large.
3. Anatomical—dissection and macroscopic observations supplemented by histological examination of stained material and electronmicroscopy.
4. Morphological—comparison of homologous parts of the central nervous system developed to a variable extent in different animals may give pertinent information about their function.
5. Stimulation—the study of the effects of electrical stimulation of the central nervous system in the conscious patient has been carried out extensively.

CHAPTER 32

THE FOREBRAIN

THE CEREBRAL HEMISPHERES (Figs. 32.1, 32.2, 32.3)

The cerebral hemispheres lie on either side of the midsagittal plane, covered superiorly by the bones of the skull vault and lying inferiorly on the bones of the anterior and middle cranial fossae and on the upper surface of the tentorium cerebelli. The diencephalon, lying in the midline, is partly embedded in the hemispheres. The hemispheres are partly separated by the **median longitudinal fissure** within which lies a fold of

FIG. 32.1
The right cerebral hemisphere, lateral aspect.

dura, the falx cerebri, and are joined together by a broad band of fibres, the **corpus callosum.** The corpus callosum overlies the diencephalon and the midbrain and is separated from them by a horizontal cleft, the transverse fissure. The basal nuclei and the rhinencephalon (smell brain) are deeper structures of the hemispheres lying near its medial side, being closely applied to the C-shaped lateral ventricle, and lateral to the diencephalon.

The **hemispheres** have an outer layer of grey matter, the **cerebral cortex;** its thickness varies from 1–4 mm at different sites. The cortex is greatly convoluted: grooves, the sulci, separate ridges of brain tissue, the gyri, and about two-thirds of the total surface area is hidden from view in the sulci.

Each hemisphere has frontal, occipital and temporal poles; lateral, medial and inferior surfaces; and frontal, parietal, occipital and temporal lobes. The lobes are named after the closely related bones of the skull. The frontal and occipital poles are the anterior and posterior extremities of the hemisphere. The inferiorly-placed temporal pole lies under the frontal lobe on the floor of the middle cranial fossa.

349

On the convex **lateral surface** the deep **lateral sulcus** extends upwards and backwards and divides frontal from temporal lobes. The margins of the sulcus overlap the deeply placed **insula,** an area of cortex which has become submerged during the enlargement of the hemispheres. The **central sulcus** passes downwards and forwards from the superior border towards the lateral sulcus and separates **precentral** and **post-central gyri,** concerned with motor and somatosensory functions respectively. These gyri are limited by pre- and post-central sulci. Sulci above and parallel to the lateral sulcus divide the surface into superior, middle

Corpus callosum — Genu / Body / Splenium

Parieto-occipital sulcus

Calcarine sulcus

Pineal body

Parahippocampal gyrus

Interthalamic connection

Fornix

Paracentral lobule

Cingulate gyrus

Septum pellucidum

Rostrum of corpus callosum

Anterior commissure

Lamina terminalis

Optic chiasma

Interventricular foramen

Uncus

FIG. 32.2
The left cerebral hemisphere, medial aspect.

and inferior frontal gyri. Sulci below and parallel to the lateral sulcus divide the surface into the superior, middle and inferior temporal gyri. A part of the superior temporal gyrus is concerned with auditory function.

A prominent feature of the flat **medial surface** is the corpus callosum. The **cingulate gyrus** lies above and parallel to the corpus callosum. The central sulcus extends for a short distance on to the surface and the cortex around it is known as the **paracentral lobule;** it also is concerned with motor and somatosensory functions. The deep **calcarine sulcus** extends horizontally backwards from behind the corpus callosum to the occipital pole. The **parieto-occipital sulcus** passes obliquely upwards from about its middle to the superior margin of the surface. The cortex overlying both margins of the posterior half of the calcarine sulcus, and that along the inferior margin of its anterior half, is concerned with visual functions.

The **inferior surface** is separated from the midbrain by a deep **hippocampal sulcus.** The **parahippocampal gyrus** borders the sulcus and is separated laterally by the longitudinal, **collateral sulcus** from the rest of the cortex. Anteriorly the parahippocampal gyrus is continued into the **uncus,** which is a short medially projecting recurved part. The uncus is bounded laterally by the **rhinal sulcus,** which is usually continuous posteriorly with the collateral sulcus. The olfactory bulb and tract lie on the anterior part of the frontal lobe and the sulcus in which they lie separates the gyrus rectus medially from the short irregular gyri laterally. The olfactory tract divides posteriorly into medial and lateral olfactory striae and the area of cortex between the striae gives passage to a number of vessels entering the brain substance. It is known as the **anterior perforated substance.**

Grey Matter of the Hemispheres

Microscopical examination of the cerebral isocortex shows that the neurons are not distributed evenly nor are they all the same size and

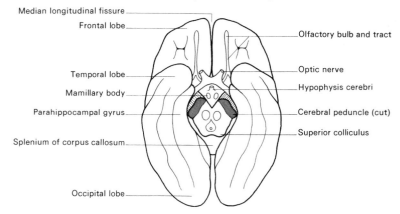

Median longitudinal fissure

Frontal lobe

Olfactory bulb and tract

Temporal lobe

Optic nerve

Mamillary body

Hypophysis cerebri

Parahippocampal gyrus

Cerebral peduncle (cut)

Superior colliculus

Splenium of corpus callosum

Occipital lobe

Fig. 32.3
The inferior aspect of the brain after removal of the hind brain.

shape. Most areas of isocortex have their neurons arranged in six layers (laminae). Layer I (molecular) is subpial and composed of a few stellate (granular) neurons and the apical dendrites of deeper pyramidal cells. Layers II and IV are the external and internal granular layers; their numerous granular cells are small with short multibranched intracortical axons. Layers III and V are the external and internal pyramidal layers; their pyramidal cells have a large apical and a number of smaller basal dendrites and their axons pass into the adjacent white matter. The very large pyramidal (Betz) cells of the motor areas are found in layer V. The innermost (fusiform) layer VI is composed of multipolar neurons and abuts on the white matter. The pattern of the entering fibres also varies from area to area. Two tangentially placed plexuses are described, the outer in layer IV and the inner in layer V; because of the prominent outer layer in the cortex around the calcarine sulcus it is referred to as the **striate area.**

In the sensory areas the granular (stellate) cells are most numerous. The motor areas have a preponderance of the pyramidal cells and are sometimes referred to as the agranular cortex. Using histological criteria it is possible to identify **sensorimotor cortex** around the central sulcus,

351

the **visual cortex** around the calcarine sulcus and the **auditory cortex** on the superior temporal gyrus. Other cortical areas are less well defined.

White Matter of the Hemispheres

The nerve fibres of the hemispheres are of three groups: commissural, association, and projection.

Commissural fibres unite the two hemispheres across the midline; they comprise the corpus callosum and the anterior and fornix (hippo-campal) commissures. The habenular and posterior commissures belong to the diencephalon.

The **corpus callosum** is a broad band of fibres passing between corresponding cortical areas of the two hemispheres. It lies at the base of the median longitudinal fissure and above the diencephalon and mid-brain. In midsagittal section it is the shape of a hook lying horizontally with its bend anteriorly and its point downwards. The pointed portion is known as the rostrum, the bend as the genu, the horizontal part as the body and the expanded posterior end as the splenium. The callosum extends into each hemisphere; the anterior fibres passing forwards from the genu into the frontal pole and known as the forceps minor. A thick posterior bundle of fibres, known as the forceps major, passes backwards from the splenium into the occipital poles. The thinner lateral expansion of the body of the callosum between these two bundles is known as the radiation. The rostrum of the corpus callosum fuses inferiorly with the lamina terminalis. A bundle of fibres within the lamina, the **anterior commissure,** unites the piriform areas (p. 355) and the olfactory tracts of the two sides. The **fornix (hippocampal) commissure** is found on the undersurface of the corpus callosum where the two crura of the fornix meet. Fibres here pass across the midline between the two hippocampi.

Association fibres may be long or short, uniting adjacent or widely separated gyri of the same hemisphere.

Projection fibres ascend from or descend to lower-lying parts of the central nervous system. Many form a well-defined band, the **internal capsule,** lying between the lentiform nucleus laterally and the thalamus and caudate nucleus medially. Superiorly its fibres fan out as the corona radiata interdigitating with the fibres of the corpus callosum. In horizontal section the capsule is V-shaped. It possesses an anterior limb (between the caudate nucleus and the lentiform nucleus and crossed by fibres and grey matter uniting the two structures), an apex (the genu) pointing medially, and a posterior limb lying between the thalamus and the lentiform nucleus (Fig. 32.4).

The anterior limb carries (a) frontopontine fibres from the frontal pole to the pons, and (b) fibres from the thalamus (medial and ventro-anterior nuclei) to the frontal lobe. The posterior limb carries from before backwards, (a) pyramidal fibres from the motor cortex which pass to the cranial nerve nuclei (corticonuclear fibres situated at the genu) and to the spinal cells (corticospinal fibres), (b) somatosensory fibres passing from the thalamus (ventroposterior nucleus) to the postcentral (somato-sensory) cortex, (c) temporopontine fibres from the temporal lobe to the pons, (d) the auditory radiations passing from the medial geniculate body under the lentiform nucleus, to the superior temporal gyrus, (*e*) the visual radiations passing from the lateral geniculate body around the posterior horn of the lateral ventricle to the visual cortex.

THE BASAL NUCLEI (Figs. 32.4, 32.5)

These nuclear masses lie within the substance of the cerebral hemispheres. The caudate and lentiform nuclei are connected across the anterior limb of the internal capsule and, because of the striated appear-

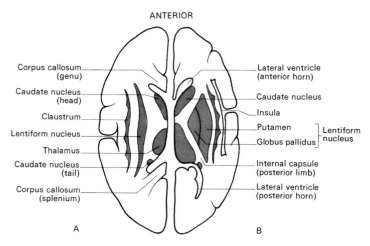

FIG. 32.4

Horizontal sections through the forebrain. A, at the level of the genu and splenium of the corpus callosum and B, through the intraventricular foramen.

ance so produced, are collectively known as the **corpus striatum.** They form part of the extrapyramidal system and are possibly involved in the regulation of movement. The amygdaloid body with its olfactory and hypothalamic connections, and the claustrum, a part of the insular cortex, developmentally and functionally are not part of the basal nuclei but are usually described with them. Diseases of the basal nuclei are said to produce abnormal movement (spontaneous tremors) which affect muscle activity, particularly that involved in posture, manual tasks and speech.

The **caudate nucleus** is C-shaped and lies within the concavity of the lateral ventricle. It has an expanded head, a narrow body and a tail. The globular head lies above the anterior perforated substance in front of the thalamus, medial to the anterior limb of the internal capsule, and bulges medially into the anterior horn of the lateral ventricle. The body passes backwards over the thalamus in the floor of the lateral ventricle. The narrow tail curls downwards and then forwards within the concavity of the ventricle and comes to lie in the roof of its inferior horn. The thalamostriate vein runs in a groove between the thalamus and the caudate nucleus and, near the interventricular foramen, it joins the choroidal vein to form the internal cerebral vein. The caudate nucleus receives fibres from the cortex and sends efferent fibres mainly to the globus pallidus part of the lentiform nucleus.

The **lentiform nucleus** is roughly lens-shaped with its less convex surface facing laterally and its more convex surface applied to the genu of the internal capsule. Anteromedially it is united across the anterior limb

Corpus callosum

Lateral ventricle (body)

Internal capsule

Third ventricle

Caudate nucleus (tail)

Hippocampus

Red nucleus

Pons

Fornix

Choroid plexus of lateral ventricle

Caudate nucleus

Putamen ⎤
Globus ⎬ Lentiform
pallidus ⎦ nucleus

Claustrum

Lateral ventricle (inferior horn)

Thalamus

Pyramidal decussation

FIG. 32.5
Diagrammatic lay-out of the main relations of the pyramidal tracts (oblique coronal section).

of the internal capsule to the head of the caudate nucleus and postero-medially separated by the posterior limb of the capsule from the thalamus. Superomedially it is covered by the internal capsule. Inferiorly, the anterior commissure and white matter of the temporal lobe separate it from the inferior horn of the lateral ventricle. The lentiform nucleus is divided into an outer putamen and an inner globus pallidus. The **putamen** receives fibres from the caudate nucleus and the cortex; its efferents pass to the globus pallidus. The **globus pallidus** receives fibres from the caudate nucleus, the putamen and the substantia nigra and its efferent fibres pass to the thalamus (ventrolateral and ventro-anterior nuclei), hypothalamus, subthalamus, substantia nigra and reticular formation.

The **claustrum** is a thin sheet of grey matter lying between the lenti-form nucleus and the insular cortex. It is closely linked to the insula.

The **amygdaloid body** is an oval nuclear mass situated at the end of the tail of the caudate nucleus and overlying the anterior extremity of the inferior horn of the lateral ventricle. It is in contact with and receives fibres from the uncus and lateral olfactory stria and communicates with its fellow of the opposite side through the anterior commissure. Most of its efferent fibres pass in the stria terminalis, a narrow bundle lying alongside the thalamostriate vein, to the hypothalamus and septal nuclei. The amygdaloid body is probably concerned in emotional behaviour and should be classified with the limbic system.

THE LIMBIC SYSTEM

This system of interconnected centres surrounds the medial part of the hemisphere. It includes structures (the amygdaloid body) which are probably connected with the olfactory brain (rhinencephalon) but influence emotion, and other structures which are probably connected with behavioural and visceral factors involved in emotion. These latter structures include the complex of the hippocampus, fornix, hypothalamus, cingulate and parahippocampal gyri. Efferents from many of these centres pass to the reticular formation of the midbrain.

The **olfactory bulb** lies on the undersurface of the frontal lobe and lies over the cribriform plate of the ethmoid bone. It receives the olfactory nerves after they have pierced the plate and a number of synapses occur in the bulb. The olfactory tract passes backwards from the bulb over the surface of the brain and divides into medial and lateral olfactory striae in front of the anterior perforated substance. The medial stria has two components. One passes through the anterior commissure to the olfactory bulb of the opposite side and the other passes to the cortex of the medial part of the hemisphere just anterior to the lamina terminalis. This area is known as the **paraterminal gyrus** and the nuclei it contains, the **septal nuclei.** The lateral stria passes to the **prepiriform cortex,** i.e. the frontal lip and the floor of the lateral sulcus in front of the uncus. It is probable that direct olfactory impulses extend no further than this area. The prepiriform cortex is continuous posteriorly, over the anterior part of the insula, with the uncus and parahippocampal gyrus. The cortex of the anterior insula, the uncus and the anterior part of the parahippocampal gyrus is known as the **piriform cortex.** The amygdaloid body (see above) lies deep to the uncus and receives a small contribution from the lateral olfactory stria.

The **hippocampus** is a cylindrical nuclear mass lying mainly in the floor of the inferior horn of the lateral ventricle (it should not be confused with the parahippocampal gyrus, p. 350). Its anterior part is wide and resembles a paw (pes hippocampi) and it narrows posteriorly. The axons from the hippocampus lie on its surface (the alveus) and then form the fimbria and the crus. The two crura meet on the undersurface of the corpus callosum to form the fornix. Decussating fibres form the commissure of the fornix. The fibres in the fornix diverge anteriorly into the columns of the fornix which pass around the interventricular foramina and end in the hypothalamus and mamillary bodies. The fornix system is the main efferent pathway of the hippocampus.

A midline triangular partition, the **septum pellucidum,** passes between the columns of the fornix and the undersurface of the corpus callosum. It is formed of two laminae enclosing a narrow cavity. The septum separates the anterior horns of the two lateral ventricles.

355

THE DIENCEPHALON

This medial part of the forebrain comprises the structures surrounding the third ventricle, namely, the two thalami, the hypothalamus, epithalamus, and subthalamus. The ventricle is limited anteriorly by the thin **lamina terminalis,** the rostral limit of the primitive neural cavity.

THE THALAMUS (Figs. 32.4, 32.5)

The two thalami are nuclear masses situated on the sides of the superior part of the third ventricle. Each thalamus is egg-shaped, having a larger posterior end. Its long axis is almost at right angles to that of the brain stem. The narrow anterior end reaches to the interventricular foramen. The posterior end projects backwards and laterally over the midbrain as the **pulvinar.** There are two small swellings on its inferior surface, the **medial** and **lateral geniculate bodies.**

The arched upper surface is related to the stria medullaris (the line of attachment of the roof of the third ventricle) medially, part of the floor of the transverse fissure, the thalamostriate vein and the stria terminalis, the floor of the lateral ventricle, and the body of the caudate nucleus laterally. A prominent anterior tubercle is found near the interventricular foramen and a dorsal groove passes backwards from the tubercle.

The inferior surface lies on the hypothalamus, subthalamus and midbrain from before backwards. The medial surfaces of the two thalami are parallel and border the third ventricle, usually being united across it by a glial mass, the connexus interthalamicus. The lateral surface is applied to the posterior limb of the internal capsule which separates it from the lentiform nucleus.

Thalamic nuclei: a band of white matter, the **internal medullary lamina,** passes downwards and medially from the dorsal groove through the anterior two-thirds of each thalamus. It splits anterosuperiorly to enclose the anterior thalamic nucleus lying beneath the anterior tubercle. Medial to the lamina are the medial (dorsomedial) nucleus, the central (centromedial) nucleus and, near the wall of the ventricle, the midline nuclei. Lateral and inferior to the lamina are the lateral and ventral nuclear masses. The lateral and medial geniculate bodies are thalamic nuclei which have been cut off from the back of the ventral nucleus but may be grouped together with it as part of a ventral nuclear complex. A thin nuclear layer over the lateral surface of the thalamus is known as the reticular nucleus. Amongst the fibres of the internal lamina are nuclei which together are called the intralaminar nuclei. The central nucleus is partly surrounded by these laminar fibres.

In summary, there are four large nuclear masses, the ventral nuclear complex, the lateral, anterior and medial nuclei, and three nuclear layers, the thalamic reticular nuclei laterally, the midline nuclei medially and the intralaminar group (including the central nucleus) centrally.

1. The **ventral nuclear complex**

(*a*) The **ventral nucleus**—includes ventroposterior, ventrolateral and ventro-anterior nuclei. The ventroposterior nucleus receives the medial, spinal and trigeminal lemnisci, and its efferents pass to the somato-sensory cortex. The ventrolateral nucleus receives fibres from the superior cerebellar peduncle and the globus pallidus, its efferents pass to the motor cortex. The ventro-anterior nucleus also receives fibres from the globus pallidus but other connections are ill-defined.

(*b*) The **medial geniculate body**—is a relay station in the auditory pathway, receiving fibres from the lateral lemniscus. Its efferents pass as the auditory radiation to the superior temporal gyrus.

(*c*) The **lateral geniculate body**—receives fibres from the optic tract, and its efferents pass as the visual radiation to the visual cortex.

2. The **lateral nuclear complex**—includes the pulvinar, and its afferent fibres are from other thalamic nuclei especially the ventral nuclear complex. Its efferent fibres are distributed to the cortex of the occipital, parietal and temporal lobes.

3. The **anterior nucleus**—receives afferent fibres from the mamillary body in the mamillothalamic tract, and its efferents pass to the cingulate gyrus.

4. The **medial (dorsomedial) nucleus**—probably receives afferent fibres from the hypothalamus and globus pallidus, and its efferents pass to the frontal cortex.

5. The **thalamic retinacular nuclei**—receive afferents from other thalamic nuclei. Their efferents pass in a diffuse manner to all parts of the cortex.

6. The **midline nuclei**—may receive fibres from the hypothalamus.

7. The **intralaminar nuclei** (including the central nucleus)—receive afferent fibres from the ascending reticular formation and other thalamic nuclei. Many of the ascending fibres are concerned with pain sensations. The efferents pass to the striate body and to the cortex.

From its numerous connections, the thalamus is seen to be a large relay station for all sensory tracts, and some forms of crude sensation may here reach conscious level. It also takes part in extrapyramidal path-ways involving the cerebellum and basal nuclei as well as the cerebral cortex.

THE HYPOTHALAMUS

This forms the floor and inferior part of the lateral wall of the third ventricle. It is separated on the ventricular wall from the thalamus by the **hypothalamic sulcus** and is continuous posteriorly with the sub-thalamus. Anteriorly is the optic chiasma and behind this an elevation (the tuber cinereum) gives rise to the stalk (the infundibulum) of the hypophysis cerebri. Two small elevations, the mamillary bodies, lie behind the tuber cinereum and separate it from the posterior perforated substance and the cerebral peduncles.

The anterior columns of the fornix fan out in the hypothalamus dividing each side into medial and lateral parts. The medial parts have a number of named nuclear groups: the more obvious being the pre-optic, supra-optic and paraventricular nuclei above and behind the optic chiasma. Efferent fibres from these nuclei pass to the posterior lobe of the hypophysis cerebri, influencing hormonal secretions.

Afferent fibres pass to the hypothalamus from the orbital surface of the frontal cortex, the septal nuclei, the hippocampus (through the fornix) and the amygdaloid body (through the stria terminalis). Efferent fibres as well as passing to the posterior lobe of the pituitary gland also pass in the median forebrain bundle and dorsal longitudinal fasciculus to the midbrain reticular nuclei. Fibres from the mamillary bodies pass to the anterior nucleus of each thalamus (mamillothalamic tracts) and the midbrain (mamillotegmental tracts) There is also a portal system of veins between some hypothalamic nuclei and the pituitary gland.

The hypothalamus plays an important rôle in the regulation of the autonomic nervous system, the anterior part controlling mainly the parasympathetic system and the posterior region the sympathetic system. It also influences most endocrine glands.

THE HYPOPHYSIS CEREBRI

The hypophysis cerebri (pituitary gland) is an endocrine gland situated in the hypophyseal fossa of the body of the sphenoid bone between the two cavernous sinuses. It is somewhat spherical in shape and is connected to the tuber cinereum by the infundibulum. The infundibulum pierces a sheet of dura, the diaphragma sellae, which covers the organ. The hypophysis receives its blood supply from two main sources: (1) the internal carotid artery, (2) vessels in the tuber cinereum. A portal circulation exists between the hypothalamus and the hypophysis. Venous blood eventually drains to the cavernous sinus.

The gland possesses anterior, middle and posterior lobes. The anterior has acidophil, basophil, and chromophobe cells. Their secretions influence the thyroid and adrenal glands, the gonads, and also include growth and lactogenic factors. Secretions from the intermediate (middle) portion of the gland possibly influence 'pigment reactions'. The posterior lobe consists of modified ependymal cells. Its activity is controlled by the hypothalamus, receiving nerve fibres from it. The posterior lobe hormones raise blood pressure, decrease urine production and contract the uterus.

The hypophysis cerebri develops by the fusion of a diverticulum from the diencephalon forming the posterior lobe and a diverticulum from the stomadeum (Rathke's pouch) forming the anterior and middle lobes. Tumours of the hypophysis cerebri may produce pressure effects on the adjacent optic chiasma. They usually also secrete excessive amounts of one or more circulating hormones.

The **epithalamus** is situated in the posterior wall of the third ventricle between the posterior ends of the thalami. It comprises the habenular nuclei and commissure, the posterior commissure and the pineal body. The **habenular nuclei** receive the stria medullaris, a narrow bundle of fibres passing backwards over the thalamus from the septal

nuclei. Its efferents pass through the habenular commissure to the interpeduncular nucleus of the subthalamus. The **posterior commissure**
unites the two superior colliculi, the pretectal regions and the medial
longitudinal bundles of the two sides. The **pineal body** develops as an
outgrowth from the third ventricle. It is an oval mass lying between the
superior colliculi. Its functions, although uncertain, are probably concerned with the secretion of serotonin and other active substances. The

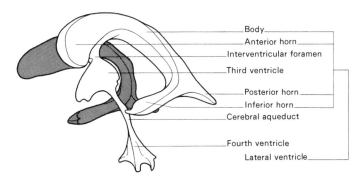

FIG. 32.6
Diagram of a model of the ventricular system of brain. The right lateral ventricle is stippled.

pineal body is frequently calcified and is a useful radiological landmark.
Its displacement may indicate an intracranial space-occupying lesion.

The **subthalamus** adjoins the midbrain, lying behind the hypothalamus and above the posterior perforated substance between the
cerebral peduncles. It contains the subthalamic and interpeduncular
nuclei which receive fibres from the globus pallidus and the habenular
nuclei. Its efferent fibres pass to the reticular formation of the brain stem.

THE LATERAL VENTRICLE (Figs. 32.5, 32.6, 32.7)

This is the cavity of the cerebral hemisphere and lies towards its
medial side and below the corpus callosum. Each ventricle is united to
the cavity of the diencephalon (third ventricle) through an **interventricular foramen.** Each lateral ventricle is basically C-shaped with
an anterior concavity. For descriptive purposes it is divided into an
anterior horn, projecting into the frontal lobe, a body arching backwards,
and an inferior horn projecting into the temporal lobe. From the posterior
convexity a posterior horn, of variable form, extends backwards into the
occipital lobe.

The **anterior horn** is that part of the ventricle in front of the
interventricular foramen. It is separated from its fellow of the opposite
side by the septum pellucidum. Its roof and anterior wall are formed by
the genu of the corpus callosum, and inferolaterally the head of the
caudate nucleus projects into the cavity.

The **body** is roofed by the corpus callosum, and its floor, which meets
the roof laterally, is formed by the body of the caudate nucleus laterally

and the thalamus medially, with the stria terminalis and the thalamo-striate vein in the groove between. Medially are the septum pellucidum and the fornix below which the choroid plexus is invaginated into the cavity.

FIG. 32.7 A, B, and C

Lumbar air encephalogram. Air, introduced into the subarachnoid space through a lumbar puncture (p. 387), is seen outlining the various aspects of the ventricular system. The patient's head has been positioned in different ways for the air to float through the CSF and fill each region in turn.

1. Air in 3rd ventricle
2. Air in lateral ventricle
3. Air in inferior horn of lateral ventricle

4. Air filling basal cisterns
5. Air filling 4th ventricle

The **posterior horn** is covered superiorly and laterally by the radiation of the corpus callosum which separates the ventricle from the optic radiation. Inferomedially there are two longitudinal ridges in the cavity, an upper formed by the forceps major of the corpus callosum, and the lower by the infolding of the wall over the calcarine sulcus.

The floor of the **inferior horn** is formed by the hippocampus, and its lateral wall by the radiation of the corpus callosum. Its roof is formed

posteriorly by the tail of the caudate nucleus, the stria terminalis and temporal lobe white matter, and anteriorly by the amygdaloid body. The medial wall is invaginated by the choroid plexus.

The **choroid plexus** of the lateral ventricle is invaginated into the cavity between interventricular foramen above and the tip of the inferior horn below. The arched line of invagination is known as the **choroidal fissure.** The medial ependymal wall of the fissure is attached to the edge of the fornix, fimbria and alveus on the one hand and to the region of the stria terminalis and the thalamostriate vein on the other.

After trephining the skull and inserting an instrument, it is possible to replace the cerebrospinal fluid in the lateral ventricles with air so that their shape can be investigated radiologically. By suitable positioning of the patient's head, the third and fourth ventricles can also be demonstrated. The position of a space-occupying lesion may be identified by the displacement of the ventricles as demonstrated by these radio-logical techniques. Air introduced through a lumbar puncture needle will also find its way into the ventricular system.

THE THIRD VENTRICLE (Figs. 32.2, 32.5, 32.6, 32.7)

This is the cavity of the diencephalon. It communicates with the lateral ventricles through the interventricular foramina, and with the fourth ventricle through the cerebral aqueduct. It forms a midline vertical slit between the two thalami superiorly and has the hypo-thalamus inferiorly..The cavity is crossed by the connexus interthalamicus (when this is present).

It is bounded anteriorly by the lamina terminalis with the anterior commissure. Its floor is formed, from before backwards, by the optic chiasma, tuber cinereum, mamillary bodies and posterior perforated substance. The cavity is recessed into the optic chiasma and the infundi-bulum. The short posterior wall is formed by the pineal body with the habenular and posterior commissures. The cavity is recessed above and within the pineal stalk. Inferiorly the ventricle communicates with the aqueduct and superiorly the ependymal roof is invaginated to form the choroid plexus of the third ventricle.

CHAPTER 33

THE BRAIN STEM AND CEREBELLUM

BRAIN STEM

The brain stem (Fig. 33.1), formed of the midbrain, pons and medulla from above downwards, is continuous above with the diencephalon and below with the spinal cord. Posteriorly the cerebellum is united to it by three pairs of cerebellar peduncles. The brain stem and cerebellum lie in the posterior cranial fossa.

The brain stem contains the nuclei and central connections of the third to the twelfth cranial nerves, and nuclei associated with the visual

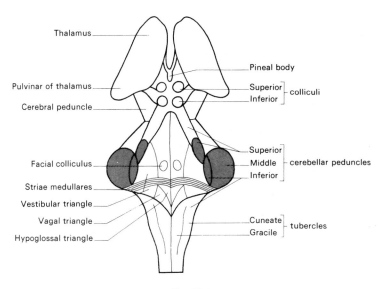

FIG. 33.1

Diagram showing some of the structures on the dorsal surface of the brain stem. The cerebellum has been removed, thus exposing the floor of the 4th ventricle.

and auditory systems and with the extrapyramidal system. It gives passage to ascending and descending fibres between the forebrain and spinal cord, and afferent and efferent cerebellar fibres. The region also contains a large number of scattered nuclei situated between the previous structures and collectively known as the reticular formation (p. 377).

THE MIDBRAIN (Figs. 33.2, 33.3)

This is a short narrow region which joins the forebrain to the hindbrain through the opening in the tentorium cerebelli. It is largely overhung by the cerebral hemispheres. Its dorsal surface possesses four small elevations, the paired superior and inferior colliculi. The superior colliculi lie between the geniculate bodies of the two thalami. A ridge, the inferior brachium, passes from the inferior colliculus to the medial geniculate body. A similar but less well-defined ridge joins the lateral geniculate body to the superior colliculus. The ventral surface of the midbrain has a pair of converging fibre bundles, the cerebral peduncles.

Mesencephalic nucleus of 5th — Superior colliculus
3rd nucleus — Inferior brachium
Tectospinal decussation — Spinal lemniscus
Red nucleus — Medial lemniscus
Substantia nigra — Rubroreticular decussation
Cerebral peduncle
Oculomotor nerves

Fig. 33.2

Diagram of a cross-section through the superior colliculi of the midbrain. P, pyramid fibres; F.P. and T.P. frontopontine and temporopontine fibres.

Between them, the surface is pierced by a number of blood vessels and is known as the **posterior perforated substance.** The cavity of the midbrain is the narrow **aqueduct** which unites the third and fourth ventricles. It is surrounded by the peri-aqueductal grey matter. The part of the midbrain dorsal to the aqueduct contains the colliculi, and is known as the **tectum.** The part ventral to the aqueduct, but excluding the cerebral peduncles, is known as the **tegmentum.** The peduncles form the **base.**

Nuclei

(*a*) The **oculomotor nucleus** has somatic and visceral parts and lies in the upper part of the midbrain ventral to the aqueduct. It consists of (i) central and lateral nuclei supplying all extra-ocular muscles except superior oblique and lateral rectus, (ii) parasympathetic nuclei (autonomic nuclei) supplying the sphincter pupillae and ciliary muscles. The oculomotor fibres pass anteriorly through the tegmentum and leave the brain stem between the cerebral peduncles.

(*b*) The **trochlear nucleus** lies on the side of the midline in the lower midbrain ventral to the aqueduct. The fibres first pass dorsally and decussate below the inferior colliculi before emerging and passing ventrally again around the cerebral peduncles to supply superior oblique.

(*c*) The **mesencephalic nucleus** of the trigeminal nerve lies lateral to and along the whole length of the peri-aqueductal grey matter. The tract lies lateral to the nucleus. It carries proprioceptive fibres from the muscles of mastication.

(*d*) The **red nuclei** are a pair of oval nuclear masses most obvious in the upper tegmentum. They receive afferents from the cerebellum through the superior cerebellar peduncles, and from the globus pallidus. Their efferents pass in the rubroreticular and rubrospinal tracts to the lower brain stem reticular formation and the spinal cord. The nuclei form part of the extrapyramidal system.

(*e*) The **substantia nigra** is a pigment-containing nuclear area separating the tegmentum and the cerebral peduncles of each side. It is also part of the extrapyramidal system and receives fibres from the basal nuclei (strionigral tract) and its efferents pass to the reticular formation.

FIG. 33.3
Diagram of a cross-section through the inferior colliculi of the
midbrain.

(*f*) The **superior colliculi** receive fibres from the optic tracts and also from the visual cortex. They communicate, through the medial longitudinal bundle, with motor nuclei of the head and neck, and through the tectospinal tract with cells of the spinal cord. They are concerned with visual reflexes.

(*g*) The **inferior colliculi** receive some auditory fibres from the lateral lemniscus. Some efferent fibres enter the reticular formation while others pass through the inferior brachium to the medial geniculate body. They may be concerned with auditory reflexes.

Fibre Tracts

The **cerebral peduncles** are motor tracts which are the continuation downwards of the internal capsules. They contain the pyramidal (cortico-spinal) fibres passing from the motor cortex to cells of the spinal cord, and on either side of these the corticopontine fibres from the frontal and temporal cortex to the pontine nuclei. Scattered throughout the peduncles are corticonuclear fibres passing from the motor cortex to the cranial nerve nuclei of the opposite side.

Ascending in the lateral tegmentum are the medial, trigeminal and spinal lemnisci passing to the thalamus (ventroposterior nucleus). The **medial lemniscus** carries somatosensory fibres from the opposite side of

365

the trunk and limbs; the **trigeminal lemniscus** carries somatosensory fibres from the opposite side of the face, and the **spinal lemniscus** carries some pain and temperature fibres from the opposite side of the body. The **lateral lemniscus** is present in the lower midbrain and passes dorsally to reach the **inferior colliculus** and the medial geniculate body. It carries auditory fibres from the cochlear, trapezoid, and lateral lemniscal nuclei.

The **medial longitudinal fasciculus** lies in the tegmentum adjacent to the 3rd and 4th cranial nerve nuclei. Many of its fibres carry impulses from the vestibular nuclei to the cranial nuclei (especially those concerned with the positioning of the eyeball) and to the upper spinal cord (concerned with the position of the head in space). Alongside the medial longitudinal fasciculus are fibres which descend from the hypothalamus to the lower autonomic nuclei.

Three tracts decussate in the midbrain:

(i) the superior cerebellar peduncles, passing from the cerebellum to the red nucleus, thalamus and globus pallidus, decussate in the lower midbrain.

(ii) the rubroreticular and rubrospinal tracts, passing from the red nucleus to the cells of the spinal cord, decussate in the upper midbrain.

(iii) the tectospinal tracts, passing from the superior (and inferior) colliculi to the motor nuclei of the brain stem and spinal cord, decussate dorsal to the rubroreticular decussation.

The midbrain contains many large and important ascending and descending fibre tracts; its cranial nerve nuclei control most of the eye muscles. The red nucleus and the substantia nigra are involved in extrapyramidal activities and the tectal nuclei in visual and auditory reflexes. Many of the nuclei of the reticular formation activate (arouse) the cerebral cortex and have facilitatory or inhibitory effects on other centres.

THE PONS (Figs. 33.4, 33.5)

Anteriorly the pons forms a prominent convexity between the midbrain and the medulla, and is composed mainly of transversely running fibres which pass backwards and laterally to become the middle cerebellar peduncles. The trigeminal nerve emerges from the middle of the pons at the junction of the middle cerebellar peduncle and the pons. The abducent, facial and vestibulocochlear nerves emerge, from medial to lateral, at the lower border of the pons. The posterior surface of the pons forms part of the floor of the fourth ventricle, and the cerebellum lies behind.

In transverse section the pons has a ventral (basilar) part and a dorsal (tegmental) part. The **basilar part** of the pons is in continuity above with the cerebral peduncles of the midbrain, the pyramidal fibres being split into small scattered bundles and the corticopontine fibres ending in numerous **pontine nuclei.** Pontocerebellar fibres arise from these nuclei, cross the midline and sweep dorsally to form the middle cerebellar peduncle. The **tegmental part** is the continuation upwards of the medulla and contains the nuclei of the trigeminal, abducent, facial and vestibulocochlear nerves.

Nuclei

(a) The **trigeminal motor nucleus** supplies the muscles of mastication and the **sensory nuclei** receive somatosensory fibres from the face and scalp. The **superior sensory nucleus** is situated in the midpons region and the **mesencephalic nucleus** extends upwards into the midbrain. The **spinal nucleus** extends downwards through the medulla. The mesencephalic nucleus is concerned with proprioceptive impulses, the spinal nucleus with most pain and temperature impulses and the superior with all the other somatosensory impulses. Axons of the trigeminal nuclei join the medial and spinal lemnisci as the trigeminal lemniscus.

(b) The **abducent nucleus** supplies the lateral rectus, and is situated dorsally near the midline under the floor of the fourth ventricle. The fibres pass ventrally to emerge at the lower border of the pons.

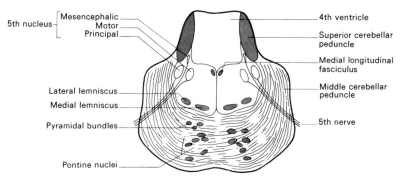

FIG. 33.4
Diagram of a cross-section through the middle of the
pons, showing the trigeminal nuclei.

(c) The **facial motor nucleus** supplies mainly the muscles of facial expression and is situated in the lateral tegmentum. The **superior salivary nucleus** supplies parasympathetic fibres to the submandibular and sublingual glands and is associated with the facial nucleus. The nucleus for the taste fibres of the anterior two-thirds of the tongue, the **nucleus of the tractus solitarius,** lies lateral to the motor nucleus. The motor fibres make a dorsal loop over the abducent nucleus before leaving the lower pons anterolaterally in company with the parasympathetic and taste fibres.

(d) The **dorsal** and **ventral cochlear nuclei** receive auditory fibres from the inner ear, and lie in the lower part of the pons on the inferior cerebellar peduncle. The nuclei lie on the floor of the lateral recess of the fourth ventricle. Most axons cross the midline in a compact bundle the **trapezoid body.** Some secondary cochlear fibres from the cochlear nuclei cross in the trapezoid body or in more dorsally placed bundles but end in nuclei near the trapezoid body, known as trapezoid nuclei. Fibres from the cochlear and trapezoid nuclei form a tract, the **lateral**

367

lemniscus, which ascends through the pons and lower midbrain to the inferior colliculus and medial geniculate body.

(*e*) The **vestibular nuclei** receive vestibular fibres from the inner ear and lie under the lateral part of the floor of the fourth ventricle in both the pons and medulla. The large lateral part gives rise to the vestibulospinal tract, the fibres of which pass uncrossed to the cells of the spinal cord. Fibres from all parts of the nuclei pass to the medial longitudinal fasciculus (and medial lemniscus) of both sides. Many fibres pass uncrossed in the inferior cerebellar peduncle to the anterior lobe, vermis and flocculonodular lobe of the cerebellum. The nuclei also receive fibres from the fastigial nuclei of the cerebellum.

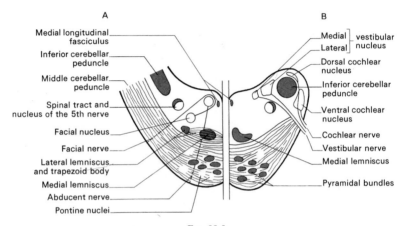

A

Medial longitudinal fasciculus
Inferior cerebellar peduncle
Middle cerebellar peduncle
Spinal tract and nucleus of the 5th nerve
Facial nucleus
Facial nerve
Lateral lemniscus and trapezoid body
Medial lemniscus
Abducent nerve
Pontine nuclei

B

Medial ⎤ vestibular
Lateral ⎦ nucleus
Dorsal cochlear nucleus
Inferior cerebellar peduncle
Ventral cochlear nucleus
Cochlear nerve
Vestibular nerve
Medial lemniscus
Pyramidal bundles

FIG. 33.5

Diagram of cross-sections through A, the lower pons; B, the lateral recess of the 4th ventricle.

Tegmental Fibre Tracts

The trapezoid body and lateral lemniscus have been discussed with the cochlear nuclei. The **medial longitudinal fasciculus** lies dorsally near the midline in the floor of the brain stem cavity. It receives fibres from the motor nuclei supplying the extra-ocular muscles, the vestibular nuclei and the cells of the cervical spinal cord. The two bundles communicate with each other through the posterior commissure. They are associated with reflex control of eye and head movements. The medial lemniscus becomes more laterally and ventrally placed as it ascends the pons; the spinal lemniscus lies lateral to it. The anterior spinocerebellar tract ascends through the lateral tegmentum to enter the superior cerebellar peduncle.

THE MEDULLA OBLONGATA (Figs. 33.5, 33.6, 33.7, 33.8)

The medulla oblongata narrows rapidly between the pons and the foramen magnum where it becomes continuous with the spinal cord.

368

The upper part (open medulla) mostly forms the floor of the fourth ventricle. Posteriorly it has a thin ependymal roof (inferior medullary velum) below, and the cerebellum above. The lower part (closed medulla) has a narrow central canal surrounded by grey matter and outside this by white matter. The basic structure of the lower medulla is similar to that of the spinal cord.

The **anterior median fissure** begins at the lower edge of the pons and continues into the cord. In the upper medulla, it is flanked by the **pyramids**—containing bundles of pyramidal fibres. Lower down most of the fibres cross the fissure as they pass downwards, posteriorly and laterally into the cord. Lateral to the pyramid is an oval mass, the **olive,**

Dorsal vagal nucleus

Spinal tract and nucleus of 5th nerve

Nucleus ambiguus

Lateral reticular nucleus

Medial lemniscus

Pyramid

12th nucleus

Inferior cerebellar peduncle

Nucleus of the tractus solitarius

Medial longitudinal fasciculus

10th nerve

Olivary nucleus

12th nerve

Fig. 33.6
Diagram of a cross-section through the open medulla at the level of the olivary nucleus.

and posterolateral to the olive is the **inferior cerebellar peduncle** passing upwards into the cerebellum. The **posterior median sulcus** runs downwards from the lower recess of the fourth ventricle into the cord. On each side of it is a small ridge—the **gracile tubercle**—and lateral to it, the **cuneate tubercle.**

The rootlets of the hypoglossal nerve leave the medulla in the groove between the pyramid and the olive, and the rootlets of the glosso-pharyngeal and vagus nerves leave in the groove between the olive and the inferior cerebellar peduncle.

INTERNAL STRUCTURE

The central canal is wide above, where it forms part of the fourth ventricle, but narrows inferiorly. The embryological pattern of alar and basal plates is found in the lower medulla but is modified above where the alar plates lie lateral to the basal plates, the roof plate being much attenuated. The roof plate remains as the ependymal inferior medullary velum. Above this, the embryonic ventricular roof develops into the cerebellum.

Nuclei

(*a*) The **spinal nucleus** of the trigeminal nerve lies posterolaterally and extends throughout the medulla; inferiorly it is continuous with the posterior horn of the spinal cord.

(*b*) The **hypoglossal nucleus** lies in the floor of the fourth ventricle near the midline; it supplies the muscles of the tongue.

(*c*) The fibres travelling in the glossopharyngeal and vagus nerves arise in a complex group of nuclei. The most rostral fibres go into the glossopharyngeal nerve and the most caudal run for a short distance with the accessory nerve. Lateral to the hypoglossal nucleus is the **dorsal vagal nucleus** (visceral efferent). Most of its fibres travel in the vagus. Some cells (salivary) associated with the upper end of this nucleus send their axons into the glossopharyngeal nerve. They are the preganglionic secretomotor fibres to the parotid gland and synapse in the otic ganglion. Alongside the motor nucleus is the **dorsal sensory vagal nucleus** (visceral afferent). Some of its fibres come from the glossopharyngeal nerve, but most come from the vagus. Lateral to it is the **tractus solitarius** and its **nucleus** (special visceral afferent—taste) receiving fibres from the glossopharyngeal nerve (back of tongue) and the vagus nerve (region of the epiglottis). Fibres from the chorda tympani branch of the facial nerve end in the rostral extension of this nucleus. Situated ventrally between the hypoglossal and dorsal vagal nuclei is a group of cells forming the **nucleus ambiguus** (special visceral efferent). Their axons pass to the muscles of the palate, pharynx and larynx in the glossopharyngeal and vagus nerves. These muscles are derived from pharyngeal arch mesoderm.

(*d*) The **gracile** and **cuneate nuclei** are situated posteriorly in the lower half of the medulla, the gracile being the more medially placed. They receive sensory fibres from the posterior column of the spinal cord; their efferents pass ventrally across the midline as internal arcuate fibres to form the **medial lemniscus** and pass rostrally to the thalamus (ventroposterior nucleus). The **accessory cuneate nucleus** receives proprioceptive fibres from the neck region; its efferents pass uncrossed in the inferior cerebellar peduncle to the cerebellum.

(*e*) The **olivary nucleus** is large, irregular and cup-shaped, forming a prominence on the lateral surface. Its open part faces medially and from it efferent fibres pass across the midline as internal arcuate fibres to enter the inferior cerebellar peduncle. Lateral to the olivary nucleus is the lateral reticular nucleus which sends fibres into both inferior cerebellar peduncles.

The vestibular and cochlear nuclei are considered with the pons (p. 367).

White Matter

The **pyramid** is a large bundle of fibres forming the prominence on the anterior surface of the medulla. It is a convergence of the numerous bundles traversing the basal part of the pons. Inferiorly most of the fibres of the two pyramids decussate, passing posteriorly across the medulla to form the lateral corticospinal tract which passes to the cells of the spinal cord. The uncrossed pyramidal fibres continue as the anterior corticospinal tract. As the decussating fibres pass laterally they cut across the anterior horn of grey matter. Corticonuclear fibres run with the pyramidal fibres and end in the contralateral cranial nerve motor nuclei.

Many of the fibres crossing the midline in the region of the open medulla are called **internal arcuate fibres.** Most go to the thalamus (passing from the gracile and cuneate nuclei through the medial lemniscus) or to the cerebellum (passing from the olivary nuclei and the reticular formation through the inferior cerebellar peduncle).

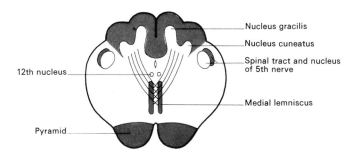

Nucleus gracilis

Nucleus cuneatus

Spinal tract and nucleus of 5th nerve

12th nucleus

Medial lemniscus

Pyramid

FIG. 33.7
Diagram of a cross-section through the closed medulla at the level of the sensory decussation.

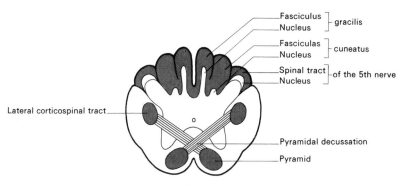

Fasciculus ⎤
Nucleus ⎦ gracilis

Fasciculas ⎤
Nucleus ⎦ cuneatus

Spinal tract ⎤
Nucleus ⎦ of the 5th nerve

Lateral corticospinal tract

Pyramidal decussation

Pyramid

FIG. 33.8
Diagram of a cross-section through the closed medulla at the level of the motor decussation.

The **medial longitudinal fasciculus** descends dorsally near the midline, separated from the medial lemniscus by the tectospinal tract. All three tracts lie alongside the midline. The **spinal tract of the trigeminal nerve** overlies the lateral aspect of its nucleus; it descends from the pons and is continuous with the dorsolateral tract of the spinal cord. The **posterior spinocerebellar tract** ascends from the spinal cord and passes uncrossed in the inferior cerebellar peduncle to the cerebellum. The **anterior spinocerebellar tract** ascends through the medulla, pons

371

and midbrain and reaches the cerebellum through the superior cerebellar peduncle.

Other tracts passing through the medulla include the spinothalamic which ascend from the spinal cord to the thalamus (ventroposterior nucleus), the vestibulospinal which descends from the lateral vestibular nucleus to the cells of the spinal cord, and the rubroreticular tract which descends from the red nucleus to the cells of the spinal cord.

THE CEREBELLUM

The cerebellum fills the larger part of the posterior cranial fossa and is attached to the back of the brain stem by three paired fibre bundles. These are the superior, middle and inferior cerebellar peduncles passing to the midbrain, pons and medulla respectively. The cavity of the fourth ventricle lies between the cerebellum posteriorly, and the pons and medulla anteriorly; laterally the cavity passes over the inferior cerebellar peduncle to form the lateral recess of the ventricle.

The cerebellum is divided into a midline coiled **vermis** and two laterally placed **hemispheres.** The ends of the vermis overlie the superior and inferior medullary vela roofing the fourth ventricle. When the vermis is cut vertically, a deep sulcus, the **fissura prima,** can be followed across the upper surface of the cerebellum. It divides the vermis and hemispheres into **anterior** and **middle lobes,** the anterior lying above and in front of the fissure. A further subdivision of the organ, the **flocculonodular lobe,** lies caudal to the **posterolateral fissure** across the lower surface of the cerebellum. The nodule is the most caudal part of the vermis and the flocculi are narrow lateral extensions from it.

The cerebellum has an outer covering of grey matter, the **cortex,** which is greatly convoluted, the visible surface representing only about a sixth of the cortical area. The sulci are parallel and the ridges between them are known as **folia.** The cellular arrangement of the cerebellar cortex is very uniform, there being three layers—inner granular, middle Purkinje and outer molecular. Most afferent fibres to the cerebellar cortex end in the granular layer and in the outer molecular layer where the profuse dendritic network of the Purkinje cells is situated. The axons of the large, flask-shaped Purkinje cells pass to the central nuclei of the cerebellum. These nuclei of each side comprise the large laterally placed **dentate nucleus** bordered medially by the **globose** and **emboliform** nuclei (together known as the nucleus interpositum) and the medially placed **fastigial** (roof) **nucleus.** The Purkinje fibres of the vermis project on to the fastigial nuclei, and an adjacent cortical band of each hemisphere (the paramedial zone) projects to the nucleus interpositum. The remainder of each hemisphere projects to the dentate nucleus.

AFFERENT CONNECTIONS
The cerebellum has four main groups of afferent connections.

1. Cerebral cortical fibres—synapse in the pontine nuclei whose axons pass in the middle cerebellar peduncle of the opposite side to all parts of the cerebellum save the flocculonodular lobe.

2. Olivary fibres—cross the medulla as the upper group of internal arcuate fibres and pass through the inferior cerebellar peduncle to all parts of the cerebellum. The olivary nuclei receive afferent fibres from the motor cortex, the red nucleus, peri-aqueductal grey matter of the mid-brain and the spinal cord.

3. Spinal fibres

(a) The posterior spinocerebellar tract, originating in the cells of the thoracic nucleus, pass uncrossed through the inferior cerebellar peduncle to the vermis and paramedian zone of the anterior and middle lobes.

(b) Fibres ascending in the dorsal column of the upper part of the spinal cord synapse in the accessory cuneate nucleus whose axons pass uncrossed in the inferior cerebellar peduncle to the vermis and paramedian zone of the anterior and middle lobes.

(c) The anterior spinocerebellar tract originates in the posterior horn of the opposite side and passes in the superior cerebellar peduncle mainly to the vermis of the anterior lobe.

(d) Fibres from the anterolateral part of the spinal cord synapse in the lateral reticular nucleus whose axons pass in the inferior cerebellar peduncle of the opposite side to all parts of the cerebellum.

4. Vestibular fibres—from the vestibular nuclei, pass mainly to the flocculonodular lobe.

EFFERENT CONNECTIONS

Efferent cerebellar fibres from the **dentate nucleus** and **nucleus interpositum** enter the superior cerebellar peduncle and decussate in the lower midbrain. They end in the red nucleus, thalamus (ventrolateral nucleus) and the globus pallidus. From the latter two regions impulses pass to the motor cortex. Some fibres end in reticular nuclei of the pons and medulla. Fibres from the **fastigial nuclei** pass in both superior and inferior cerebellar peduncles to the vestibular nuclei and reticular nuclei of the pons and medulla.

From the above information, the fibre content of the cerebellar peduncles may be summarised:

1. The **superior cerebellar peduncle** contains efferent fibres from all cerebellar nuclei and also the anterior spinocerebellar tract.

2. The **middle cerebellar peduncle** carries pontocerebellar fibres.

3. The **inferior cerebellar peduncle** carries the posterior spinocerebellar tract, fibres of the accessory cuneate and lateral reticular nuclei, afferent and efferent vestibular connections and olivocerebellar fibres.

The cerebellum, through its corticopontine connections, receives information on corticospinal activity. Simultaneously, through its pro-prioceptive spinal and vestibular connections it is informed of the effect of the corticospinal activity on the muscles of the body. It is able to compare this information and, through its efferent tracts, influence the cortical and subcortical motor centres. Thus the cerebellum can modify the pattern of a movement as it is taking place, ensuring maximum efficiency with minimum effort. Disease of the cerebellum interferes with the co-ordination of voluntary movement; patients show an intention tremor.

THE FOURTH VENTRICLE (Figs. 32.6, 33.1)

This is the cavity of the hind brain. It communicates superiorly with the third ventricle through the cerebral aqueduct and is continuous inferiorly with the central canal of the spinal cord. When looked at from behind the cavity is somewhat diamond-shaped, bounded superolaterally by the superior cerebellar peduncles, inferolaterally by the inferior cerebellar peduncles and inferiorly by the gracile and cuneate tubercles.

The **roof** of the cavity extends backwards into the cerebellum; superiorly it is formed by a glial sheet stretching between the superior cerebellar peduncles (the **superior medullary velum**) and inferiorly by a thin ependymal sheet between the inferior cerebellar peduncles (the **inferior medullary velum**). The lateral angles of the roof are evaginated to form the **lateral recesses** which pass outwards round the inferior cerebellar peduncles. The inferior velum is invaginated by the blood vessels and pia mater to form the choroid plexus of the ventricle. A lateral opening in the tip of each lateral recess and a median opening in the inferior medullary velum allow cerebrospinal fluid to pass from the ventricular system to the subarachnoid space.

The diamond-shaped **floor** of the ventricle is formed above by the pons and below by the medulla. A **median sulcus** grooves its length and a number of fibres, the **striae medullares,** pass transversely across it into the lateral recess. On either side of the median sulcus, below the striae medullares a small depression, the **inferior fovea,** is present. Two diverging sulci descend from the fovea dividing the area below the striae into a medial **hypoglossal triangle,** an intermediate **vagal triangle** and a lateral **vestibular area.** They overlie their respective cranial nerve nuclei.

Just above the striae medullares an elevation, the **facial colliculus,** is present on each side of the median sulcus. It is formed by facial nerve fibres arching over the abducent nucleus.

CHAPTER 34

THE SPINAL CORD AND RETICULAR FORMATION

THE SPINAL CORD (Fig. 34.1)
The spinal cord lies within the vertebral canal and extends from the foramen magnum to the level of the second lumbar vertebra after which a fibrous remnant, the filum terminale, descends to be attached to the back of the coccyx. The cord is about 45 cm long. It is cylindrical in shape, flattened slightly anteroposteriorly, and has cervical and lumbar enlargements where the nerves supplying the upper and lower limbs originate. The enlargements lie opposite the lower cervical and lower thoracic vertebrae. Since the spinal cord is shorter than the vertebral canal, the nerves descend with increasing obliquity before leaving the canal through the intervertebral foramina. The collection of lower lumbar, sacral and coccygeal nerves below the spinal cord, with the filum terminale, is known as the **cauda equina.** The cord has an **anterior median fissure** and a **posterior median sulcus.** On its sides the rootlets of the spinal nerves emerge from **anterolateral** and **posterolateral sulci.** There is proportionately more grey matter in the cervical and lumbar enlargements corresponding to the large nerve roots supplying the limbs.

Grey Matter
The grey matter of the spinal cord is arranged around the central canal and projects towards the anterolateral and posterolateral sulci to form paired **anterior** and **posterior horns.** The cells of the former are mainly motor in function and of the latter mainly sensory. A small-celled region, the **gelatinous substance,** overlies the posterior horn. In the thoracic and sacral regions a small lateral projection, the **lateral horn,** is present; its cells give rise to preganglionic autonomic nerve fibres. In the thoracic region a large group of large, closely-packed cells, the **thoracic nucleus,** is present at the base of the posterior horn. Proprioceptive fibres from muscle spindles end on the cells of this nucleus and the efferent fibres form the posterior spinocerebellar tract mainly of the same side. However, the majority of the nerve cells in the grey matter are intercalated (intermediate) neurons.

White Matter (Fig. 34.1)
The anterior and posterior horns and the emerging spinal rootlets divide the white matter into three columns (funiculi) on each side. An anterior funiculus lies between the anterior horn and the median fissure, a lateral between the anterior and posterior horns and a posterior between the posterior horn and the posterior sulcus. The anterior median fissure incompletely separates the anterior columns, the remaining communication being called the anterior white commissure. The posterior median

septum completely separates the posterior columns. Each posterior column is further divided in the cervical and upper thoracic regions into a **fasciculus cuneatus** laterally and a **fasciculus gracilis** medially. Between the gelatinous substance and the surface of the cord is the **dorsolateral tract.** The region closely surrounding the grey matter is known as the **fasciculus proprius.**

The fibres of the white matter are grouped into tracts (Fig. 34.1) which ascend and descend in the cord. Most of these tracts cannot be

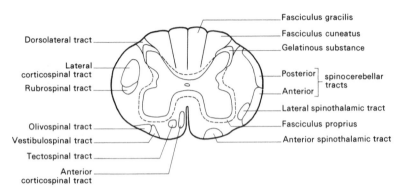

Fasciculus gracilis
Fasciculus cuneatus
Gelatinous substance
Dorsolateral tract
Lateral corticospinal tract
Rubrospinal tract
Posterior ⌉ spinocerebellar
Anterior ⌋ tracts
Lateral spinothalamic tract
Olivospinal tract
Vestibulospinal tract
Tectospinal tract
Anterior corticospinal tract
Fasciculus proprius
Anterior spinothalamic tract

Fɪɢ. 34.1

Diagram of a cross-section of the spinal cord, showing the main ascending pathways on the right and the main descending pathways on the left side of the diagram.

identified in normal material. Pathological and experimental lesions have helped to define some of these tracts. Many of the fibres have their cell bodies within the spinal cord or brain. The entering dorsal root fibres of spinal nerves divide into a large ascending branch and a small descending branch. Both of these give off innumerable collateral branches which take part in intrasegmental and intersegmental reflexes.

The **posterior column** contains:

(*a*) Mainly ascending fibres associated with touch, pressure, vibration, and proprioception. Their cell bodies lie in the dorsal root ganglia and they pass to the gracile and cuneate nuclei in the medulla.

(*b*) Intersegmental and intrasegmental fibres.

The **lateral column** contains:

(*a*) Peripherally placed

(i) anterior and posterior spinocerebellar tracts—associated with proprioception. The anterior tract, whose cell bodies lie in the posterior horn of the opposite side, enter the cerebellum in the superior cerebellar peduncle. The posterior tract has its cell bodies in the thoracic nucleus of the same side and passes uncrossed to the cerebellum in the inferior cerebellar peduncle.

(ii) dorsolateral fasciculus—a mixed bundle of fibres. Some axons arise in the dorsal root ganglia (possibly carrying pain and thermal impulses) but most axons probably arise in or near the gelatinous substance (pro-

376

priospinal fibres). All the axons run for short distances before ending in the posterior horn.

(iii) lateral spinothalamic tract—associated with pain and temperature. Its cell bodies lie in the posterior horn of the opposite side and its fibres have crossed in the anterior white commissure to ascend to the thalamus in the spinal lemniscus.

(b) Centrally placed

(i) lateral corticospinal (crossed pyramidal) tract—motor fibres whose cell bodies lie in the cerebral motor cortex. The fibres have crossed in the medulla and descend to the grey matter of the cord. Many of the fibres in the lateral corticospinal tract end at the base of the posterior horn where they synapse with cells whose short axons end amongst the anterior horn cells.

(ii) reticulospinal and rubrospinal tracts—contain extrapyramidal motor fibres descending to the cells of the spinal cord. They come from the red nucleus in the midbrain and from scattered reticular nuclei.

The **anterior column** contains:

(a) Anterior corticospinal (uncrossed pyramidal) tract. This is found in the cervical and upper thoracic regions and is formed of descending fibres from the motor cortex. They cross almost horizontally in the anterior white commissure to the contralateral anterior horn region.

(b) Vestibulospinal, olivospinal and tectospinal tracts are extrapyramidal fibres passing to the anterior horn region from nuclei in the brain stem.

(c) Anterior spinothalamic tract carries touch fibres. Its cells lie in the posterior horn of the opposite side and its fibres pass in the spinal lemniscus to the thalamus.

The fibres of the fasciculus proprius surround the grey matter and form intrasegmental and intersegmental connections in the spinal cord.

The anterior and posterior spinothalamic tracts together are sometimes called the **spinal lemniscus.** With other adjacent fibres whose connections are with the olivary and the vestibular nuclei and the tectum of the midbrain, the spinothalamic complex is referred to as the **anterolateral system.**

THE RETICULAR FORMATION

The reticular formation is the name given to a large number of ill-defined groups of neurons situated between the larger nuclear masses of the brain stem and around the grey matter of the spinal cord.

With expanding knowledge of the nervous system the widespread activity of the reticular formation has become recognised and the accurate mapping of its nuclear groups and fibre tracts has been undertaken. Over a hundred nuclear groups have been described, the larger groups (such as the lateral reticular nucleus of the medulla) being more easily recognised. The neurons are of a variety of sizes having prolific dendritic trees and axons with numerous collateral branches. Ascending axons pass through the dendritic fields of descending neurons probably influencing their activity. Similarly descending axons tend to pass through the dendritic fields of ascending neurons.

Ascending neurons of the reticular formation receive collaterals from all afferent pathways, especially those of the trigeminal nerve, and also from the cerebellum. They project to the intralaminar thalamic nuclei and from there project diffusely to all parts of the cerebral cortex. There is a marked lack of organisation in this system, stimulation producing no specific local response but giving rise to widespread cortical activity (cortical arousal) and wakefulness. Enlarging lesions of the midbrain or increasing pressure on the midbrain reduce this cortical activity and lead to progressive stupor.

Descending neurons receive fibres from the motor cortex, either directly from the corticonuclear and corticospinal pathways or via the basal nuclei. They also receive cerebellar fibres, especially from the anterior lobe and fastigial nuclei. The descending pathways have both ipsilateral and contralateral effects on the spinal anterior horn cells which may inhibit or facilitate spinal motor activity governing, in particular, postural adjustments.

CHAPTER 35

THE AFFERENT AND EFFERENT PATHWAYS

Axons run for variable distances within the spinal cord and brain stem. Most are short intrasegmental and intersegmental fibres but many run for long distances uniting the brain and lower spinal segments. In the central nervous system there appears some functional localisation of the fibres. Short intrasegmental and intersegmental fibres lie close to the grey matter of the cord in the fasciculus proprius; many ascending fibres lie in the posterior column and the periphery of the lateral column; and many descending fibres lie in the anterior column and the intermediate part of the lateral column.

Most of the information entering the central nervous system is employed in reflex, automatic and unconscious ways, only a small amount reaching conciousness. Similarly on the motor side of the central nervous system, only a small proportion of the descending pathways are directly involved in voluntary, conscious activity.

The pathways are so arranged that each cerebral hemisphere controls muscles of the opposite half of the body and also receives information from the opposite side. The primary sensory and motor areas of the cortex show a marked degree of anatomical localisation. In the sensori-motor cortex around the central sulcus the lower limb is represented near the top, the trunk and upper limb about the middle, and the head and neck are at the lower parts of the gyri. Though the limbs and trunk are represented in an inverted position, the head and neck are not inverted.

The areas of cortex represented are proportional to the complexity of the muscle activity and the acuteness of the sensory detection. The more 'important' parts, e.g. lips, tongue, thumb and index finger, have larger representations than the buttock, foot and back. The macula of the eye has a larger representation on the calcarine gyri than all the peripheral retina.

In most humans, one hemisphere appears to be dominant. This usually determines the 'handedness' of the individual and is the side of the brain most concerned with speech processes and memory.

AFFERENT PATHWAYS

The afferent pathways of the central nervous system are involved in the conduction of information received by the peripheral nerve endings about environmental conditions. Some of these receptors are simple, free nerve endings while others are very elaborate end organs (such as the encapsulated corpuscles and the muscle spindles). The extent to which a particular 'sensation' is dependent on a single form of nerve ending or on the summation of information from a variety of endings is in many cases undecided. The stretch receptors of muscle are specific in function while the free nerve endings of the cornea, mostly identical in structure, can distinguish touch, pain, hotness and coldness.

Most of the somatosensory pathways ascending the spinal cord and brain stem may be grouped under three headings: (a) pathways for touch and pressure, (b) pathways for pain, hotness and coldness, (c) proprioceptive pathways. Those pathways reaching the cerebral cortex are usually formed of a chain of three sets of neurons.

In addition, some of the cranial nerves contain pathways for olfaction, vision, taste, balance and hearing, the so-called special senses.

Touch and pressure fibres in a spinal nerve have their cell bodies in the dorsal root ganglion. The central branches ascend in the posterior column of the spinal cord and synapse in the gracile or cuneate nuclei in the medulla. In the posterior column, fibres from the lower limb lie medial to those from the trunk, upper limb and neck.

The second set of neurons has its cell bodies in the gracile and cuneate nuclei. The axons swing round the central grey matter, cross the midline and then ascend as the medial lemniscus to the thalamus (ventroposterior nucleus). The third set of neurons has its cell bodies in the thalamic nucleus and the axons ascend through the internal capsule to the cortex of the postcentral gyrus.

Other touch fibres enter the cord and synapse in the posterior horn. The second neurons cross the midline and ascend in the anterior spinothalamic tract to the ventral thalamic nucleus. The third set of neurons projects to the postcentral gyrus.

Touch fibres in the trigeminal nerve have their cell bodies in the trigeminal ganglion and their central branches end in the superior sensory trigeminal nucleus. The second set of axons cross the midline, join the medial side of the medial lemniscus and end in the ventral thalamic nucleus. The third set of axons project to the lower part of the postcentral gyrus.

Pain and temperature fibres in a spinal nerve have their cell bodies in the dorsal root ganglion. The central fibres enter the cord and ascend for a short distance in the dorsolateral tract before synapsing in the posterior horn. The second set of axons cross the cord in the anterior white commissure and form the lateral spinothalamic tract. The fibres ascend the cord, pass through the brain stem as the spinal lemniscus and synapse in the thalamus (ventroposterior nucleus). A third set of axons pass through the internal capsule to the postcentral cortical gyrus.

Pain and temperature fibres in the trigeminal nerve have their cell bodies in the trigeminal ganglion. Their central branches enter the pons and descend into the upper cord as the spinal tract of the trigeminal nerve (cf. the spinal dorsolateral tract). Their fibres synapse in the spinal nucleus of the trigeminal nerve (cf. the posterior horn), whose axons cross the midline and join the spinal lemniscus. The fibres end in the ventroposterior thalamic nucleus.

The impulses of some pain-carrying fibres are relayed in the reticular formation to the intralaminar thalamic nuclei and thence to most areas of the cortex. This nonlemniscal pathway is a much more diffuse projection system.

Some **proprioceptive information** may reach a conscious level (cerebral cortex) but most is utilised by the cord and cerebellum and never reaches consciousness. Conscious proprioceptive fibres reach the cerebral cortex by the same pathways as do touch and pressure fibres in the posterior columns.

Unconscious proprioceptive fibres in a spinal nerve have their cell bodies in the dorsal root ganglion and their impulses reach the cerebellum by one of three pathways.

(*a*) Branches of the first neuron may ascend in the posterior column of the spinal cord to the accessory cuneate nucleus in the medulla. Fibres arising here pass in the ipsilateral inferior cerebellar peduncle to the cerebellum (vermis and paramedian zone of the anterior and middle lobes). This is an uncrossed pathway for impulses from the upper limb and upper trunk.

(*b*) The first neuron may synapse in the posterior horn of grey matter. A second neuron arising here crosses immediately and ascends in the anterior spinocerebellar tract. The tract reaches the cerebellum (vermis of the anterior lobe) via the superior cerebellar peduncle. This is mainly a crossed pathway.

(*c*) The first neuron may synapse in the thoracic nucleus of the posterior horn of grey matter. A second axon arising here passes to the ipsilateral posterior spinocerebellar tract and thence through the inferior cerebellar peduncle to the cerebellum (vermis and paramedian zones of anterior and middle lobes). This is mainly an uncrossed pathway.

Proprioceptive fibres are also present in the trigeminal nerve, especially the mandibular division. The cell bodies of the first set of neurons are in the trigeminal ganglia. Information reaches the cerebellum and thalamus but the paths in the brain stem are ill-defined. The mesencephalic trigeminal nucleus is concerned with passing on proprioceptive impulses.

PATHWAYS OF THE SPECIAL SENSES

Olfactory impulses from the sensory mucosa in the upper part of each nasal cavity pass along the olfactory nerves to an olfactory bulb. Impulses are transmitted along the olfactory tracts and their subsequent passage is ill-defined, but it seems unlikely that primary olfactory projection areas extend beyond the prepiriform cortex (p. 355).

Visual impulses from the retina pass to the optic nerve. The two optic nerves undergo partial decussation at the optic chiasma; the nasal fibres of each hemiretina cross to the opposite side. The optic tracts, which pass backwards from the chiasma, thus contain ipsilateral temporal fibres and contralateral nasal fibres. Each tract skirts the midbrain and passes mainly to the lateral geniculate body of the thalamus. Some fibres, however, pass beyond the thalamus to the superior colliculus and pretectal region of the midbrain. These fibres are probably concerned with visual reflex pathways.

Fibres arising in the lateral geniculate body form the optic radiation which passes through the posterior limb of the internal capsule, then lateral to the posterior horn of the lateral ventricle, and reaches the visual cortex. This borders the calcarine sulcus on the medial surface of the occipital lobe (striate cortex).

Impulses arising from parts of the retinae receiving light from the left visual fields are relayed in the right geniculate body to the visual (striate) area of the right occipital pole. The lower halves of the retinae receive impulses from upper visual fields and the impulses are projected through the geniculate bodies to the lower lips of the calcarine sulci of both sides.

Taste impulses carried in the seventh, ninth and tenth cranial nerves pass to the nucleus of the tractus solitarius. Further connections are ill-defined but probably pass via the thalamus to the insular cortex. Many connections are made with centres controlling visceral activities.

Auditory impulses from the spiral organ in the cochlear duct pass through the bipolar neurons of the cochlear nerve to the dorsal and ventral cochlear nuclei in the floor of the lateral recess of the fourth ventricle. Secondary neurons arising here cross the midline mostly as a ventrally placed decussating bundle, the trapezoid body. These fibres synapse in the trapezoid nuclei (embedded in the trapezoid body) and in the nuclei of the lateral lemniscus. Some fibres cross the brain stem dorsal to the trapezoid body and synapse in the contralateral trapezoid nucleus. The axons from these nuclear groups form the lateral lemniscus which ascends to the medial geniculate body and the inferior colliculus. Neurons from the medial geniculate body pass in the posterior limb of the internal capsule to the cortex of the superior temporal gyrus.

Vestibular impulses arising in the specialised organs of balance in the saccule, utricle and semicircular ducts pass through the bipolar neurons of the vestibular nerve to the vestibular nuclei situated in the floor of the fourth ventricle. These nuclei comprise lateral, medial, superior and inferior groups. The lateral has secondary connections with the spinal cord through the vestibulospinal tract and all nuclei have connections which pass in the inferior cerebellar peduncle to the flocculonodular lobe of the cerebellum. Connections between the nuclei and the medial longitudinal bundle are concerned with reflex movements of the eyes, head and neck. Other fibres probably lead to the thalamus and thence to the cortex (superior temporal gyrus).

EFFERENT PATHWAYS

Efferent pathways passing from the cerebral cortex to the brain stem and spinal cord form two complementary systems, the pyramidal and the extrapyramidal.

Pyramidal fibres arise mainly from the pyramidal cells of the motor cortex. They pass through the internal capsule, the middle part of the cerebral peduncle and are split into smaller bundles by the transversely running fibres of the basilar part of the pons. The bundles reunite in the upper medulla to form the prominent pyramid. Most of the fibres decussate just above the junction of the medulla and spinal cord and form the lateral corticospinal tract. A smaller number of fibres do not cross in the lower medulla but descend as the anterior corticospinal tract and decussate later, at the appropriate segmental level. Some pyramidal fibres (corticonuclear) leave the main tract in the brain stem and end near the cranial nerve motor nuclei.

Many pyramidal fibres (corticonuclear, and lateral and anterior corticospinal) probably end in intermediate neurons in the region of the cranial nerve motor nuclei or of the anterior horn cells. The intermediate neurons serve as a second neuron in the pyramidal pathways. Some pyramidal fibres synapse directly with the final neurons. The final neuron (lower motor neuron) is the cranial motor neuron or anterior horn cell whose axon passes to the motor end plates of striated muscle.

The **extrapyramidal system** is the name given to groups of fibres passing from the motor cortex via subcortical nuclear masses to the lower motor neurons. The subcortical nuclei are found in the basal nuclei and the subthalamus of the forebrain; the substantia nigra, red nucleus and reticular nuclei of the midbrain; the reticular and lateral vestibular nuclei of the hindbrain. This system has obvious cerebellar connections. The main descending pathways are the rubro-reticulospinal and vestibulospinal tracts.

Other descending pathways leave (a) the tectum of the midbrain (especially the superior colliculi) and descend in the tectospinal tracts, (b) the olivary nuclei of the medulla and descend as the olivospinal tracts.

Cerebellar efferent pathways are considered on page 373.

The efferent pathway of the **autonomic nervous system,** innervating smooth muscle, cardiac muscle and most glands, are ill-defined. Certain cortical areas, particularly the inferior surface of the frontal lobe, are closely linked with the hypothalamus from which autonomic fibres descend. Sympathetic fibres originate in the posterior parts of the hypothalamus and descend to the thoracolumbar outflow (T1–L2), synapsing on the lateral horn cells of these segments. Parasympathetic fibres originate in the anterior parts of the hypothalamus and descend to the craniosacral outflow. The cranial fibres synapse in the 3rd, 7th, 9th and 10th cranial nerve nuclei and the sacral fibres synapse in the lateral horn cells of the 2nd, 3rd and 4th sacral segments.

CHAPTER 36

THE MENINGES AND BLOOD SUPPLY

Three membranes form a protective covering around the brain and spinal cord, an outer dense fibrous dura mater, an intermediate delicate avascular arachnoid and an inner delicate vascular pia mater. The dura and arachnoid are separated by a potential subdural space and the arachnoid and pia by a wider subarachnoid space containing cerebrospinal fluid. The arachnoid and pia can be looked on as different parts of one enclosing membrane the pia-arachnoid (cf. visceral and parietal peritoneum).

THE DURA MATER

Cranial

The cranial dura mater is in two layers. The outer (endocranial) layer is the periosteum on the inner surface of the cranial bones and is thus continuous with the periosteum on the outer surface of the skull through the foramina and sutures. The inner (cerebral) layer of dura mater is continuous with that of the spinal cord. In most areas the two layers are firmly adherent but in places they are separated to enclose the venous sinuses. The inner layer is folded to form the falx cerebri and the tentorium cerebelli, and is stretched between the clinoid processes as the diaphragma sellae.

The **falx cerebri** lies in the midsagittal plane and separates the two cerebral hemispheres. It is attached to the vault of the skull from the crista galli to the internal occipital protuberance. It is sickle-shaped, narrower at its anterior end, and posteriorly blends with the upper surface of the tentorium cerebelli. The inferior sagittal sinus lies within the lower free border and the superior sagittal sinus within the attachment of the fold to the vault.

The **tentorium cerebelli** roofs in the posterior cranial fossa and separates the cerebral hemispheres from the cerebellum. Anteriorly is a hole for the midbrain. It thus has attached and free borders. The attached border extends from each posterior clinoid process along the superior border of the petrous temporal bone and then round to the internal occipital protuberance. The free border is at a higher level than the attached; it runs around the posterior and lateral aspects of the midbrain and then goes forward to reach the anterior clinoid processes. The superior petrosal and transverse venous sinuses lie along the attached border of the fold and the midline straight sinus descends backwards between its layers to the internal occipital protuberance.

The **diaphragma sellae** is attached to the four clinoid processes and forms a roof for the hypophyseal fossa. In the midline it is evaginated to surround the pituitary gland and here forms the medial walls of the cavernous sinuses.

The cerebral layer of dura forms a sheath around the cranial nerves as they leave the skull. The sheath so formed around the optic nerve extends to the sclera.

The cranial dura mater receives its blood supply from anterior ethmoidal, middle and accessory meningeal, internal carotid and verte-

A   B   C

FIG. 36.1

Myelogram. Radiopaque material has been injected into the subarachnoid space through a lumbar puncture needle (p. 386) which has then been withdrawn. By tilting the patient this material which is more dense than CSF, can be used to outline the various parts of the subarachnoid space. A–lower end of subarachnoid space, B–lumbar region, C–cervical region.

1. 4th lumbar vertebra	3. Meningeal sheath of nerve root
2. Lower end of subarachnoid space	4. 1st rib

bral arteries. It is innervated by meningeal branches of the trigeminal, glossopharyngeal, vagal and upper three cervical nerves from before backwards.

Spinal

The spinal dura matter is continuous at the foramen magnum with the cerebral layer of cranial dura and extends downwards to the level of the second sacral vertebra. It lies within the vertebral canal separated from its walls by extradural fat and the internal vertebral venous plexus (p. 38). It is pierced by the ventral and dorsal roots of the spinal nerves and the filum terminale, and ensheaths these structures and the mixed spinal nerves as far as the intervertebral foramina. The spinal nerves and filum terminale help to stabilise the dural sac within the vertebral canal.

THE ARACHNOID

This is closely applied to the cranial and spinal dura mater and fine trabeculae pass from it to the pia mater. In places the arachnoid herniates through the dura mater, forming arachnoid villi which come into contact with the endothelium of the cranial venous sinuses, especially the superior sagittal sinus and its lateral recesses. The clusters of villi seen in later life are known as arachnoid granulations. The villi filter the cerebrospinal fluid back into the venous channels.

THE PIA MATER

This is closely applied to the surface of the brain and spinal cord. It extends into the sulci of the brain and the anterior median fissure of the cords and invests the cranial and spinal nerves, their roots and the filum terminale. On each side of the spinal cord the pia forms a serrated fold, the **ligamentum denticulatum.** The ligament runs the whole length of the cord and is attached to the dura mater, between the spinal nerves, by its serrations which pierce the arachnoid. The ligament helps to stabilise the spinal cord within the dural sheath.

Grey and white matter are absent over the roof of the third and fourth ventricles and the medial wall of the lateral ventricles, and here the pia mater lies on the ependymal lining of the ventricles. The two layers fuse and are invaginated into the cavities by blood vessels. The folds so formed are known as **choroid plexuses.** The ependymal cells take on a secretory appearance and are concerned with the production of cerebrospinal fluid. A forward-projecting fold of pia extends into the transverse fissure below the corpus callosum and is known as the **tela choroidea.** Choroidal arteries and the great cerebral vein lie in the tela. Lateral and inferior extensions of the tela invaginate the lateral and third ventricles forming their choroidal plexuses. A single median and two lateral apertures in the pia and ependyma of the roof of the fourth ventricle allow cerebrospinal fluid to pass from the ventricular system to the subarachnoid space.

The **subarachnoid space** is filled with cerebrospinal fluid and is narrowest over the cerebral hemispheres. In some regions, where the arachnoid stretches over subdivisions of the brain, larger spaces (**cisterns**) are formed. The larger of these are the **cerebellomedullary cistern** (**cisterna magna**) in the angle between the cerebellum and the medulla, the **interpeduncular** between the cerebral peduncles, and the **pontine** in front of the pons. The **lumbar cistern,** below the spinal cord, contains the cauda equina. A hollow needle can be pushed forwards in the midline between the spines of the lower lumbar vertebrae and after passing through the interspinous ligaments, it enters the extradural space. The needle then pierces the dura and arachnoid and enters the subarachnoid space. In this way a sample of cerebrospinal fluid can be aspirated for examination, the procedure being known as a lumbar puncture. A local anaesthetic can be introduced through such a needle into either the extradural or subarachnoid space to produce regional anaesthesia; the procedures are known as epidural and spinal anaesthetic techniques respectively. Air, or other contrast media may be introduced into the subarachnoid space to help radiological diagnosis (Fig. 36.1).

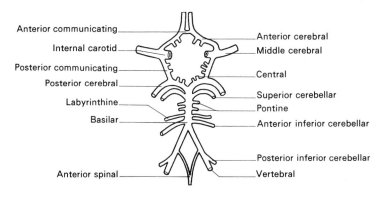

Fig. 36.2
Diagrammatic lay-out of the arterial circle on the base of the brain. The larger branches are shown.

CIRCULATION OF THE CEREBROSPINAL FLUID

Most of the cerebrospinal fluid is produced by the choroid plexuses of the ventricles by active secretion of the modified ependymal cells. It passes through the cavities of the brain and then through the apertures in the roof of the fourth ventricle into the subarachnoid space. The fluid circulates around the outside of the brain and spinal cord, and is returned to the blood stream either through the arachnoid villi and granulations or directly to the small veins. Some fluid may be absorbed into perineural lymph vessels. Interference with the circulation of cerebrospinal fluid produces a condition known as hydrocephalus. If the blockage is within the ventricular system (such as with pressure from a tumour) the ventricles will become dilated proximal to the level of obstruction—a condition known as internal hydrocephalus. Blockage of the arachnoid granulations (as with infection) produces communicating (external) hydrocephalus.

THE BLOOD SUPPLY OF THE BRAIN

Owing to the unyielding nature of the skull and spinal dura, and the relative incompressibility of the brain and cerebrospinal fluid, the vascular system is very susceptible to changes in intracranial pressure. The pattern of the vessels and the rate of flow through them can be investigated radiologically after the injection of radiopaque substances into the large arteries in the neck. Local cerebral ischaemia (see p. 15) occurring as a result of cerebral or general degenerative arterial disease may produce variable degrees of muscle weakness, speech disturbance, somatosensory and visual loss, the condition being known as a 'stroke'. Similar symptoms may be produced by pressure on a cortical area resulting from injury, local inflammation, or a tumour.

Fig. 36.3

Right carotid arteriogram, anteroposterior view. Radiopaque material has been introduced into the common carotid artery in the neck.

1. Internal carotid artery
2. Middle cerebral artery
3. Anterior cerebral arteries

Arterial Supply (Figs. 36.2, 36.3, 36.4)

The brain receives its blood from the two internal carotid and the two vertebral arteries.

Internal carotid artery (see also page 336)—enters the cranial cavity through the carotid canal in the petrous temporal bone, traverses the cavernous sinus, piercing its roof near the anterior clinoid process, and then divides into anterior and middle cerebral arteries (Fig. 36.4).

BRANCHES

(i) **anterior cerebral artery**—passes forwards towards the midline and then upwards around the rostrum and genu of the corpus callosum to divide into two terminal branches running backwards on the corpus callosum and in the cingulate sulcus. The artery supplies the medial aspect

FIG. 36.4

Left carotid arteriogram, lateral view. Arterial phase. Radiopaque material has been introduced into the common carotid artery in the neck. Part of the anaesthetic tube is seen in the lower right corner.

1. Internal carotid artery
2. Anterior cerebral arteries
3. Branches of anterior cerebral artery above the corpus callosum
4. Middle cerebral artery
5. Posterior communicating artery

of the frontal and parietal lobes as far back as the parieto-occipital sulcus, and a small part of the adjacent lateral surface. The two anterior cerebral anteries are united near their origin by the short **anterior communicating artery.**

(ii) **middle cerebral artery**—passes laterally into the lateral sulcus in which it crosses the insula and temporal pole and turns upwards and backwards across the lateral aspect of the hemisphere. The artery supplies the inferior surface of the frontal lobe, the insula and all save the periphery of the lateral surface of the hemisphere.

(iii) **ophthalmic artery**—see page 280.

(iv) **anterior choroidal artery**—passes backwards with the optic tract and contributes to the blood supply of the choroid plexus in the inferior horn of the lateral ventricle.

FIG. 36.5

Vertebral arteriogram, anteroposterior view. The radiopaque material has been introduced into a vertebral artery. The contralateral artery is also demonstrated since the material is introduced under pressure and some passes retrogradely down to the other side.

1. Vertebral arteries (in foramina transversarii)	3. Basilar artery
	4. Superior cerebellar artery
2. Vertebral arteries inside skull	5. Posterior cerebral artery

(v) **posterior communicating artery**—passes backwards to the posterior cerebral artery.

(vi) branches to the pituitary gland, meninges and trigeminal ganglion.

Vertebral artery (see also page 331)—enters the cranial cavity through the foramen magnum, passes forwards, upwards and medially on to the basal part of the occipital bone and unites with its fellow of the opposite side at the lower border of the pons to form the basilar artery (Figs. 36.5, 36.6).

BRANCHES

(i) **anterior spinal artery**—a single vessel is formed by the union of branches from both vertebral arteries. It descends in front of the medulla to reach and supply the spinal cord.

(ii) **posterior inferior cerebellar artery**—passes posteriorly to supply the posterolateral part of the medulla, the lower cerebellum, a choroidal branch to the fourth ventricle, and a posterior spinal branch which descends to the spinal cord.

FIG. 36.6
Vertebral arteriogram, lateral view (see Fig. 36.5).

1. R & L vertebral arteries
2. Vertebral loops round lateral mass of the atlas
3. Basilar artery
4. Superior cerebellar artery
5. Posterior cerebral arteries

Basilar artery—ascends in front of the pons and divides near its upper border into the two posterior cerebral arteries.

BRANCHES

(i) **anterior inferior cerebellar artery**—passes backwards to its named area.

(ii) **pontine branches.**

(iii) **labyrinthine artery**—passes through the internal acoustic meatus to the inner ear.

(iv) **superior cerebellar artery**—passes backwards around the cerebral peduncles to supply the superior surface of the cerebellum.

391

(v) **posterior cerebral artery**—passes backwards around the cerebral peduncles to reach and supply the medial surface of the occipital lobe. Branches supply the inferior surfaces of the occipital and temporal lobes and the adjacent lateral surface. Its posterior choroidal branch passes into the tela choroidea to reach the choroid plexuses of the third and lateral ventricles.

The principal arteries supplying the forebrain form an anastomotic ring, the **circle of Willis,** around the optic chiasma and the pituitary gland (Fig. 36.2). It is formed by the stem of the anterior and middle cerebral arteries of each side anterolaterally, the posterior cerebral arteries posteriorly, the anterior communicating artery uniting the two anterior cerebral arteries, and the posterior communicating arteries uniting the corresponding posterior cerebral arteries to the middle cerebral or internal carotid arteries. The pattern of this anastomosis however is variable. A number of branches from the ring and its larger tributaries pass upwards into the nuclear masses of the forebrain, entering the brain mainly through the anterior and posterior perforated substances.

Venous Drainage

The veins draining the hemispheres may be divided into superficial and deep groups which anastomose freely and drain to the cranial venous sinuses.

The **superficial group:**

(i) the superior cerebral veins, passing to the superior sagittal sinus.

(ii) the superficial middle cerebral vein passing in the lateral sulcus to the cavernous sinus.

(iii) the inferior cerebral veins passing to the transverse sinus. Superior and inferior anastomotic veins join the superficial middle cerebral vein to the superior sagittal and transverse sinuses.

The **deep group:**

(i) the anterior cerebral vein, draining the region supplied by its artery, joins

(ii) the deep middle cerebral vein, lying deeply in the lateral sulcus and forms the basal vein. This passes backwards round the midbrain and joins the great cerebral vein near the pineal gland.

(iii) each internal cerebral vein receives the thalamostriate vein, draining the caudate nucleus and thalamus, and the choroidal veins of the lateral and third ventricles.

(iv) the **great cerebral vein,** formed when the two internal cerebral veins join, opens into the straight sinus.

THE CRANIAL VENOUS SINUSES

These lie either between the two layers of cranial dura mater or within a fold of the cerebral layer. The sinuses receive venous blood from adjacent parts of the brain and communicate via other sinuses and emissary veins with the exterior of the skull. The sinuses may be unpaired or paired.

UNPAIRED SINUSES

(i) **superior sagittal sinus**—passes backwards in the upper border of the falx cerebri to reach the internal occipital protuberance where it usually joins the right transverse sinus. Its walls are invaginated by many arachnoid granulations (p. 386), as are the lateral recesses of the sinus.

(ii) **inferior sagittal sinus**—passes backwards in the lower border of the falx cerebri to join the straight sinus at the attachment of the falx to the tentorium.

FIG. 36.7

Left carotid arteriogram—later exposure. Venous phase (see Fig. 36.4). Part of the anaesthetic tube is seen in the lower right corner.

1. Superior cerebral veins
2. Superior anastomatic vein
3. Internal cerebral vein
4. Origin of great cerebral vein

(iii) **straight sinus**—runs downwards within the tentorium cerebelli to the internal occipital protuberance, usually joining the left transverse sinus.

(iv) **basilar sinus**—is a network of sinuses lying on the basal part of the occipital bone and uniting the two inferior petrosal sinuses.

(v) **intercavernous sinuses**—unite the cavernous sinuses anterior and posterior to the pituitary gland.

PAIRED SINUSES

(i) **transverse sinus**—commences at the internal occipital protuberance, the right usually continuous with the superior sagittal sinus and the

393

left with the straight sinus. Each runs along the attached border of the tentorium, grooving the occipital and parietal bones, to the lateral part of the petrous temporal bone where it becomes the sigmoid sinus. The two transverse sinuses often communicate at the internal occipital protuberance to form the confluence of the sinuses.

(ii) **sigmoid sinus**—is a continuation of the transverse sinus and is formed at the lateral end of the superior border of the petrous temporal

FIG. 36.8
Coronal section through the pituitary fossa showing the structures related to the cavernous sinus (shown in stipple).

bone. It curves downwards and then forwards, grooving the inner surface of the mastoid process, to reach the jugular foramen where it becomes the internal jugular vein.

(iii) **cavernous sinus** (Fig. 36.8)—lies on the body of the sphenoid bone lateral to the pituitary gland. It is traversed by the internal carotid artery, the oculomotor, trochlear and abducent nerves and the ophthalmic and maxillary branches of the trigeminal nerve. It extends from the apex of the petrous temporal bone and the opening of the carotid canal forwards to the superior orbital fissure. Its roof is formed by the diaphragma sellae which lies under the hypothalamus and it is pierced by the internal carotid artery. Its lateral wall is related to the temporal lobe of the brain and within this wall lie the oculomotor, trochlear, ophthalmic and maxillary nerves. Posteriorly the wall is related to the trigeminal ganglion. The internal carotid artery passes upwards and forwards through the sinus and pierces its roof near the anterior clinoid process. The abducent nerve passes forwards and downwards through the sinus lateral to the artery.

The sinus receives the ophthalmic veins, the sphenoparietal sinus, the superficial middle cerebral vein and smaller veins from the adjacent parts of the brain. It drains via emissary veins to the pterygoid venous plexus, and via the superior and inferior petrosal sinuses to the transverse sinus and internal jugular vein respectively. The two sinuses intercommunicate via the intercavernous sinuses.

(iv) **inferior petrosal sinus**—arises from the cavernous sinus, descends over the petro-occipital suture, passes through the jugular foramen and joins the internal jugular vein.

394

(v) **superior petrosal sinus**—passes along the superior border of the petrous temporal bone uniting the cavernous and transverse sinuses.

(vi) **sphenoparietal sinus**—runs along the edge of the lesser wing of the sphenoid bone to the cavernous sinus.

(vii) **occipital sinus**—passes from the transverse sinus near the internal occipital protuberance, around the foramen magnum to the sigmoid sinus.

Emissary veins—pass through most foramina of the skull and unite the intracranial venous sinuses with the veins outside the skull. They include the condylar, parietal and mastoid veins, and venous plexuses passing through the foramen ovale, foramen lacerum and hypoglossal foramen.

Diploic veins—are present in the frontal, parietal and occipital bones. They drain the diploë and communicate with the veins of the scalp and the dura.

BLOOD SUPPLY OF THE SPINAL CORD

Arterial supply—is from a single **anterior spinal artery** (derived from both vertebral arteries) and two **posterior spinal arteries** (branches of the posterior inferior cerebellar arteries). The anterior artery descends in the anterior median fissure and each posterior artery behind the posterior spinal nerve rootlets. These three arteries are reinforced in different regions by branches passing through the intervertebral foramina from the vertebral, deep cervical, posterior intercostal, lumbar and lateral sacral arteries. The lumbar arteries provide a rich supply to the lumbar enlargement.

Venous drainage—is via large midline anterior and posterior spinal veins, and smaller channels near the emergence of the rootlets. They drain to the internal vertebral venous plexus (p. 38).

INDEX

Abdomen, 86
Abdominal wall, anterior, 86
— —posterior, 125
Abduction, definition of, 16
Abnormality (see Chap. 2 and specific structure)
Accommodation, 277
Acetabulum, 131
Achilles tendon, 245
Acoustic meatus, external, 31, 263, 269, 308
— —internal, 269, 313
Acromion, 167
Adduction, definition of, 16
Adenoids, 299, 300
Aditus to antrum, 309
—to omental bursa, 93
Adrenal (see Suprarenal gland)
Ala of ilium, 131, 212
—of nose, 282
Alar plate, 346, 369
Alimentary canal, 22, 69, 95, 139
Allantois, 22
Allocortex, 347
Alveolar duct, 80
—sac, 80
Alveus, 355
Amnioblasts, 19
Amniotic cavity, 18, 19
Ampulla of bile duct, 116, 117
—of ductus, 150
—of rectum, 139
—of semicircular ducts, 310
—of uterine tube, 146
—of vas (see Ampulla of ductus)
Amygdaloid body, 354
Anaemia, 14
Anaesthesia, epidural, 387
—spinal, 387
Anal canal, 139
—columns, 140
—membrane, 22, 27
—sphincter, external, 140
— —internal, 139
—triangle, 152
—valvules, 140
Anastomosis, 14
—marginal, 109
—portal-systemic, 111, 140
—scapular, 179
Anatomical position, 16

—snuff box, 193
Aneurysm, 129
Angina, 57
Angioblasts, 27
Angle of mandible, 266
—infrasternal, 42
—of rib, 43
—sternal, 42
—subpubic, 136
Anococcygeal body, 139, 152
Anorectal canal, 139
Ansa cervicalis, 323, 338
—hypoglossi (see Ansa cervicalis)
—subclavia, 340
Anteflexion, definition of, 144
Anterior, definition of, 16
Anteversion, definition of, 144
Antrum, mastoid (tympanic), 310
—maxillary (see Sinus, maxillary)
—pyloric, 95
Anulus fibrosus, 36
—ovalis (see Limbus ovalis)
Aorta, abdominal, 127
—arch, 29, 64
—ascending, 63
—descending, 64
—dorsal, 28
—ventral, 29, 129
Aortic arches, 29
—knuckle, 74
Aperture of fourth ventricle, 374, 387
—nasal, anterior (nostril), 263, 282
— —posterior (choana), 264, 298
—pyloric, 164
Apex of fibula, 228
—of heart, 52
—of lung, 75, 77
—of petromastoid, 269
—of sacrum, 134
Aponeurosis, 4
—bicipital, 181, 182, 186, 207
—epicranial, 272
—palatine, 288
—palmar, 189, 203, 207
—plantar, 251
Appendices epiploicae, 101
Appendix, vermiform, 104
Aqueduct, cerebral, 362, 364, 374
—of midbrain (see Aqueduct, cerebral)
Aqueous humor, 277
Arachnoid granulations, 386

Arachnoid (*continued*)
—mater, 386
—villi, 386
Arch of aorta, 29, 64
—aortic, 301
—of atlas, 327
—coraco-acromial, 173
—cricoid, 304
—of fauces, 285, 287
—of foot, lateral longitudinal, 237, 251
——medial longitudinal, 239, 250
——transverse, 251
—jugular venous, 338
—palatoglossal, 285, 287
—palatopharyngeal, 287
—palmar, deep, 194, 206
——superficial, 194, 203, 206
—pharyngeal, 29, 267, 301
—plantar, 252
—pubic, 133
—subpubic, 136
—superciliary, 263
—venous, dorsal of foot, 254
——dorsal of hand, 207
——plantar, 254
—vertebral, 33, 34
—zygomatic, 263
Arcuate fibres, internal, 37
—line, 88, 131, 133
Area, auricular, of ilium, 131
—bare, of liver, 92
—cortical (*see* Cortex)
—intercondylar, 227
—striate, 351
Areola, 50
Areolar tissue, 4
Arteriogram, 56, 57, 65, 105, 107, 109, 125, 159, 224, 240, 332, 388, 390, 393
Arteriosclerosis, 15, 333
Artery, 14
—acromiothoracic, 178
—adrenal (*see* Artery, suprarenal)
—alveolar, inferior, 335
——superior, 335
—appendicular, 104, 108
—aorta (*see* Aorta)
——arch, 301
—ascending lumbar (*see* Artery, lumbar)
—auditory, internal (*see* Artery, labyrinthine)
—auricular, posterior, 335
—axial, 212
—axillary, 178
—basilar, 311, 331, 391
—brachial, 178, 182
—brachiocephalic, 64, 331, 333
—bronchial, 64
—of bulb, 157
—caecal, anterior, 108
——posterior, 108
—carotid, common, 333

——external, 334
——internal, 312, 336, 388
—central, of retina, 278, 280, 314
—cerebellar, anterior inferior, 391
——posterior inferior, 391
——superior, 391
—cerebral, anterior, 389
——middle, 389
——posterior, 392
—cervical, deep, 333
——transverse, 333
—choroidal, anterior, 390
——posterior, 392
—ciliary, 280
—circumflex, femoral, lateral, 225
———medial, 225
——of heart, 55
——humeral, anterior, 179
———posterior, 179
——iliac, deep, 160
——scapular, 179
—coeliac, 29, 97, 106
—colic, left, 108
——middle, 108
——right, 108
—communicating, anterior, 389
——posterior, 390
—coronary, left, 55
——right, 55
—costocervical, 333
—cremasteric, 90
—cystic, 106
—deep, of penis, 157
—dental (*see* Artery, alveolar)
—diagonal, 56
—diaphragmatic, 64, 128
—digital, of foot, 252
——of hand, 206
—dorsal, of penis, 157
——of tongue, 289
—dorsalis pedis, 241, 252
—of ductus deferens, 90
—epigastric, inferior, 160
——superior, 47
—ethmoidal, anterior, 280, 312
——posterior, 280
—facial, 334
——transverse, 335
—femoral, 224
—gastric, left, 97, 106
——right, 97, 106
——short, 97
—gastroduodenal, 106
—gastro-epiploic, 97, 106, 107
—gluteal, superior, 160
——inferior, 160
—gonadal (*see* Artery, ovarian or Artery, testicular)
—hepatic, 106, 115
—ileal, 108
—ileocolic, 108

Artery (*continued*)
—iliac, common, 158
——external, 160, 224
——internal, 158
—iliolumbar, 160
—innominate (*see* Artery brachiocephalic)
—intercostal, anterior, 47
——highest (superior), 333
——posterior, 46
—interosseous, anterior, 194
——common, 194
——posterior, 195
—interventricular, anterior, 55
——posterior, 55
—jejunal, 108
—labial, 157
—labyrinthine, 311, 391
—lacrimal, 280
—laryngeal, superior, 334
—lingual, 289, 334
—lumbar, 128
—mammary, internal (*see* Artery thoracic, internal)
—marginal, left, 55
——right, 55
—maxillary, 335
—meningeal, accessory, 335
——middle, 335
—mediastinal, 64
—mesenteric, inferior, 29, 108
——superior, 29, 107
—metacarpal, palmar, 206
—metatarsal, dorsal, 252
——plantar, 252
—musculophrenic, 47
—nodal, 56
—obturator, 159, 222
—occipital, 335
—oesophageal, 64
—ophthalmic, 278, 280
—ovarian, 128
—palatine, 335
—palmar, digital, 206
——metacarpal, 206
—pancreatic, 107
—pancreaticoduodenal, inferior, 108
——superior, 106
—perforating, of thigh, 225
—peroneal, 241
—of pharyngeal arches, 29
—pharyngeal, ascending, 334
—phrenic, 64, 128
—plantar, digital, 252
——lateral, 252
——medial, 252
——metatarsal, 252
—pontine, 391
—popliteal, 241
—profunda brachii, 182
——femoris, 220, 225
—pterygopalatine, 335

—pudendal, internal, 152, 157, 160
—pulmonary, 65
—radial, 194
—rectal, inferior, 140, 157
——middle, 140, 158
——superior, 108, 140
—renal, 128
—retinal, central, 278, 280, 314
—sacral, lateral, 160
——median, 128
—scrotal, 157
—short gastric, 47, 106
—sigmoid, 108
—sphenopalatine (*see* Artery, pterygopalatine)
—spinal, anterior, 391, 395
——posterior, 391 395
—splenic, 97, 106
—subclavian, 44, 178, 331
—subcostal, 64, 88
—subscapular, 179
—supra-orbital, 280
—suprarenal, 128
—suprascapular, 179, 333
—supratrochlear, 280
—temporal, superficial, 335
—testicular, 128
—thoracic, internal, 47
——lateral, 178
——superior, 178
—thyrocervical, 179, 333
—thyroid, inferior, 328, 333
——superior, 328, 334
—tibial, anterior, 241
——posterior, 241
—transverse, colli (cervical), 179, 333
——facial, 335
—ulnar, 194
—umbilical, obliterated, 159
—uterine, 158
—vaginal, 158
—of vas deferens (*see* Artery of ductus deferens)
—vertebral, 34, 327, 331, 390
—vesical, inferior, 158
——superior, 158
—vitelline, 28, 29
Arthritis, 10, 217
Articular disc, 9, 170, 185, 200, 295
—meniscus, of knee, 231
—tubercle, 265, 269, 295
Arytenoid cartilage, 304
Astrocyte, 12
Atlas vertebra, 34
Atrium, left, 54
—right, 52
Auditory cortex, 351, 382
—meatus (*see* Acoustic meatus)
—nuclei (*see* Nucleus, cochlear)
—ossicles, 309
—pathways, 382

Auditory (*continued*)
—radiation, 352
—tube, 269, 298, 300, 309
Auricle of ear, 305
—of heart, 52, 54
Auricular appendage, 52, 54
Autonomic nervous system, 12, 81, 163, 339, 344, 358
Axilla, 178
Axis vertebra, 35
Axon, 11, 344
—hillock, 11

Band, iliotibial, 218, 254
—septomarginal (moderator), 53
Bare area, of liver, 92, 111, 115
Basal ganglia (*see* Nucleus, basal)
—plate, 346, 369
Base of heart, 52
—of lung, 75
—of midbrain, 364
—of pons, 366
Basis pedunculi (*see* Peduncle, cerebral)
Betz cell, 351
Bile, canaliculi, 116
—duct, 117
Biliary system, 116
Bladder, gall, 117
—urinary, 141
Blastocyst, 19
Blastomere, 19
Blinking, 274
Blood, 13
—fetal, 32
Body, amygdaloid, 354
—anococcygeal, 152
—of bone, 8
—carotid, 333
—ciliary, 277
—of corpus callosum, 352
—geniculate, lateral, 356, 357
——medial, 356, 357
—of hyoid bone, 272
—of mandible, 266
—mamillary, 357
—of pancreas, 119
—perineal, 148, 152, 155
—pineal, 347, 359
—of pubis, 133
—restiform (*see* Peduncle, cerebellar, inferior)
—of sphenoid, 268
—stalk, 20, 28
—of sternum, 42
—of stomach, 95
—of talus, 245
—trapezoid, 367
—of uterus, 144
—of ventricle (lateral), 359
—of vertebra, 33
—vitreous, 277

Bone, 5
—blood forming, 5
—development of, 8
—marrow, 5, 14
Bones (named)
—atlas, 34
—axis, 35
—calcaneus, 245
—capitate, 198
—carpus, 198
—classification, 5
—clavicle, 166
—concha, inferior, 271, 283
—cuboid, 246
—coccyx, 134
—cuneiform, 246
—ethmoid, 271
—femur, 213
—fibula, 228
—frontal, 270
—hamate, 198
—humerus, 167
—hip, 131, 212
—hyoid, 272
—ilium, 131
—incus, 309
—innominate (*see* Bones, hip)
—ischium, 132
—lacrimal, 271
—lunate, 198
—malleus, 309
—mandible, 266
—maxilla, 267
—metacarpal, 198
—metatarsal, 246
—nasal, 270
—navicular, 245
—occipital, 269
—palatine, 271
—parietal, 270
—patella, 227
—phalanges, of foot, 246
——of hand, 198
—pisiform, 198
—pneumatic, 5
—pubis, 133
—radius, 184
—ribs, 43
—sacrum, 133
—scaphoid, 198
—scapula, 167
—sesamoid, 6, 198, 205, 227, 250, 252
—skull, 262
—sphenoid, 268
—stapes, 309
—sternum, 42
—talus, 245
—tarsus, 245
—temporal, 269
—tibia, 227
—trapezium, 198

Bones (*continued*)
—trapezoid, 198
—triquetral, 198
—turbinate (*see* Bones, concha, inferior)
—ulna, 185
—vomer, 271, 283
—zygomatic, 270
Brachium conjunctivum (*see* Peduncle, cerebellar, superior)
—inferior, 363, 365
—pontis (*see* Peduncle, cerebellar, middle)
—superior, 363
Brain, 344
—stem, 344, 363
Breast, 50, 178
Bregma, 262
Brim of pelvis, 136
Bronchi, extrapulmonary, 70
—intrapulmonary, 75
Bronchioles, 80
Bronchopulmonary segment, 75
Bronchogram, 78, 79
Bronchoscopy, 71
Buccopharyngeal membrane, 20, 29, 31
Bud, liver, 30
—limb, 31
—lung, 29
—pancreas, 24, 30
—ureteric, 26
Bulb, jugular, 337
—olfactory, 350, 355
—of penis, 153
—vestibular, 155
Bulbus cordis, 60
Bulla ethmoidalis, 271, 283
Bundle, atrioventricular (of His), 59
—medial longitudinal (*see* Fasciculus)
Bunion, 250
Bursa, 9
—calcaneal, 238
—gastrocnemius, 231, 234
—hyoid, 305
—infrapatellar, 234
—of knee, 234
—metatarsophalangeal, 250
—omental, 30, 93
—popliteal, 231, 234, 238
—prepatellar, 234
—psoas (iliopectineal), 216, 217
—radial, 190
—semimembranosus, 234
—subacromial, 173
—subscapular, 173, 176
—suprapatellar, 231, 234
—triceps, 182
—ulnar, 190

Caecum, 104
Calcaneus, 245
Calcitonin, 302
Calyx, renal, 121

Canal, alimentary, 29, 95
—anal, 139, 148
—anorectal, 27
—atrioventricular, 60
—carotid, 265, 269
—central, 374
—condylar, 270, 314
—epididymis, 90
—for facial nerve, 309
—femoral, 223
—hypoglossal, 270, 314
—incisive (*see* Foramen, incisive)
—inguinal, 89
—mandibular, 318
—neurenteric, 21
—notochordal, 21
—optic, 277
—palatine, greater, 283
—pericardioperitoneal, 24, 29
—pterygoid, 320
—pudendal, 152
—pyloric, 95
—sacral, 134
—semicircular, 310
—subsartorial, 224, 225
—vertebral, 38
Canaliculi, bile, 116
—lacrimal, 281
Cancer, 2
Cap of duodenum, 96, 99
Capillaries, 14
Capitate, 198
Capitulum, 170
Capsule, Bowman's, 124
—internal, 352
—of kidney, 123
—of lens, 277
—of liver, 115
—of lymph node, 15
—of prostate, 149
—of spleen, 119
—of thyroid, 328
—of tonsil, 300
Cardiac notch of left lung, 75
Carina, 69, 78
Cardiogenic mesoderm, 20
Carpus, 198
Cartilage, 4
—costal, 44
—elastic, 5
—fibrocartilage, 5
—hyaline, 4, 303
—of larynx, arytenoid, 304
——cricoid, 304
——epiglottic, 304
——thyroid, 303
—Meckel's, 267
—nasal, 282
—semilunar, of knee (*see* Menisci of knee)
—septal, 275, 283
—tracheal, 329

Cartilage (*continued*)
—yellow (elastic), 5, 303
Caruncula lacrimalis, 280
Cauda equina, 375
Caudal, definition of, 16
Caudate lobe of liver, 113
—nucleus, 353
—process, of liver, 113
Cavity, abdominal, 86, 91
—amniotic, 19, 22
—coelomic, extra-embryonic, 19
——intra-embryonic, 24
—cranial, 312
—exocoelomic, 19
—glenoid, 167
—medullary, 5
—nasal, 282
—oral, 285
—orbital, 276
—pelvic, 136
—pericardial, 20, 24
—peritoneal, 26
—pleural, 24, 52
—thoracic, 52
—tympanic, 308
—ventricular, 359
C-cells, 302
Cell, 2
—astrocyte, 12
—Betz, 351
—of blood, 14
—chondrocyte, 4
—chromaffin, 124
—ependymal, 12
—fat, 4
—fibroblast, 4
—germ, 27, 91, 148
—goblet, 3, 112
—granular, 351, 372
—of lymph, 14, 15
—macrophage, 4
—mast, 4
—mastoid air, 310
—microglia, 12
—mobile, 16
—monocyte, 14, 15
—neuron, 11, 344
—oligodendroglia, 11, 12
—osteoblast, 5
—osteoclast, 8
—osteocyte, 5
—oxyntic, 98
—perikaryon, 11
—plasma, 4
—platelets, 14
—Purkinje, 372
—pyramidal, 351
—Schwann, 11
—thymocyte, 69
Cementum, 286
Central nervous system, 11, 344

Centre, cortical (*see* Cortex)
—ossification, 7, 8
Centrosome, 2
Cerebellum, 344, 346, 372
Cerebral localisation, 379
Cerebrospinal fluid, 374
Cerebrum, 349
Cervix of uterus, 144
Chain, circular lymph, 341
—deep cervical lymph, 290, 329, 330, 341
—sympathetic (*see* Trunk, sympathetic)
Chamber, anterior, of eye, 277
—posterior, of eye, 277
Chewing, 296
Chiasma, optic, 314, 357
Cholecystogram, 116, 118
Choanae (*see* Aperture, posterior nasal)
Chondrocranium, 266
Chorda tympani, 265, 290, 292, 296, 318, 320
Chorion, 20
Choroid of eye, 277
Choroid plexus, 12, 347, 386
——of fourth ventricle, 374
——of lateral ventricle, 347, 362
——of third ventricle, 347, 362
Choroidal fissure, 347, 362
Chromosomes, 2, 19
Ciliary body, 277
—ganglion, 314, 340
Circular lymph chain, 341
Circulation, cerebrospinal fluid, 387
—portal, 15, 110, 358
Circulatory system, 14
——fetal, 61
Circulus arteriosus, 392
Circumduction, definition of, 16
Cistern, cerebellomedullary, 386
—chyli, 82, 162
—magna, 386
—interpeduncular, 386
—lumbar, 386
—pontine, 386
—subarachnoid, 386
Claustrum, 354
Clavicle, 166
Clefts, exocoelomic, 19
—intratonsillar, 300
—pharyngeal, 31, 301
—pudendal, 148
Clitoris, 27, 155
Cloaca, 26, 30, 141, 143
Cloacal eminence, 27
—membrane, 22
—swelling, 27
Coccyx, 133
Cochlea, 310
—duct, 310
Coelome, extra-embryonic, 19
—intra-embryonic, 24
Colliculus facialis, 374

Colliculus (*continued*)
—inferior, 365, 366
—superior, 359, 365
Colon, ascending, 104
—descending, 104
—pelvic (*see* Colon, sigmoid)
—sigmoid, 105
—transverse, 104
Column, anal, 140
—branchial, 346
—of fornix, 358
—motor, 346
—renal, 123
—sensory, 346
—somatic, 346
—of spinal cord, anterior, 346, 375, 376
———lateral, 346, 375, 376
———posterior, 346, 375, 376
—vertebral, 33, 37
—visceral, 346
Commissure, anterior, 347, 352, 355
——white, 375
—corpus callosum, 347, 352
—of fornix, 347, 352
—habenular, 352, 358
—hippocampal (*see* Commissure of fornix)
—optic (*see* Chiasma, optic)
—posterior, 352, 359
Concha, nasal, inferior, 271, 283
——middle, 271, 283
——superior, 271, 283
Conducting system of heart, 58
Condyle of femur, 214
—of mandible, 295
—of tibia, 227
—occipital, 270
Cone of retina, 277, 279
—of light, 308
Confluence of sinuses, 394
Conjugate, 136
Conjunctiva, 281
Connective tissue, 4
Connexus interthalamic, 356
Conus elasticus, 304
Copula, 290
Cord of brachial plexus, 179
—false vocal, 305
—nephrogenic, 26
—spermatic, 89
—spinal, 11
—tendinous, 53
—umbilical, 20
—vocal, 304
Cornea, 277
Cornu, hyoid, 272
—sacral, 134
—thyroid, 303
Corona radiata, 352
Corpora quadrigemina (*see* Colliculus)
Corpus callosum, 347, 352
—cavernosum, 153

—luteum, 148
—mamillare, 357
—spongiosum, 153
—striatum, 353
—trapezoideum, 367
Corpuscles, Hassall's, 69
Cortex, agranular, 351
—allocortex, 347
—auditory, 351, 382
—cerebellar, 344, 372
—cerebral, 344, 349, 351
—hippocampal, 347
—isocortex, 347, 351
—of lymph node, 15
—motor, 350, 351, 382
—neocortex (*see* Cortex, isocortex)
—olfactory, 381
—prepiriform, 355, 381
—piriform, 347, 355
—renal, 123
—sensorimotor, 351, 379
—somatosensory, 380
—striate, 351, 382
—suprarenal, 124
—of thymus, 69
—vestibular, 382
—visual, 352, 379, 382
Costal cartilages, 44
Cotyledon, 32
Cranial, definition of, 16
—fossae, 312
—nerves, 314, 344
Craniotomy, 335
Crest, iliac, 131
——tubercle of, 131
—infratemporal, 263
—intertrochanteric, 213
—neural, 31, 124
—obturator, 133
—pubic, 133
—sacral, median, 134
—supinator, 185
—supramastoid, 263
—trochanteric (*see* Crest, intertrochanteric)
—urethral, 150, 155
Cricoid cartilage, 304
Crista galli, 271, 312
—terminalis, 53
Cristae, 311
Crown-heel length, 32
Crown-rump length, 23
Crus of clitoris, 155
—of diaphragm, 49
—of fornix, 355
—of inguinal ligament, 87
—of penis, 153
Cubital fossa, 182, 186
Cuboid bone, 246
Cumulus oophorus, 148
Cuneiform bones, 246
Cup, optic (*see* Disc, optic)

Curvature, gastric, greater, 95
——lesser, 95
—of vertebral column, 37
Cushions, endocardial, 61
Cusps of heart (*see* Valvules)
Cutaneous nerve supply, of head and neck, 339
———of lower limb, 208
———of upper limb, 258
Cyst, exocoelomic, 19
Cytoplasm, 2
Cytotrophoblast, 20

Decidua basalis, 20, 32
—capsularis, 20, 32
—parietalis, 20, 32
Decidual reaction, 20, 32
Deciduous teeth, 286
Decussation of cerebellar peduncle, superior, 366
—lemniscal, 370
—motor, 370
—optic (*see* Chiasma, optic)
—of pyramids, 370
—sensory, 370
—tegmental, dorsal, 366
——ventral, 366
—trochlear, 364
Defaecation, 141
Definitive yolk sac, 19
Degenerative arterial disease, 129
Deglutition, 302
Dendrites, 11, 344
Dens, 35
Dentate ligament, 386
—nucleus, 372
Dentine, 286
Dentition, 286
Dermatome, 23
Dermamyotome, 23
Development (*see* Chap. 2 and also specific structure or organ)
—of face, 274
—of forebrain, 346
—of gut and derivation, 30, 301
—of heart and pericardium, 27, 59
—of long bone, 8
—of peritoneum, 26, 94
—of pharynx, 301
—of central nervous system, 345, 346
—of skull, 266, 267
—of urogenital system, 26
Dermis, 3
Diaphragm, 26, 42, 49
—mouth, 290
—pelvic, 138
—urogenital, 152
Diaphragma sellae, 384
Diaphysis, 8
Diencephalon, 344, 356
Digits, 31

Diploë, 5
Disc, embryonic, 20
—intra-articular, 9, 170, 171, 185, 187, 200, 295
—intervertebral, 9, 36
—optic, 277
—triangular, 185
Dislocation, 10
—ankle, 248
—hip, 216
—mandible, 296
—shoulder, 173
Diverticulum, respiratory, 29, 306
—tracheobronchial, 29
Divisions of brachial plexus, 179
Dome of diaphragm, 49, 76
—of pleura, 72
Dominence, cerebral, 379
Dorsal, definition of, 16
Dorsal expansion of fingers, 191
——of toes, 236
Dorsiflexion of foot, 16, 235, 250
Dorsum sellae, 268
Drum, ear, 308
Duct, alveolar, 80
—bile, 117
—cochlear, 310
—collecting, 123
—cystic, 117
—efferent, of testis, 91
—ejaculatory, 150
—endolymphatic, 311
—epididymis (*see* Canal, epididymis)
—frontonasal, 283, 284
—hepatic, common, 117
——left, 116, 117
——right, 116, 117
—interlobular, 116
—lacrimal, 281
—lactiferous, 51
—lymphatic, right, 66, 82, 337
—mesonephric, 26, 91
—Müllerian (*see* Duct, paramesonephric)
—nasolacrimal, 271, 277, 282, 283
—pancreatic, 120
——accessory, 120
—paramesonephric, 26, 146
—parotid, 291
—renal, 123
—semicircular, 311
—sublingual, 294
—submandibular, 293
—thoracic, 66, 82, 337
—thyroglossal, 329
—vitelline, 22
—vitello-intestinal, 24
—Wolffian (*see* Duct, mesonephric)
Ductus arteriosus, 61, 64, 301
—deferens, 90, 150
—reuniens, 311
—venosus, 61

Duodenum, 29, 98
Dura mater, cerebral, 384
— —spinal, 385

Ear, drum, 308
—external, 308
—internal, 310
—middle, 308
Ectoderm, 19, 292, 301
Ectodermal germ layer, 19
Ejaculation, 151
Ejaculatory duct, 150
Elbow, 184
Embolus, 15, 256
Embryoblast, 19
Embryology (see Chap 2, and also specific
        structure or organ)
Embryonic period, 22
Eminence, arcuate, 313
—cloacal, 27
—frontal (see Tuberosity, frontal)
—hypothenar, 204
—iliopubic, 131, 133
—parietal (see Tuberosity, parietal)
—thenar, 204
—tibial (see Area, intercondylar)
Enamel, 286
Encephalogram, 360
Endocardial cushions, 61
Endocardium, 59
Endoderm, 19, 29, 294, 301
Endodermal germ layer, 19, 29
Endolymph, 310
Endometrium, 20, 146
Endomysium, 10
Endoplasmic reticulum, 2
Endoscopy, 71
Endothelium, 3
Enema, 16, 102
Enlargement, cervical, 375
—lumbar, 375
Ependyma, 12, 345
Epicardium, 59
Epicondyle, femoral, 214
—humeral, 170
Epicranial aponeurosis, 272
Epidermis, 3
Epididymis, 90, 150
Epigastrium, 86
Epiglottis, 303
Epimere, 23
Epimysium, 10
Epiphyseal plates, 8
Epiphysis, 8
—slipped, 8, 185
Epithalamus, 358
Epithelium, 2
—germinal, 27, 91, 148
—olfactory, 282, 284
Epitympanic recess, 309
Ethmoid bone, 271

Eversion of foot, 249
Exocoelomic cavity, 19
—cleft, 18
Expansion, extensor, of fingers, 191
— —of toes, 236
Expiration, 46, 49, 50
Extension, definition of, 16
Extra-embryonic coelome, 19
—mesoderm, 19
—somatopleure, 19
—splanchnopleure, 19
Extrahepatic biliary system, 116
Extrapyramidal system, 353, 383
Extravasation of urine, 153
Eyeball, 277
Eyelashes, 281
Eyelids, 280

Face, 272
Facet, articular, 35
—costal, 35
—patellar, 214
Fallopian tube (see Tube, uterine)
Falx cerebri, 349, 384
—inguinal, 87
Fascia, 4
—abdominal, 86
—axillary, 207, 324
—bulbar, 153, 278
—carotid sheath, 324
—cervical, 145, 291, 324
—clavipectoral, 178, 207
—cremasteric, 89
—cribriform, 223
—deep, of lower limb, 254
— —of upper limb, 207
—iliac, 137
—lata, 87, 223, 254
—lumbar (see Fascia, thoracolumbar)
—orbital (see Fascia, bulbar)
—palmar, 189, 203, 207
—of parotid gland, 291
—pelvic, 139, 143
—perineal, 137, 152, 153
—perirenal, 121
—pharyngobasilar, 298
—plantar, 251
—popliteal, 235
—pretracheal, 324, 328
—prevertebral, 324
—prostatic, 149
—psoas, 49, 126
—rectovesical, 150
—renal, 121
—sheath of eyeball, 153, 278
— —of rectus abdominis, 86
—spermatic, external, 90
— —internal, 89
—temporal, 263, 297
—thoracolumbar, 126, 175
—transversalis, 87, 88, 121

Fasciculus, cuneatus, 376
—dorsolateral, 376
—gracilis, 376
—medial longitudinal, 359, 366, 368, 370
—proprius, 376
Fat pads, elbow, 186
——knee, 233
——orbital, 276
——perirenal, 121
Fauces, pillars (arches) of, 285
Femur, 213
Fenestra cochleae, 309
—vestibuli, 309
Fetal circulation, 61
—period, 32
Fetus, 32
Fibres, arcuate, internal, 370
—afferent, cerebellar, 372
——cerebral, 357
—association, 352
—cerebellar, 372
—collagen, 4
—commissural, 347, 352
—corticonuclear, 365
—corticopontine, 366
—corticospinal, 365
—efferent, cerebellar, 373
——cerebral, 382
—elastic, 4
—extrapyramidal, 364, 383
—frontopontine, 365
—intersegmental, 378
—intrasegmental, 378
—of medulla, 370
—of midbrain, 365
—olivary, 373
—of pons, 368
—pontocerebellar, 366
—projection, 347, 352
—Purkinje, 59
—pyramidal, 365, 382
—reticular, 4
—spinal, 373
—temporopontine, 365
—tissue, 4
—vestibular, 373
—zonular, 277
Fibroblast, 4
Fibrocartilage, 5, 170
Fibula, 228
Filum terminale, 375
Fimbria of brain, 355
—of ovary, 146
Fissura prima, 372
Fissure (see also Sulcus)
—anterior median, 369, 375
—cerebellar, 372
—cerebral (see Sulcus, cerebral)
—choroidal, 347, 362
—for ligamentum teres, 113
—for ligamentum venosum, 92, 113

—of liver, 113
—of lungs, 75
—medial longitudinal, 349
—oval, 285
—orbital, inferior, 263, 277
——superior, 277, 312
—palpebral, 280
—petrosquamous, 265
—petrotympanic, 265, 296
—portal (see Porta hepatis)
—posterolateral, 372
—primary, of cerebellum, 372
—pterygomaxillary, 263
—squamotympanic, 265, 295
—transverse, 349, 356
Flexion, definition of, 16
Flexure, duodenojejunal, 101
—cervical, 345
—colic, left (splenic), 102, 104
——right (hepatic), 102, 104
—mesencephalic, 345
—pontine, 345
Flocculus, 372
Floor of fourth ventricle, 374
—of mouth, 290
—of pelvis, 138
Fluid, cerebrospinal, 374
—lacrimal, 281
—synovial, 9
Foetus (see Fetus)
Fold, alar, 231
—anal, 27
—ary-epiglottic, 299
—false vocal, 305
—glosso-epiglottic, 288
—head, 22
—infrapatellar, synovial, 231
—infundibulopelvic (see Ligament, suspensory)
—medial genital, 27
—palatoglossal (see Arch, palatoglossal)
—palatopharyngeal (see Arch, palatopharyngeal)
—semilunar, 281
—spiral, 117
—sublingual, 285
—tail, 22
—urethral, 27
—urorectal, 26
—vestibular, 305
—vocal, 304
Follicles, lymphoid, 15
—ovarian, 148
Folia, 372
Fontanelles, anterior, 262
—posterior, 263
Foot, 244
Footplate (stapes), 309
Foramen caecum (tongue), 288, 290
—carotid (see Canal, carotid)
—condylar, 314

Foramen (*continued*)
—epiploic, 93
—of fourth ventricle, 374, 387
—hypoglossal, 265
—incisive, 264, 283, 287
—infra-orbital, 263, 267
—interventricular, 62, 347, 359
—intervertebral, 33
—jugular, 265, 313
—lacerum, 265, 312
—magnum, 265, 269, 313
—mandibular, 266, 318
—mastoid, 314
—mental, 263, 266
—obturator, 131, 133, 213
—optic (*see* Canal, optic)
—ovale, of heart, 61
— —of skull, 264, 313
—palatine, greater, 264, 283, 287
— —lesser, 264, 287
—parietal emissary, 395
—rotundum, 313
—sacral, 133
—sphenopalatine, 271, 283
—spinosum, 264, 313
—stylomastoid, 265, 269, 319
—supra-orbital, 263
—transversarium, 34
—vertebral, 33
Forceps major, 352
—minor, 352
Forearm, 184
Forebrain, 344, 349
Foregut, 29
Formatio reticularis, 366, 377
Fornix of brain, 355, 358
—of conjunctiva, 281
—of vagina, 144, 148
Fossa, acetabular, 131, 213
—coronoid, 169, 186
—cranial, anterior, 312
— —middle, 312
— —posterior, 313
—cubital, 182, 186
—digastric, 267
—digital (*see* Fossa, malleolar)
—duodenal, 101
—glenoid (*see* Fossa, mandibular)
—hypophyseal, 268, 312
—iliac, 131
—infraspinous, 167, 176
—infratemporal, 263, 297
—ischiorectal, 152
—intrabulbar, 155
—jugular, 269
—lacrimal, 281
—mandibular, 264, 269
—malleolar, 228
—navicular, 155
—olecranon, 169, 186
—ovalis, of heart, 53

—peritoneal, 94
—piriform, 299
—pituitary (hypophyseal), 268, 312
—popliteal, 235
—pterygoid, 264
—pterygopalatine, 263, 283
—radial, 169
—rectovesical, 94
—retromolar, 285
—rhomboid (*see* Floor of fourth ventricle)
—sublingual, 266
—submandibular, 266
—supraspinous, 167, 176
—temporal, 263
Fovea centralis, 277
—of head of femur, 213, 216
—inferior, 374
Fracture, 5
Frenulum of penis, 153
—of tongue, 285, 288
Frontal bone, 270
Fundus of stomach, 95
—of uterus, 144
Funiculus, anterior, 375
—lateral, 375
—posterior, 375

Galea aponeurotica (*see* Epicranial aponeurosis)
Gall bladder, 117
Ganglion, 344
—aortic, 81
—autonomic, 12
—basal (*see* Nucleus, basal)
—cervical, 339
—ciliary, 314, 340
—cochlear, 312, 320
—coeliac, 82
—cranial, parasympathetic, 340
—dorsal root, 12, 48
—facial (geniculate), 319
—glossopharyngeal, 320
—otic, 292, 318, 321, 341
—parasympathetic, 340
—pelvic autonomic, 163
—posterior root (*see* Ganglion, dorsal r
—pterygopalatine, 281, 299, 316, 317
    340
—sphenopalatine (*see* Ganglion, p
    palatine)
—spiral, 320
—stellate, 81, 340
—submandibular, 292, 318, 340
—sympathetic, cervical, 339
— —lumbar, 163
— —pelvic, 163
— —sacral, 163
— —thoracic, 81
—trigeminal (semilunar), 269, 3
—vagus, 321
—vestibular, 312, 320

Gastrojejunostomy, 164
Gastroscope, 98
Gelatinous substance, 375
Geniculate body, lateral, 356, 357
—medial, 356, 357
Genital tubercle, 27
Genu of corpus callosum, 352
—of internal capsule, 352
Germ disc, 19
—layers, 19, 20, 29, 31
Girdle, pectoral, 8, 166
—pelvic, 8, 135, 212
Gland, 3
—adrenal (*see* Gland, suprarenal)
—apocrine, 4
—Brunner's (*see* Gland, duodenal)
—bulbo-urethral, 155
—cardiac, 98
—ceruminous, 308
—duodenal, 101
—endocrine, 3
—epicrine, 4
—exocrine, 3
—gastric, 98
—holocrine, 4
—hypophysis cerebri, 31, 358
—islets of Langerhans, 120
—lacrimal, 281, 316, 340
—liver, 113
—lymph (*see* Lymph nodes)
—mammary, 4, 50
—Meibomian (*see* Gland, tarsal)
—mesocrine, 4
—mucous, 112
—oesophageal, 330
—ovary, 147
—of palate, 288
—pancreas, 119
—parathyroid, 329
—parotid, 291, 318, 341
—pineal (*see* Pineal body)
—pituitary (*see* Hypophysis cerebri)
—prostate, 27
—pyloric, 98
—salivary, 291
—sebaceous, 4
—sublingual, 294, 341
—submandibular, 293, 341
—suprarenal, 124
—sweat, 3
—tarsal, 281
—testis, 90
—thymus, 69
—thyroid, 329
—vestibular, greater, 155
Glans clitoris, 27, 155
—penis, 27, 153
Globus pallidus, 354
Glomerulus, 123
Golgi apparatus, 2
Granulations, arachnoid, 312, 386

Gravity, centre of, 212, 259
Grey matter (*see* Cortex, cerebellar and
     Cortex, cerebral)
——horns of, spinal cord, 375
——peri-aqueductal, 364
Grips, 206
Groove, atrioventricular (*see* Sulcus,
     coronary)
—carotid, 312, 336
—costal, 43
—of cuboid, 246
—deltopectoral, 174
—intertubercular, 169, 174
—interventricular, 52, 55
—meningeal, 312
—neural, 345
—obturator, 127, 132, 159, 213
—optic, 268, 312
—pharyngeal, 29
—radial, 169, 182
—subclavian, 44
—urethral, 155
Gubernaculum of ovary, 148
—of testis, 91
Gums, 286
Gutter, paracolic, left, 105
——right, 104, 115
—paravertebral, 75
Gyrus, cingulate, 350
—frontal, 350
— h i p p o c a m p a l   (*see*   G y r u s,
     parahippocampal)
—insula, 350
—parahippocampal, 350
—paraterminal, 355
—postcentral, 350
—precentral, 350
—rectus, 351
—temporal, 350

Haemorrhage, cerebral, 388
—extradural, 325
—oesophageal, 111
—rectal, 111, 140
Haemorrhoids, 140
Haemothorax, 48
Hamate bone, 198
Hamulus, pterygoid, 264, 288
Hand, 198
Handedness, 379
Head, 262
—of femur, 213
—of fibula, 228
—of humerus, 167
—of pancreas, 119
—of radius, 184
—of rib, 43
—of talus, 245
—of ulna, 185
Head fold, 22
—process, 21

Heart, 28, 52
Heel, 251
Heel strike, 259
Helicotrema, 310
Hemisphere, cerebellar, 372
—cerebral, 349
Henson's node. 20
Hepatic portal system, 110
Hernia, diaphragmatic, 95
—femoral, 223
—hiatus, 95
—inguinal, 90
Heuser's membrane, 19
Hiatus hernia, 95
—sacral, 134
—semilunaris, 283
Hillock, axon, 11
Hilus of kidney, 121
—of liver, 113
—of lung, 75
—of lymph node, 15
—of spleen, 118, 120
Hindbrain, 344
Hindgut, 30
Hip bone, 131, 212
Hippocampus, 347, 355
Hook of hamate, 198
Horn, grey, anterior, 346, 375
——lateral, 346, 375
——posterior, 346, 375
—of hyoid, greater, 272
——lesser, 272
—of lateral ventricle, 359
—of thyroid, superior, 303
——inferior, 303
—see also Cornu
Humerus, 167
Humor, aqueous, 277
—vitreous (see Body, vitreous)
Hydrocephalus, 387
Hymen, 148
Hypophysis cerebri, 31, 358
Hyoid bone, 272
Hypochondrium, 86
Hypomere, 23
Hypoparathyroidism, 329
Hypothalamus, 357
Hysterosalpingogram, 147

Ileum, 101
Ilium, 131
Incisions, abdominal, 88
—thoracic, 48
Incisura angularis (see Notch, angular)
Incus, 309
Infarction, 15
—cardiac, 57
—cerebral, 388
Inferior, definition of, 16
Inflammation, 15

Information, sources of, on central nervous
    system, 347
Infundibulum, of hypophysis cerebri, 347,
    357
—of right ventricle, 53
—of uterine tube, 146
Infusions, arm veins, 207
Inguinal canal, 89
—falx, 87
—ligament, 87
Inlet, of pelvis, 136
—of thorax, 42
Inner cell mass, 19
Innominate bone (see Hip bone)
Inspiration, 46, 49, 50
Insula, 350
Intercostal space, 46
Intermediate cell mass, 26
Intermittent claudication, 225
Internal capsule, 352
Intervertebral disc, 36, 38
Intervillous space, 32
Intestine, large, 101
—small, 98
Intra-articular disc, 9
Intra-embryonic coelome, 24
—mesoderm, 23
Inversion of foot, 249
Iris, 277
Ischaemia, 15, 387
Ischium, 132
Islets (of Langerhans), 120
Isocortex, 347, 351
Isthmus, fauceal, 285, 299, 302
—oropharyngeal (see Isthmus, fauceal)
—pharyngeal, 288, 302
—of thyroid gland, 328
—of uterine tube, 146

Jejunum, 101
Joint, acromioclavicular, 171
—ankle, 247
—atlanto-axial, 37
—atlanto-occipital, 37
—calcaneocuboid, 249
—carpometacarpal, 201
—costochondral, 45
—costotransverse, 45
—costovertebral, 45
—crico-arytenoid, 304
—cricothyroid, 304
—elbow, 186
—hip, 215
—intercarpal, 200
—interphalangeal, of foot, 249
——of hand, 202
—intertarsal, 248
—intervertebral, 36
—knee, 228
—mandibular (see Joint, temporomandibu-
    lar)

Joint (*continued*)
—manubriosternal, 45
—metacarpophalangeal, 202
—metatarsophalangeal, 249
—midcarpal, 200
—midtarsal, 248
—of pelvis, 135, 136
—radiocarpal (wrist), 200
—radioulnar, distal, 187
——proximal, 187
—of ribs, 45
—sacrococcygeal, 135
—sacro-iliac, 135
—shoulder, 171, 177
—sternoclavicular, 170
—of sternum, 45
—subtalar, 246
—symphysis pubis, 136
—talocalcaneal, posterior, 246
—talocalcaneonavicular, 246
—tarsometatarsal, 249
—temporomandibular, 295
—of thoracic cage, 45
—tibiofibular, inferior, 235
——superior, 235
—vertebral, 36
—wrist, 200
—xiphisternal, 45
Joints, bony, 9
—cartilaginous, 9
—classification of, 9
—fibrous, 9
—movement of, 9
—stability of, 10
—synovial, 9

Karyoplasm, 2
Kidney, 121
Knot, primitive, 20

Labia majora, 27, 155
—minora, 27, 155
Labioscrotal swelling, 27
Labrum, acetabular, 215
—glenoidal, 171
Labyrinth, bony, 310
—ethmoidal, 271, 283
—membranous, 310
Lacrimal apparatus, 281
—bone, 271
Lactation, 51
Lambda, 263
Lamina, alar, 346
—basal, 346
—cricoid, 304
—dental, 287
—medullary, internal, 356
—spiral, 310
—terminalis, 346, 356
—thalamic, 356
—thyroid, 303

—vertebral, 33
Laryngeal prominence, 303
—sinus, 305
Laryngopharynx, 298
Larynx, 303
Lateral, definition of, 16
—geniculate body, 356, 357
—plate mesoderm, 23
Layer, cortical, cerebellar, 372
——cerebral, 357
—ectodermal germ, 19, 31
—endodermal germ, 19, 29
—ependymal, 345
—granular, 351, 372
—mantle, 345
—marginal, 345
—mesodermal germ, 20, 23
—molecular, 372
—Purkinje, 372
Lemniscus, lateral, 357, 365, 367
—medial, 365, 370
—spinal, 365, 377
—trigeminal, 365, 367
Lesion, 2
Lens, 31, 277
Ligament, 4
—acromioclavicular, 171
—alar, 37
—annular, 185, 187
—apical, 37
—arcuate, lateral, 44, 49, 126
——medial, 49, 126
—ary-epiglottic, 305
—bifurcated, 249
—of bladder, 142, 143
—broad, 94, 144, 148
—calcaneofibular, 247
—calcaneonavicular (spring), 249, 251
—cervical, lateral (cardinal), 145
—check, of axis (alar), 37
——of eyeball, 278
—collateral, of elbow, 186
——of finger, 202
——of knee, 230
——of toe, 249
——of wrist, 200
—conus elasticus, 304
—coracoclavicular, 167, 171
—coracohumeral, 171
—coronary, of knee, 229
——of liver, 92, 114
—costoclavicular, 167, 170
—costotransverse, 45
—cricothyroid, 304
—cruciate, of knee, 231
——atlanto-occipital, 37
—deep transverse, of palm, 202, 203
——of sole, 249
—deltoid, 247
—falciform, 30, 92, 94, 113
—of head of femur, 213, 216

Ligament (*continued*)
—gastrolienal (*see* Ligament, gastrosplenic)
—gastrosplenic, 92, 118
—glenohumeral, 171
—iliofemoral, 135, 215
—iliolumbar, 135
—infundibulopelvic (*see* Ligament, suspensary of ovary)
—inguinal, 87, 223
— —pectineal part of, 87
—interclavicular, 170
—interosseous, tibiofibular, 228
— —talocalcaneal, 248
— —sacro-iliac, 134
—interspinous, 37
—intertransverse, 37
—ischiofemoral, 216
—lacunar, 87
—lateral, of ankle, 247
— —of temporomandibular joint, 295
— —of uterus (cardinal), 145
—lienorenal, 92, 118
—of liver, 92
—longitudinal, anterior, 37, 324
— —posterior, 37
—medial, of ankle (deltoid), 247
—oblique popliteal, 229
—of ovary, 144, 147, 148
—palmar, deep transverse, 202
— —of finger, 202
— —of wrist, 200
—palpebral, 274, 281
—patellar, 223, 230
—pectineal, part of inguinal, 87
—phrenicocolic, 105, 118
—plantar, deep transverse, 249, 251
— —long, 249, 251
— —short, 249, 251
—pterygomandibular (*see* Raphé, pterygomandibular)
—pubocervical, 143, 145
—pubofemoral, 216
—puboprostatic, 143, 149
—pubovesical, 143, 145
—pulmonary, 75
—round, of liver, 114
— —of uterus, 144, 145, 148
—sacro-iliac, 135
—sacrospinous, 135, 213
—sacrotuberous, 135, 213
—sphenomandibular, 264, 295, 318
—spring (*see* Ligament, calcaneonavicular)
—sternoclavicular, 170
—stylohyoid, 272, 298, 301
—stylomandibular, 291, 295
—supraspinous, 37
—suspensory, of eyeball, 278
— —of lens, 277
— —of ovary, 144
— —of penis, 153
—talocalcaneal, interosseous, 248

—talofibular, anterior, 247
— —posterior, 247
—temporomandibular (*see* Ligament, lateral)
—teres, of femur, 213, 216
— —of liver, 114
—thyrohyoid, 305
—tibiofibular, inferior, 235
— —interosseous, 235
— —superior, 235
— —transverse, 247
—transverse, of acetabulum, 215
— —of atlas, 35, 37
— —deep, of palm, 202
— — —of sole, 249
— —humeral, 171
— —tibiofibular, 247
—triangular, of liver, left, 92, 115
— —right, 115
—umbilical, median, 27, 142
—uterine, lateral (cardinal), 145
—uterosacral, 145
—of uterus, 145
—vestibular, 305
—vocal, 304
Ligamentum arteriosum, 64
—denticulatum, 386
—flavum, 37
—nuchae, 34, 175, 324, 327
—teres, 114
—venosum, 92
Limbic system, 355
Limbs, lower, 211
—upper, 165
Limbus ovalis, 53
Line, arcuate, of abdomen, 88
— —of pelvis, 131, 133
—epiphyseal (*see* Plate, epiphyseal)
—gluteal, 212
—intertubercular (*see* Line, transtubercular)
—intertrochanteric, 213
—lateral, 86
—midaxillary, 73
—midclavicular, 73
—mylohyoid, 266
—nuchal, inferior, 265, 269
— —superior, 175, 265, 269
—oblique, of radius, 185
— —of thyroid cartilage, 303
— —of tibia, 228
—paravertebral, 73
—pectineal, 133
—subcostal, 86
—soleal, of tibia, 228
—supracondylar, 213
—supracristal, 38
—temporal, 263
—transpyloric, 86
—transtubercular, 86
—trochanteric (*see* Line intertrochanteric)
—of weight, 212, 234

Linea alba, 88
—aspera, 213
Lingual swellings, lateral, 290
Lingula of lung, 75
—of mandible, 266
Lips, 273
Liver, 113
Lobe, caudate, 113
—of cerebellum, 372
—of cerebrum, 349
—flocculonodular, 372
—of liver, 113
—of lung, 75
—of pituitary, 358
—of prostate, 149
—quadrate, 113
—thyroid, 329
Lobule of ear, 308
—of liver, 115
—paracentral, 350
Locking of knee joint, 233
Loop of Henle, 123
Lower limb, 211
Lumbar puncture, 38, 362, 384
Lunate bone, 198
Lungs, 73
Lung bud, 29, 80
Lymph, 15
—follicles, aggregated, 15, 101, 104, 112
Lymph drainage (see also specific structure)
——of abdomen and pelvis, 162
——of breast, 50, 209
——of gut, 111, 140
——of head and neck, 341
——of limbs, lower, 256
———upper, 209
——of mammary gland, 50, 209
——of thorax, 82
——of tongue, 290
Lymph nodes, 15
——abdominal, 111
——aortic, 111, 162
——apical, 209
——axillary, 51, 209
——bronchopulmonary, 80
——central, 209
——cervical, deep, 290, 329, 330, 341
———superficial, 342
——circular chain of, 341
——coeliac, 98, 111, 119, 120, 330
——cubital, 209
——diaphragmatic, 82
——hepatic, 115
——hilar, 80
——iliac, common, 162
———external, 162, 257
———internal, 162
——infraclavicular, 209
——inguinal, deep, 257
———superficial, lower, 257
————upper, 162, 256

——intercostal, 82
——jugular, anterior, 342
———external, 342
———internal, 341
——jugulodigastric, 290, 342
——jugulo-omohyoid, 290, 342
——lateral axillary, 209
——mediastinal, anterior, 82, 162
———posterior, 82, 330
——mesenteric, inferior, 111
———superior, 111
——occipital, 341
——para-aortic, 162
——parasternal, 82
——paratracheal, 329, 342
——parotid, deep, 341
———superficial, 291, 341
——pectoral, 51, 209
——popliteal, 257
——pre-aortic, 98, 108, 111, 162
——pre-auricular (see Lymph node, parotid, superficial)
——pretracheal, 329, 342
——retro-auricular, 341
——retropharyngeal, 284, 290, 341
——sacral, 162
——scapular (see Lymph node, subscapular)
——submandibular, 284, 290, 341
——submental, 290, 341
——subscapular, 209
——supraclavicular, 342
——suprapancreatic, 119, 120
——supratrochlear (see Lymph node, [cubital]
——thoracic, 82
——tracheobronchial, 80, 82, 330, 342
——trochlear, 209
Lymph trunk, bronchomediastinal, 82
——cisterna chyli, 162
——intestinal, 162
——jugular, 342
——lumbar, 162
——mediastinal, 80
——right, 83
——subclavian, 209
——thoracic, 82, 209
Lymphangiogram, 161, 256
Lymphoedema, 15, 209, 257

Macula of eyeball, 277, 379
—of saccule, 311
—of utricle, 311
Malignant disease, 2
Malleolus of fibula, 228
—of tibia, 228
Malleus, 309
Mammary gland, 50
Mamillary body, 357
Mandible, 266
Manubrium, 42
Margin, infra-orbital, 263
—supra-orbital, 263

Marrow, bone, 14
Mass, lateral, of atlas, 34
——of sacrum, 133
Massa intermedia (see Connexus inter-
    thalamic)
Mastication, 296
Mastoid air cells, 310
—antrum, 310
—process, 264, 269
Matter, grey (see Cortex, cerebellar, and
    Cortex, cerebral)
——peri-aqueductal, 364
——of spinal cord, 375
—white, 344
Maxilla, 267
Meatus, acoustic, external, 31, 263, 269, 308
——internal, 269, 313
—of nose, inferior, 283
——middle, 283
——superior, 283
Medial, definition of, 16
—geniculate body, 356, 357
—genital fold, 27
Media, contrast, 16
Median, definition of, 16
Mediastinum of testis, 91
—of thorax, 52
Medulla of bone, 5
—of kidney, 123
—of lymph node, 15
—oblongata, 344, 368
—of suprarenal, 124
—of thymus, 69
Medullary velum, inferior, 368, 374
——superior, 374
Membrane, anal, 22, 27, 31
—ary-epiglottic, 305
—atlanto-occipital, anterior, 37
——posterior, 34, 37, 327
—basilar, 311
—buccopharyngeal, 20, 29, 31
—cloacal, 22, 31
—conus elasticus, 304
—cricothyroid, 304
—Heuser's, 19
—intercostal, external (anterior), 46
——internal (posterior), 46
—interosseous, of forearm, 187
——of leg, 235
—mucous, 3
—obturator, 138, 213
—perineal, 152
—peri-odontal, 286
—pleuropericardial, 26
—pleuroperitoneal, 26
—serous, 3
—suprapleural, 77
—synovial, 9
—thyrohyoid, 305
—tympanic, 308
—urogenital, 22, 27

—vestibular (see Membrane, ary-epiglottic)
Membrana tectoria, vertebral, 37
——of inner ear, 311
Memory, 379
Meninges of brain, 384
—of spinal cord, 385
Menisci of knee, 231
—torn, 234
Mesencephalon (see Midbrain)
Mesenchyme, primary, 19
Mesentery of appendix, 104
—of colon, sigmoid, 93
——transverse, 92
—dorsal, of gut, 26
——of pericardium, 28
—of small intestine, 92, 101
—ventral, of gut, 26, 94
Meso-appendix, 104
Mesocardium, 60
Mesocolon, sigmoid, 93
—transverse, 92
Mesoderm, cardiogenic, 20
—extra-embryonic, 19
—intermediate, 26
—intra-embryonic, 23
—lateral plate, 23, 24
—paraxial, 23
—pharyngeal, 301
—primitive, 23
—somatopleuric, 24
—somitic, 23
—splanchnopleuric, 22
Mesodermal germ layer, 20, 23
Mesonephric duct (Wolffian), 26, 91
Mesonephros, 26
Mesothelium, 3
—coelomic, 91, 124
Mesovarium, 144, 147
Metacarpus, 198
Metanephros, 26
Metaphysis, 8
Metatarsus, 246
Microglia, 12
Micturition, 144
Midbrain, 344, 363
Midgut, 30
—primitive, 29
Mitochondria, 2
Mitral valve, 55
Moderator band, 53
Modiolus, 310
Mons pubis, 155
Morula, 19
Mouth, 285
Movement at joints, 16
Mucous membrane, 3
Mullerian (paramesonephric) duct, 26, 146
Muscle, action, 10
—cardiac, 11
—smooth, 11
—striated, 10

Muscle of abdominal wall, anterior, 86
——— posterior, 125
— abductor digiti minimi, of foot, 251
———— of hand, 204
— abductor hallucis, 251
—— pollicis brevis, 204
——— longus, 192
— accessorius, 250, 252
— adductor brevis, 221
—— hallucis, 251
—— longus, 221
—— magnus, 221
—— pollicis, 205
— anconeus, 184
— ary-epiglottic, 305
— biceps brachii, 181
—— femoris, 219
— brachialis, 181
— brachioradialis, 190
— buccinator, 273
— bulbar, 24, 278
— bulbospongiosus (bulbocavernosus), 154, 155
— ciliary, 277, 315, 341
— coccygeus, 139
— compressor nares, 274
— constrictors of pharynx, 298
—— of pupil, 340
— coracobrachialis, 181
— corrugator, 274
— cremaster, 89
— crico-arytenoid, lateral, 305
—— posterior, 305
— cricothyroid, 305
— cuff, 176
— dartos, 90, 154
— deltoid, 176
— depressor anguli oris, 273
—— labii inferioris, 273
— detrusor, 143
— diaphragm, 49
— digastric, anterior belly, 291, 318
—— posterior belly, 291, 320
— dilator nares, 274
— dilator pupillae, 277, 317
— erector spinae, 326
— extensor carpi radialis brevis, 191

———— ulnaris, 192
——— digiti minimi, 192
——— digitorum, 191
———— brevis, 236
———— longus, 236
——— hallucis longus, 236
——— indicis, 193
——— pollicis brevis, 192
———— longus, 193
— external oblique, 86
— extra-ocular (*see* Muscle, bulbar)
— of face, 273, 274
— flexor accessorius, 250, 252

— flexor carpi radialis, 188
——— ulnaris, 189
—— digiti minimi, 205
—— digitorum longus, 239, 252
—— digitorum profundus, 190
—— digitorum superficialis (sublimus), 189
—— hallucis brevis, 251
——— longus, 239, 252
—— pollicis brevis, 204
——— longus, 189
— frontalis, 272
— gastrocnemius, 238
— genioglossus, 288
— geniohyoid, 291
— gluteus maximus, 217
—— medius, 218
—— minimus, 218
— gracilis, 221
— hamstrings, 219
— hyoglossus, 288
— hypothenar, 204
— iliacus, 137
— iliocostalis, 326
— infrahyoid, 328
— infraspinatus, 176
— interarytenoid, 305
— intercostal, external, 46
—— innermost, 46
—— internal, 46
— internal oblique, 87
— interossei, of foot, 251
—— of hand, 205
— interspinous, 326
— intertransversus, 326
— ischiocavernosus, 154
— of larynx, 305
— latissimus dorsi, 175
— levator anguli oris, 273
—— ani, 138
—— costae, 326
—— labii superioris, 273
—— veli palatini, 288
—— palpebrae superioris, 279
—— scapulae, 175
—— longissimus capitis, 326
—— longus capitis, 327
—— colli (cervicis), 327
— lumbricals, of foot, 251
—— of hand, 190, 206
— masseter, 296
— of mastication, 296, 318
— mentalis, 273
— multifidus, 326
— muscularis mucosae, 3, 98
— mylohyoid, 290, 318
— oblique, abdominal, external, 86
——— internal, 87
—— arytenoid, 305
—— of eyeball, inferior, 279
——— superior, 279
—— of head, inferior, 327

Muscle, oblique, of head (*continued*)
———superior, 327
—obturator, externus, 218
——internus, 138
—occipitalis, 272, 320
—omohyoid, 328
—opponens digiti minimi, 205
——pollicis, 204
—orbicularis oculi, 274
——oris, 273
—palatoglossus, 288, 289
—palatopharyngeus, 288, 298
—palmaris longus, 189
—palpebral, 280
—papillary, 54
—of Passavant (*see* Muscle, sphincter, palato-
    pharyngeus)
—pectineus, 220
—pectoralis major, 174
——minor, 174
—peroneus brevis, 237
——longus, 237, 252
——tertius, 236
—piriformis, 138, 218
—plantaris, 238
—platysma, 274
—popliteus, 214, 238
—prevertebral, 327
—pronator quadratus, 190
——teres, 188
—psoas major, 125
——minor, 126
—pterygoid, lateral, 297
——medial, 297
—quadratus femoris, 218
——lumborum, 126
—quadriceps femoris, 222
—rectus abdominis, 87
——capitis anterior, 327
———lateralis, 327
———posterior, major, 326
————minor, 327
——of eyeball, 278
——femoris, 222
—rhomboid major, 175
——minor, 175
—rotatores, 326
—salpingopharyngeus, 298
—sartorius, 222
—scalenus anterior, 44, 327
——medius, 44, 327
——posterior, 44, 327
—semimembranosus, 219
—semispinalis capitis, 326
—semitendinosus, 219
—serratus anterior, 44, 174
—of sole of foot, 251
—soleus, 239
—sphincter ani, external, 140
——internal, 139
———cardiac, of stomach, 95

Muscle, sphincter (*continued*)
——oculi, 274
——oris, 273
——palatopharyngeal, 288
——pupillae, 340
——pyloric, 98
——urethral, 155
——vesical, 143
—spinalis, 326
—splenius capitis, 326
—stapedius, 309, 320
—sternocostalis (*see* Muscle, intercostal,
    innermost)
—sternocleidomastoid, 325
—sternohyoid, 328
—sternothyroid, 328
—styloglossus, 289, 301
—stylohyoid, 301, 320
—stylopharyngeus, 298, 301, 321
—subclavius, 44
—subcostalis (*see* Muscle, intercostal, inner-
    most)
—subscapularis, 176
—supinator, 192
—suprahyoid, 289, 290
—supraspinatus, 176
—suspensory, 101
—taeniae coli, 101
—temporalis, 297
—tensor fasciae latae, 217
——veli palatini, 287, 318
——tympani, 309, 318
—teres major, 176
——minor, 176
—thenar, 204
—thyro-arytenoid, 305
—thyro-epiglottic, 305
—thyrohyoid, 328
—tibialis anterior, 235, 252
——posterior, 239, 252
—of tongue, 24, 288, 322
—transversus abdominis, 87
——arytenoid, 305
——perinei, 154
——thoracis (*see* Muscle, intercostal inner-
    most)
—trapezius, 175
—triceps, 181
—vastus intermedialis, 222
——lateralis, 222
——medialis, 222
—vocalis, 305
—zygomaticus major, 274
——minor, 274
Muscularis mucosae, 3, 98
Myelin sheath, 11
Myelogram, 385
Myoblasts, 23
Myocardium, 59
Myometrium, 146
Myotome, 23, 290

Nails, 3
Nares, anterior, 263, 282
—posterior (choanae), 264
Nasal bone, 270
—cavity, 282
Nasopharynx, 298
Navicular bone, 245
—fossa, 155
Neck, 324
—cutaneous nerves, 339
—fasciae, 324
—of fibula, 228
—of femur, 213, 215
—of humerus, anatomical, 167
——surgical, 169
—of pancreas, 119
—of rib, 43
—of talus, 245
—of uterus, 144
Necrosis, 2
Neocortex (see Isocortex)
Neoplasm, 2
Nephrogenic cord, 26
Nephron, 123
Nerve, 11
—abducent, 280, 319
—accessory, 34, 322
—alveolar, inferior, 286, 318
——superior, 286, 317
—ansa cervicalis (hypoglossi), 323, 338
——subclavia, 340
—auditory (see Nerve, vestibulocochlear)
—auricular, of vagus, 322
——great, 338
——posterior, 320
—auriculotemporal, 318
—axillary, 173, 179, 181, 210
—brachial plexus, 179, 209
—buccal, of facial, 320
——of mandibular, 318
—cardiac, of vagus, 58, 69, 322
—cervical, of facial, 320
——plexus, 338
——transverse, 338
—chorda tympani, 265, 290, 292, 296, 318, 320
—ciliary, long, 278, 317
——short, 278
—circumflex (see Nerve axillary)
—cranial, 314, 344
—coccygeal plexus, 163
—cochlear (see Nerve vestibulocochlear)
—colli (see Nerve cervical)
—cutaneous of arm, lower lateral, 183
———upper lateral, 181
———medial, 180
———posterior, 183
——of calf, lateral, 242
——femoral, intermediate, 226
———lateral, 127
———medial, 226
———posterior, 219
——of forearm, lateral, 182
———medial, 180
———posterior, 183, 197
——of lower limb, summary of, 258
——palmar, 196, 197
——perforating, 163
——of upper limb, summary of, 208
—dental (see Nerve, alveolar)
—descendens cervicalis (see Nerve ansa cervicalis)
——hypoglossi (see Nerve, ansa cervicalis)
—digital, of foot, 253
——of hand, 196
—dorsal, of penis, 157
—erigentes (see Nerve, splanchnic, pelvic)
—ethmoidal, anterior, 312, 317
——posterior, 317
—facial, 319
—femoral, 127, 228, 257
—frontal, 316
—gastric (see Trunk, vagal)
—genitofemoral, 127
—glossopharyngeal, 290, 320
—gluteal, inferior, 163
——superior, 163
—hypogastric, 164
—hypoglossal, 290, 323
—iliohypogastric, 127
—ilio-inguinal, 127
—incisor, 318
—infra-orbital, 317
—infratrochlear, 317
—injuries, 170
—intercostal, 48
—intercostobrachial, 48
—interosseous, anterior, 195
——posterior, 195
—labial, 157
—lacrimal, 316, 317
—laryngeal, external, 322
——internal, 322
——recurrent, 68, 322
——superior, 322
—to latissimus dorsi (see Nerve thoracodorsal)
—lingual, 290, 318
——of glossopharyngeal, 321
—lumbar, 162
—lumbosacral plexus, 127, 162
—mandibular, of facial, 320
——of trigeminal, 318
—to masseter, 318
—maxillary, 317
—median, 179, 183, 196, 210
—meningeal branch of trigeminal, 318
—mental, 318
—musculocutaneous, of arm, 179, 182
——of leg (see Nerve, peroneal, superficial)
—mylohyoid, 318
—nasal, 317

Nerve (*continued*)
—nasociliary, 316
—nasopalatine, 317
—obturator, 127, 221, 257
—to obturator internus, 219
—occipital, greater, 327, 338
——lesser, 338
—oculomotor, 280, 315
—olfactory, 312, 314
—ophthalmic, 316
—optic, 278, 314
—palatine, 317
—palmar cutaneous branch of median, 196
——of ulnar, 197
—pectoral, medial, 174, 180
——lateral, 174
—pelvic splanchnic, 140, 163, 164
—perineal, 154
——branch of S4, 140
—peroneal, common, 242, 257
——deep, 242, 259
——superficial, 242, 259
—petrosal, deep, 312, 340
——greater, 269, 312, 313, 319, 340
——lesser, 269, 313, 341
—pharyngeal, of glossopharyngeal, 299
——of trigeminal, 317
——of vagus, 298, 322
—phrenic, 67, 179, 338
—plantar, lateral, 253
——medial, 253
—popliteal, lateral (*see* Nerve, peroneal common)
——medial (*see* Nerve, tibial)
—presacral (*see* Plexus, hypogastric)
—of pterygoid canal, 320, 340
—pudendal, 152, 157, 163
—to quadratus femoris, 219
—radial, 179, 183, 195, 210
—rami, 12, 13, 81
—rectal, inferior, 157
—renal, 81
—roots, 12
—sacral plexus (lumbosacral), 162
—saphenous, 226
—sciatic, 163, 220, 257
—scrotal, 157
—to serratus anterior (*see* Nerve thoracic, long)
—sphenopalatine, long (*see* Nerve, nasopalatine)
——short, (*see* Nerve, nasal)
—spinal, 12
—spinal accessory, 322
—spinosus (*see* Nerve, meningeal branch of trigeminal)
—splanchnic, greater, 81, 124
——lesser, 81
——least (*see* Nerve, renal), 81
——pelvic, 140, 163, 164
—subcostal, 126

—subscapular, 181
—supraclavicular, 338
—supra-orbital, 316
—suprascapular, 167, 176, 180
—supratrochlear, 316
—sural, 242
—temporal, branch of facial, 320
—thoracic, long, 180
—thoracodorsal, 181
—tibial, 241, 257
——anterior (*see* Nerve, peroneal, deep)
——posterior, (*see* Nerve, tibial)
—transverse, cervical (colli), 338
—trigeminal, 316
—trochlear, 280, 315
—tympanic, 321
—ulnar, 179, 183, 196, 210
—vagal trunk (gastric), 68, 164
—vagus, 68, 321
—vestibular (*see* Nerve, vestibulocochlear)
—vestibulocochlear, 320
—zygomatic, of facial, 320
——of maxillary, 317
Nerve injuries, cranial, 314
——facial, 320
——lower limb, 228, 257
——upper limb, 209
Nervous system, autonomic, 12
——central, 11
——development of, 31
——parasympathetic, 13
——peripheral, 11
——sympathetic, 13
Nervous tissue, 11
Neural crest, 31, 124, 345
—groove, 31, 345
—plate, 31, 345
—tube, 31, 345
Neurilemma, 11
Neurocranium, 23
Neurenteric canal, 21
Neuroglia, 11, 12
Neuron, 11, 344
—afferent, 11
—efferent, 11
—intercalated (internuncial), 11, 375
Newgrowth, 2
Nipple, 50
Node, atrioventricular, 59
—Hensen's, 20
—lymph, 15
—primitive, 20
—of Ranvier, 11
—sinu-atrial, 59
Nodule of cerebellum, 372
—of aortic valvule, 54
—of pulmonary valvule, 54
Nose, 282
Notch, acetabular, 215
—angular, 95
—cardiac, 75

Notch (*continued*)
—digastric, 265, 269
—intercondylar, 214
—jugular, 42, 170
—mandibular, 266
—mastoid, 265, 269
—radial, 184, 185
—scapular, 167
—sciatic, greater, 131, 213
——lesser, 138
—sphenopalatine, 271, 283
—supra-orbital, 263
—suprascapular, 167
—thyroid, 303
—trochlear, 185
—ulnar, 185
Notochord, 21
Nucleus, 2, 344
—abducent, 367
—accessory, 322
—ambiguus, 288, 298, 321, 370
—amygdaloid (*see* Body amygdaloid)
—anterior, 357
—basal, 347, 353
—caudate, 353
—central, 357
—cerebellar, 372
—cochlear, 320, 365, 367
—of cranial nerves (*see* individual named nuclei)
—cuneate, 370
——accessory, 370, 381
—dentate, 372
—dorsomedial, 357
—emboliform, 372
—facial, 367
—fastigial, 368, 372
—globose, 372
—glossopharyngeal, 320, 321
—gracile, 370
—habenular, 358
—hypoglossal, 369
—hypothalamic, 358
—interpeduncular, 359
—interpositum, 372
—intralaminar, 357, 378
—lateral, 357
—lentiform, 354
—of medulla, 369
—medial, 357
—mesencephalic, 364
—of midbrain, 364
—midline, 357
—oculomotor, 364
—olivary, 370
—optic, 381
—paraventricular, 358
—of pons, 366
—pontine, 366
—pre-optic, 358
—pretectal, 359, 381
—pulposus, 36
—red, 364
—reticular, 373, 377
—lateral, 370, 373
——thalamic, 357
—salivary, 319, 367
—septal, 355, 359
—of spinal cord, 375
—substantia nigra, 365
—supra-optic, 358
—thalamic, 356
—thoracic, 375
—of tractus solitarius, 290, 319, 320, 367, 370
—of trapezoid body, 365, 367
—trigeminal, mesencephalic, 364, 367
——motor, 367
——superior sensory, 367
——spinal, 367, 369
—trochlear, 364
—of vagus, 370
—ventral thalamic, 356
—vestibular, 320, 368

Occipital bone, 269
Oesophagus, abdominal, 95
—cervical, 29, 330
—thoracic, 69
Olecranon, 185
Olfactory area, 355, 381
—bulb, 355
—pathways, 381
—stria, 355
—tract, 355
Oligodendroglia, 12
Olive, 369, 370
Omental bursa (lesser sac), 30, 93, 94
Omentum, greater, 26, 92
—lesser, 30, 92, 94
Opening, diaphragmatic, 49
—inguinal, 87
—into omental bursa (aditus), 93
—nasal, 282
—saphenous, 223, 254
Operculum, 301
Opposition, 201
Optic canal, 277
—chiasma, 314
—disc, 277
—foramen (*see* Optic, canal)
—groove, 312
—nerve, 314
—pathways, 381
—tract, 381
—radiation, 353, 382
Orbit, 276
Organ, spiral, 311
Organelle, 2
Orientation, 16, 198, 201
Orifice, aortic, 55
—atrioventricular, 53

Orifice (*continued*)
—cardiac, 95
—ileocaecal, 104
—pulmonary, 53
—urethral, 143, 155
Oropharynx, 299
Ossicles, auditory, 309
Ossification, 7
—cartilaginous, 7
—membranous, 7, 167, 266, 267
Otoliths, 311
Outlet, pelvic, 136
—thoracic, 42
Ovary, 147
Ovum, 18, 148

Pacemaker of heart, 59
Pain pathways, 13, 58, 357, 376, 380
—referred, 339
Palate, hard, 264, 287
—soft, 287
Palatine bone, 271
Palm, 203
Pancreas, 30, 119
Papilla, duodenal, 99, 117
—lacrimal, 280
—renal, 121
—sublingual, 285, 293
—of tongue, 290
Paralysis, facial, 320
—limbs, 209, 228, 257
—respiratory, 115
Paramesonephric (Müllerian) duct, 26, 146
Parametrium, 144, 145
Parasympathetic nervous system, 13, 81, 164, 340
Parathyroid gland, 329
Paraxial mesoderm, 23
Parietal bone, 270
Parotid duct, 291
—gland, 291, 318, 341
Patches, Peyer's (*see* Lymph follicle, aggregated)
Patella, 227
Pathways, afferent, 379
—auditory, 382
—autonomic, 383
—efferent, 382
—extrapyramidal, 365, 383
—olfactory, 381
—optic (*see* Pathways, visual)
—pain, 13, 58, 380
—pressure, 380
—proprioceptive, 381
—pyramidal, 382
—taste, 382
—temperature, 380
—touch, 380
—vestibular, 382
—visual, 381
Pectoral girdle, 8

Pedicles, vertebral, 33
Peduncle, cerebellar, inferior, 369, 373
——middle, 366, 377
——superior, 366, 373
—cerebral, 365
Pelvic girdle, 8
Pelvis, articulated, 136
—bony, 131
—ureteric, 123
Penis, 27, 153
Perforated substance, anterior, 351
——posterior, 357, 364
Pericardial cavity, 20, 24, 26, 59
Pericardioperitoneal canal, 24, 26
Pericardium, 59
Perichondrium, 4
Perikaryon, 11
Perilymph, 310
Perimysium, 10
Perineum, 152
Period, embryonic, 22
—fetal, 31
—pre-embryonic, 18
Periosteum, 5
Peripheral nervous system, 11
Peritoneum, 91
Permanent teeth, 286
Pes hippocampi, 355
Peyer's patches (*see* Lymph follicles, aggregated)
Phalanges of foot, 246
—of hand, 198
Pharyngeal arches, 29, 301
—clefts, 31
—plexus, nervous, 299
——venous, 299, 337
—pouch, 31
Pharynx, 297, 301
Phonation, 306
Pia mater, 386
Piles, 111, 140
Pineal body, 347
Pisiform bone, 198
Pit, nasal, 274
—olfactory, 277
—primitive, 20
—tonsillar, 300
Pituitary fossa (*see* Fossa, hypophyseal)
—gland (*see* Hypophysis cerebri)
Placenta, 24, 32, 61
Placode, nasal, 274
Plane, coronal, 16
—intercristal, 38
—horizontal, 16
—lateral, 16, 86
—sagittal, 16
—subcostal, 86
—supracristal, 38
—transpyloric, 86, 98
—transtubercular, 86
—transverse, 16

Plantar flexion of foot, 16, 238, 250
Plate, alar, 346, 369
—basal, 346, 369
—cribriform, 271, 312
—epiphyseal, 8
—neural, 31
—horizontal, of palatine bone, 271
—orbital, 270
—perpendicular, 271
—prochordal, 20
—pterygoid, lateral, 264, 268
— —medial, 264, 268
—tarsal, 281
—tympanic, 264, 265
—vertical, of palatine bone, 271
Pleura, 72
Pleuropericardial membrane, 26
Pleuroperitoneal membrane, 26
Plexus, choroid, 347, 386
— —of fourth ventricle, 374
— —of lateral ventricles, 347, 352
— —of third ventricle, 347, 362
—nervous, aortic, 164
— —of Auerbach (myenteric), 111
— —brachial, 179, 209
— —cardiac, 64, 81
— —cervical, 338
— —coccygeal, 163
— —coeliac, 163
— —hypogastric, 164
— —lumbar, 127
— —lumbosacral, 127, 162, 212
— —of Meissner (submucous), 111
— —mesenteric, 107, 108
— —oesophageal, 68, 81, 321
— —pelvic, 164
— —pharyngeal, 299
— —pulmonary, 68, 81
— —sacral, 162
— —solar (see Plexus, nervous, coeliac)
— —spinal, 12
—subendocardial, 59
— —tympanic, 321
—venous, pampiniform, 90, 162
— —pelvic, 160
— —pharyngeal, 299, 337
— —prostatic, 149
— —pterygoid, 280, 283, 297, 336
— —rectal, 140
— —soleal, 238
— —suboccipital, 327, 337
— —uterine, 146
— —vaginal, 148
— —vertebral, external, 38, 160
— — —internal, 38, 160, 395
— —vesical, 143
Pneumogram, 142
Pneumothorax, 48
Point, midinguinal, 224
Poles of hemisphere, 349
Pons, 344, 366

Popliteal fossa, 235
Porta hepatis, 113
Posterior, definition of, 16
Posture, 238, 259
Pouch, perineal, deep, 154, 157
— —superficial, 152, 153, 154
—pharyngeal, 300, 301, 329
—suprapatellar (see Bursa, suprapatellar)
—of Rathke, 31
—recto-uterine (of Douglas), 94, 148
—rectovesical, 94, 150
—uterovesical, 94, 143
Pre-embryonic period, 18
Pregnancy, ectopic, 19
Prehension, 166
Premaxilla, 268, 275, 287
Prepuce, 153
Pressure, intracranial, 315, 387
—intrathoracic, 72
—venous, 337
Primary alveoli, 8
—mesenchyme, 19
—villus, 20
—yolk sac, 19
Primitive gut, 29
—knot, 20
—node, 20
—pit, 20
—streak, 20
—urogenital sinus, 26
—yolk sac (exocoelome), 19
Process, accessory, 36
—acromial, 167
—alveolar, mandibular, 266
— —maxillary, 264, 268
—articular, of vertebra, 33, 134
—of arytenoid, muscular, 304
— —vocal, 304
—caudate, 113
—clinoid, anterior, 268, 312
— —posterior, 268, 312
—condylar, 266
—coracoid, 167, 181
—coronoid, of mandible, 266
— —of ulna, 185
—frontal, 268
—frontonasal, 274, 287
—head, 21
—mastoid, 264, 269
—mamillary, 36
—mandibular, 274
—maxillary, 274, 287
—odontoid (see Dens)
—olecranon, 185
—palatine, 264, 268, 287
—premaxillary, 287
—pterygoid, 268
—spinous, vertebral, 33
— —scapular, 167
—styloid, of fifth metatarsal, 247
— —radial, 185

Process, styloid (*continued*)
——temporal, 265, 269
——ulnar, 185
—transverse, 33
—uncinate, of pancreas, 119
—xiphoid, 42
—zygomatic, 268
Processus vaginalis, 89, 91
Prochordal plate, 20
Proctodeum, 31
Prominence, laryngeal, 303
Promontory of middle ear, 309
—sacral, 134
Pronation, 185, 188
Pronephros, 26
Proprioception, 376
Prosencephalon (*see* Forebrain)
Prostate, 149
Prostatic urethra, 155
—utricle, 155
Protruded intervertebral disc, 36
Protuberance, occipital, external, 266, 269
——internal, 312
Pterion, 263
Pterygopalatine fossa, 263, 283
—ganglion, 281, 299, 316, 317, 319, 340
Pubis, 133
Pulp of spleen, 119
—of tooth, 286
Pulvinar, 356, 357
Pump, soleal, 238
Punctum lacrimalis, 280
Puncture, lumbar, 38
Pupil, 277
Purkinje cells, 372
—fibres, 59
Putamen, 354
Pyelogram, 122
Pyloric antrum, 95
—canal, 95
—sphincter, 98
Pyloroplasty, 164
Pylorus, 98
Pyramid of ear, 309
—of medulla, 369, 370
—renal, 121
Pyramidal, cell, 351
—system, 382
—tract, 365, 382

Radiation, auditory, 352
—of corpus callosum, 352
—optic (visual), 353
Radio-isotopes, 16
Radiology, 16
Radio-opaque media, 16
Radius, 184
Raised intracranial pressure, 315, 387
Ramus, anterior primary (*see* Ramus, ventral)
—communicans, 13, 81

—dorsal, 12
—ischiopubic, 133, 213
—of mandible, 266
—posterior primary (*see* Ramus, dorsal)
—ventral, 12, 179
Raphe, 10
—anococcygeal, 139, 152
—mylohyoid, 290
—pharyngeal, 298
—pterygomandibular, 264, 273, 298
Reaction, decidual, 20, 32
Recess, costodiaphragmatic, 72
—costomediastinal, 72
—duodenal, 101
—epitympanic, 309
—lateral, dural, 312, 393
——fourth ventricle, 372
—pharyngeal, 298
—piriform (*see* Fossa, piriform)
—spheno-ethmoidal, 283
—supra-optic, 362
—suprapineal, 362
Recto-uterine pouch, 94, 148
Rectovesical pouch, 94, 150
Rectum, 139
Regions, of abdomen, 86
Reflux, gastric, 95
—ureteric, 143
Respiration, 46, 49, 50
Respiratory diverticulum, 29
Restiform body (*see* Peduncle, cerebellar, inferior)
Rete testis, 91
Reticular formation, 366, 377
Retina, 277
Retinaculum, extensor, of foot, 237
——of wrist, 185, 191, 193, 207
—femoral, 215
—flexor, of foot, 240
——of wrist, 189, 203, 207
—patellar, 223, 230
—peroneal, 237
Rhinencephalon, 349, 355
Rhombencephalon (*see* Hindbrain)
Rhombic fossa (*see* Floor of fourth ventricle)
Rib, first, 43
—typical, 43
Ridge, gluteal, 212, 213
—gonadal, 27
—superciliary (*see* Arch, superciliary)
—supracondylar, of femur, 213
——of humerus, 170
Rima glottidis, 305
Ring, femoral, 223
—inguinal, deep, 89
——superficial, 87
—tendinous (orbital), 277
Rods, of retina, 279
Root of brachial plexus, 179
—of lung, 75
—of mesentery, 92

Root (*continued*)
—of spinal nerve, 12, 48
Rostral, definition of, 16
Rostrum, of corpus callosum, 352
Rotation, 16
Running, 259
Rupture (*see* Hernia)
—splenic, 119

Sac, alveolar, 80
—dural, 38
—endolymphatic, 311
—lacrimal, 271, 281
—lesser (omental bursa), 30, 93
—pericardial (*see* Cavity, pericardial)
—of peritoneum, greater, 91
— —lesser, 30, 93
—pleural (*see* Cavity, pleural)
—primitive yolk (exocoelome), 19
— —yolk (definitive), 19
Saccul tions of colon, 101
Saccule, 311
Sacrum, 133
Scala media, 310
—tympani, 310
—vestibuli, 310
Scalp, 272
Scaphoid, 198
Scapula, 167
Sclera, 277
Sclerotome, 23
Scrotal swelling, 27, 154
Scrotum, 27, 90, 154
Secondary alveoli, 8
—villus, 20
—yolk sac, 19
Segment, bronchopulmonary, 75
Sella turcica, 312
Semicircular canals, 310
—ducts, 311
Semilunar valvules, aortic, 55
— —pulmonary, 54
Seminal vesicle, 150
Seminiferous tubules, 91
Sensory pathways, 379
Septum, interatrial, 55
—intercondylar, 227, 231
—intermuscular, of arm, 182, 183
— —of leg, 235, 254
—interventricular, 55
—lucidum (*see* Septum, pellucidum)
—membranous, 55
—nasal, 275, 283
—palmar, 203
—pellucidum, 355
—posterior median (*see* Sulcus, posterior median)
—primum, 61
—secundum, 61
—spiral, 61, 310
—transversum, 26

Serotonin, 369
Sex differences, pelvis, 136
Shaft (*see* Body of bone)
Sheath, axillary, 324
—carotid, 292, 324
—femoral, 223
—fibrous flexor, 203, 207
—myelin, 11
—prostate, 149
—rectum, 139
—rectus, 86, 88
—synovial, 9
— —of foot, 237, 240
— —of hand, extensor, 193
— — —flexor, 190
Shoulder region, 166
Sialogram, 292
Sinus, aortic, 55, 63
—basilar, 393
—carotid, 333
—cavernous, 280, 315, 394
—cervical, 301
—coronary, 53, 57
—cranial air, 284
— —venous, 392
—ethmoidal, 271, 284
—frontal, 270, 284, 312
—intercavernous, 393
—lactiferous, 51
—of larynx, 305
—maxillary, 267, 284
—oblique pericardial, 54, 60
—occipital, 395
—paranasal air, 284
—petrosal, inferior, 314, 337, 393, 394
— —superior, 314, 395
—primitive urogenital, 26
—renal, 121
—sagittal, inferior, 393
— —superior, 270, 312, 392
—sigmoid, 314, 337, 394
—sphenoidal, 268, 284
—sphenoparietal, 395
—straight, 393
—tarsi, 245
—transverse, 270, 313, 314, 393
— —of percardium, 28, 60
—urogenital, 26
—venosus, 60
Sinusoid, 14
Skeleton, 8
Skin, 3, 203, 251
Skull, 262
Smell, 381
Sole, 251
Soleal pump, 238
Somatosensory area, 350, 351
—pathways, 380
Somite, 23
Sound, 306
Space, extradural, 38

Space (*continued*)
—hypothenar, 203
—intercostal, 46, 178
—intervillous, 20
—ischiorectal (*see* Fossa, ischiorectal)
—palmar, 203
—peritoneal (*see* Fossa, peritoneal)
—retrocardiac, 76
—retromolar, 285
—retropubic, 143
—subarachnoid, 374, 386
—subdural, 384
—subhepatic (hepatorenal), 94
—subphrenic, 94, 104, 114
—suprasternal, 324
—thenar, 203
Speech, 379
Spermatic cord, 89
Spermatozoa, 18, 151
Sphenoid bone, 268
Sphincter, anal, external, 140
——internal, 139
—of bile duct, 117
—cardiac, 95
—ileocaecal, 104
—laryngeal, 303
—palatopharyngeal, 288
—pupillae, 315
—pyloric, 95, 98
—urethral, 148, 154, 157
—vaginal, 148
—vesical, 143
Spina bifida, 345
Spine of ilium, 131, 213
—of ischium, 133, 213
—mental, 267
—of scapula, 167
—of sphenoid, 264
—of tibia (*see* Tuberosity, tibial)
Spinal cord, 38, 375
—nerves, 12
Spleen, 117
Splenium of corpus callosum, 352
Stalk, body, 20, 22
—optic, 347
Standing, 259
Stapes, 309
Stem villous, 32
Stenosis, 62
Sternal angle, 42
Sternotomy, 48
Sternum, 42
Stomach, 29, 95
Stomodeum, 31
Stratum granulosum, 148
Streak, primitive, 20
Stria habenularis (*see* Stria, medullaris thalami)
—medullary, 374
—medullaris thalami, 356
—olfactory, 351, 355

—terminalis, 355, 356
Stroke, 388
Stroma of ovary, 148
Styloid process, 265, 269
Subarachnoid space, 384 386
Subdural space, 384
Sublingual gland, 294, 341
Submandibular duct, 293
—gland, 293, 341
Suboccipital region, 326
Substance, perforated, anterior, 351
——posterior, 357, 364
Substantia gelatinosa, 375
—nigra, 364
Subthalamus, 357, 359
Sulcus, anterior median (*see* Fissure, anterior median)
—anterolateral, 375
—calcanei, 245
—calcarine, 350
—central, 350
—cerebellar, 372
—cerebral, 349
—collateral, 350
—coronary, 52, 55
—frontal, 350
—hippocampal, 350
—hypothalamic, 357
—interventricular, 52
—lateral, 350
—limitans, 346
—median, 374
—parieto-occipital, 350
—postcentral, 350
—posterior median, 369, 375
—posterolateral, 375
—precentral, 350
—rhinal, 350
—tali, 245
—temporal, 350
—terminalis, of heart, 53
——of tongue, 288
Superior, definition of, 16
Supination, 181, 188
Suprarenal gland, 124
Sustentaculum tali, 245
Suture, 9, 262
—coronal, 262
—lambdoid, 262
—metopic, 270
—sagittal, 262
—zygomaticofrontal, 263
Swallowing, 302
Sweating, 13
Swelling, cloacal, 27
—labioscrotal, 27
—lateral cloacal, 27
—lateral lingual, 290
—scrotal, 27, 154
Sympathetic nervous system, 13, 81, 163
—trunk, cervical, 339

Sympathetic trunk (*continued*)
— —lumbar, 163
— —sacral, 163
— —thoracic, 81
Symphysis, 9
—menti, 266
—pubis, 133, 136
Synapse, 11
Syncytiotrophoblast, 20
Syndrome, carpal tunnel, 196, 203
Synovial fluid, 9
—joint, 9
—membrane, 9
—sheath, 172, 181, 190, 191, 193, 237
System, 2
—alimentary, 29
—anterolateral, 377
—cardiovascular, 14
—extrahepatic biliary, 116
—extrapyramidal, 353
—hepatic portal, 110
—limbic, 355
—lymph, 15
—macrophage, 2, 16
—nervous, 11
—portal (hypothalamic), 358
—pyramidal, 382
—reticulo-endothelial (*see* System, macro-
        phage)

Taeniae coli, 101
Tail fold, 22
—of caudate nucleus, 353
—of pancreas, 116
Talus, 245
Tapetum (*see* Radiation of corpus callosum)
Tarsus, 245
Taste, 318, 319, 320, 321, 367
Taste buds, 290
Tears, 281
Tectum, 364
Teeth, 286
Tegmen tympani, 309, 313
Tegmentum of midbrain, 364, 366
—of pons, 366
Tela choroidea, 386
Telencephalon, 344
Temporal bone, 269
—gyrus, 350
—lobe, 350
Tendon, 4
Tendinous intersections, 87
—ring (orbital), 277
Tendon of biceps, 181, 186
—calcaneal, 239
—central, of diaphragm, 49
—conjoint, 87
—patellar, 223
—quadriceps, 222
Tentorium cerebelli, 313, 384
Tertiary villus, 20

Testis, 90
—ectopic, 90
—undescended, 90
Thalamus, 356
Thoracic cage, 45
—cavity, 42, 52
—duct, 66, 82
—inlet, 42
—outlet, 42
—nucleus, 375
—wall, 12
Thoracotomy, 48
Thorax, 42
Thrombosis, 15
—coronary, 57
Thymus, 66, 69
Thyroid cartilage, 303
—gland, 328
—isthmus, 329
—notch, 303
Tibia, 227
Tissues, 2, 4, 10, 11
Tomogram, 77
Tongue, 288
Tonsil, lingual, 290
—pharyngeal (adenoids), 299
—palatine (the tonsil), 299
—tubal, 300
Tonsillar pits, 300
Trachea, 69, 329
Tracheobronchial diverticulum, 29
Tracheostomy, 330
Tract, ascending, of spinal cord, 376
—of cerebellum, 372
—corticonuclear, 365, 370
—corticopontine, 365
—corticospinal, anterior, 370, 377, 383
— —lateral, 370, 377, 383
—descending, of spinal cord, 376
—dorsolateral, 376
—extrapyramidal, 365, 383
—iliotibial, 218, 254
—mamillotegmental, 358
—mamillothalamic, 358
—of medulla, 370
—of midbrain, 365
—olfactory, 350, 355
—olivocerebellar, 370
—olivospinal, 377
—optic, 381
—of pons, 368
—posterolateral (*see* Tract, dorsolateral)
—pyramidal, 365, 382
—reticulospinal, 372, 377
—rubrospinal, 372, 377
—solitarius, 369, 370
—of spinal cord, 376
—spinal, of trigeminal, 371
—spinocerebellar, posterior (dorsal), 371,
        375, 376
— —anterior (ventral), 371, 376

Tract (*continued*)
—spinothalamic, anterior, 372, 377
——lateral, 372, 377
—strionigral, 365
—tectospinal, 365, 371, 377
—temporopontine, 352, 365
—thalamocortical, 352, 365
—vestibulocerebellar, 368, 373
—vestibulospinal, 368, 372, 377
Tractus solitarius, 369, 370
Tragus, 308
Transverse sinus, 28, 60
Trapezium, 198
Trapezoid, body, 367
—bone, 198
—nucleus, 367
Tremor, intention, 372
—spontaneous, 353
Triangle, anal, 152
—anterior, of neck, 325
—femoral, 223
—hypoglossal, 374
—posterior, of neck, 178, 325
—suboccipital, 327
—urogenital, female, 154
——male, 153
—vagal, 374
—vestibular, 374
Tricuspid valve, 53
Trigone of bladder, 143
Triquetral, 198
Trochanter of femur, greater, 213
——lesser, 213
Trochlea of humerus, 170
—of orbit, 279
—of phalanx, 199
—of talus, 245
Trophoblast, 19
Truncus arteriosus, 60, 129
Trunk of brachial plexus, 179, 209
—coeliac, 29, 97, 106
—costocervical, 333
—jugular, 342
—lumbosacral, 127
—lymph, right, 83
—pulmonary, 65
—sympathetic, cervical, 339
——lumbar, 163
——sacral, 163
——thoracic, 81
—thyrocervical, 179, 333
—vagal (gastric nerves), 68, 81, 164, 321
Tube, auditory, 269, 298, 300, 309
—Fallopian (*see* Tube, uterine)
—neural, 34
—pharyngotympanic (*see* Tube, auditory)
—uterine, 26, 146
Tuber cinereum, 357
Tubercle, adductor, 213
—anterior thalamic, 356
—articular, 265, 269, 295

—of calcaneum, anterior, 245
——posterior, 245
—cuneate, 369
—deltoid (*see* Tuberosity, deltoid)
—dorsal, 185, 193
—genial (*see* Tubercle, mental)
—genital, 27, 154
—gracile, 369
—of iliac crest, 131
—infraglenoid, 182
—mental, 267
—of palatine bone, 271
—pharyngeal, 269, 298
—peroneal, 237, 245
—pubic, 133
—quadrate, 213
—radial (*see* Tubercle, dorsal)
—of rib, 43
—scalene, 44
—scaphoid, 198
—supraglenoid, 181
—tibial, 223
—vertebral, 34
Tuberculum impar, 290
—sellae, 312
Tuberosity, deltoid, 176
—frontal, 263
—gluteal, 213
—of humerus, greater, 167
——lesser, 169
—iliac, 131
—ischial, 132, 213
—maxillary, 264, 268
—navicular, 245
—parietal, 270
—radial (bicipital), 181, 184
—tibial, 227
Tubules, convoluted, 123
—renal (*see* Duct, renal)
—seminiferous, 91
Tumour, 2
Tunica albuginea, 91, 148, 154
—vaginalis, 90
Tunnel, carpal flexor, 196, 203
Turbinate (*see* Concha, nasal)
Tympanic antrum, 310
—cavity, 308
—membrane, 308
—plate, 269

Ulcers, duodenal, 98, 101
—gastric, 98
—varicose, 256
Ulna, 185
Umbilicus, 38
Uncus, 350
Upper limb, 165
Urachus, 27, 142, 144
Ureter, 26, 123, 142
Urethra, female, 27, 156
—male, 27, 155

Urethral crest, 150, 155
Urethrogram, 156
Urogenital diaphragm, 152
Urorectal fold, 26
Uterine tube, 26, 146
Uterovesical pouch, 94, 143
Uterus, 26, 144
Utricle of ear, 311
—prostatic, 155
Uvula of palate, 287

Vagina, 26, 148
Vagotomy, 164
Vallate papillae, 290
Valleculae, 288
Valve, anal, 140
—aortic, 55
—bicuspid (see Valve, mitral)
—cardiac, 95
—of coronary sinus, 53
—ileocaecal, 104
—of inferior vena cava, 53
—mitral, 55
—pulmonary, 54
—pyloric (see Sphincter, pyloric)
—spiral, 117
—tricuspid, 53
—venous, 14, 254, 333, 337
Valvule, anal, 140
—cardiac, 54, 55
—semilunar, 54, 55
Varicose veins, 256
Vas deferens (see Ductus deferens)
Vasectomy, 150
Vault of skull, 312
Vein, 14
—anastomotic, of cortex, 392
— —portal-systemic, 111, 140
—auricular, posterior, 337
—axillary, 179
—azygos, 67
—basal, 392
—basilic, 186, 207
—basivertebral, 33, 39
—brachial, 179, 207
—brachiocephalic, 66, 171, 333
—bronchial, 67
—cardiac, anterior, 58
— —atrial, 58
— —great, 57
— —middle, 58
— —small, 58
— —ventricular, 58
—cardinal, common, 26, 28
—cava, inferior, 49, 67
— —superior, 67
—cephalic, 174, 179, 186, 207
—cerebral, anterior, 392
— —great, 392
— —inferior, 392
— —internal, 392

— —middle, deep, 392
— — —superficial, 392
— —superior, 392
—choroidal, 392
—circumflex femoral, 225
—condylar, emissary, 395
—cortical, superficial, 392
—costal, superior, 67
—cubital, median, 182, 186, 207
—cystic, 117
—diaphragmatic, 129
—diploic, 272, 395
—dorsal, of penis, 153
—emissary, 272, 312, 314, 395
—facial, 280, 336, 337
— —anterior (see Vein, facial)
— —common (see Vein, facial)
— —posterior (see Vein, retromandibular)
—femoral, 225
—gastric, 97, 110
—gastro-epiploic, 97, 110
—gonadal, 129, 162
—hemiazygos, 67
— —accessory, 67
—hepatic, 115, 129
—iliac, common, 161
— —external, 161
— —internal, 161
—iliolumbar, 162
—innominate (see Vein, brachiocephalic)
—intercostal, anterior, 48
— —first, 48
— —posterior, 48, 67
— —superior, 67
—intervertebral, 38, 395
—jugular, anterior, 324, 338
— —external, 333, 338
— —internal, 333, 337
—lingual, 289, 337
— —dorsal, 289
—lumbar, 129
— —ascending, 67
—mastoid, emissary, 395
—marginal, 58
—maxillary, 337
—mesenteric, inferior, 110
— —superior, 110
—oblique, of left atrium, 58
—oesophageal, 111
—ophthalmic, inferior, 280
— —superior, 280
—ovarian, 148, 162
—pancreatic, 110
—pancreaticoduodenal, 110
—para-umbilical, 110, 111
—parietal, emissary, 395
—of pelvis, 160
—penis, dorsal, of, 153
—perforating, 254
—pharyngeal, 300
—phrenic, 129

Vein (*continued*)
—popliteal, 241
—portal, 97, 110, 115
—profunda femoris, 225
—prostatic, 149
—pudendal, internal, 157
—pulmonary, 67
—rectal, inferior, 140, 152
— —superior, 110, 140
—renal, 129
—retinal, 278
—retromandibular, 337
—saphenous, great (long), 223, 225, 254
— —small, (short), 241, 255
—of scalp, 336
—soleal, 238
—spinal, 395
—splenic, 110
—subcardinal, 28
—subclavian, 44, 179, 333
—subcostal, 67
—supracardinal, 28
—suprarenal, 129
—temporal, superficial, 337
—testicular, 90, 162
—thalamostriate, 356, 392
—thoracic, internal, 66
—thyroid, inferior, 66, 328
— —middle, 328, 337
— —superior, 328, 337
—umbilical, 110, 111
—varicose, 111
—ventricular, posterior, 58
—vertebral, 66, 327
—vitelline, 116
Velum, medullary, inferior, 369, 374
— —superior, 374
Vena cava, inferior, 28, 53, 129
— —superior, 53, 67
Venae cordis minimae, 58
—vorticosae, 278
Venepuncture, 182, 207
Venogram, 255
Venous drainage of abdomen, 110, 129
— —of central nervous system, 392
— —of head and neck, 336
— —of lower limb, 254
— —of pelvis, 160
— —of thorax, 66
— —of upper limb, 207
Ventral, definition of, 16
Ventricle, fourth, 374
—lateral, 346, 359
—left, 54
—primitive, 346
—right, 53
—third, 362
Vermiform appendix, 104
Vermis, 372
Vertebra, atlas, 34
—axis, 35

—cervical, 33
—coccygeal, 134
—lumbar, 36
—prominens, 35
—sacral, 133
—thoracic, 35
—typical, 33
Vertebral column, 33, 37
Vesicle, cerebral, 346
—seminal, 150
Vessel, blood, 14
—lymph, 15
Vestibular cortex, 382
—nuclei, 368
—pathways, 382
—triangle, 367
Vestibule of aorta, 55
—cardiac, 55
—of ear, 310
—mouth, 255
—nose, 282
—perineal, 155
Villi, arachnoid, 386
—intestinal, 101, 112
—primary, 20
—secondary, 20
—stem, 32
—tertiary, 20
Viscerocranium, 23
Visual pathways, 350, 381
Vitelline duct, 22
Vitreous body, 277
Vocal cords, false, 305
— —true, 304
Vocalisation, 306
Vomer, 271, 283

Walking, 259
Wall, abdominal, anterior, 86
— —posterior, 125
—pelvic, 137
—thoracic, 42
Weight, line of, 212, 216, 234, 248, 259
Willis, circle of, 387, 392
Window, oval, 309
—round, 309
Wing of sphenoid, greater, 268
— —lesser, 268, 312
Wolffian (mesonephric) duct, 26, 91
Wrist, 198, 200

Xiphoid process, 42

Yolk sac, definitive, 19
— —primitive, 19

Zona fasciculata, 124
—glomerulosa, 124
—pellucida, 18
—reticulata, 124
Zone, ependymal, 345

Zone (*continued*)
—mantle, 345
—marginal, 345
Zonular fibres, 277

Zygomatic arch, 270
—bone, 270
—process, 268
Zygote, 19

NOTES

NOTES

NOTES

NOTES

NOTES

NOTES

NOTES

NOTES

NOTES